S/NVQ Level 2

2nd Edition

Beauty Therapy

Jane Hiscock and **Frances Lovett**

Heinemann

Inspiring generations

Heinemann is an imprint of Pearson Education Limited,
a company incorporated in England and Wales, having
its registered office at Edinburgh Gate, Harlow, Essex, CM20 2JE.
Registered company number: 872828

Heinemann is a registered trademark of Pearson Education Limited

Text © Fareham College 2004

First published 2002

Revised edition 2004

2009

10 9

British Library Cataloguing in Publication Data is available from
the British Library on request.

ISBN: 978 0 435451 02 8

Page layout and illustrations by Hardlines, Charlbury, Oxon

Original illustrations © Harcourt Education Limited, 2004

Printed and bound in China (CTPS / 09)

Websites

Please note that the examples of websites suggested in this book
were up to date at the time of writing. It is essential for tutors to
preview each site before using it to ensure that the URL is still
accurate and the content is appropriate. We suggest that tutors
bookmark useful sites and consider enabling students to access
them through the school or college intranet.

Tel: 01865 888058 www.heinemann.co.uk

Contents

Acknowledgements

We have been extremely fortunate to have a continuing team of support to help us with the development of this new book, which meets the latest Beauty Therapy standards. So, in no particular order of priority, as everyone has played such an important part in both encouragement and practical application, our thanks must go to:

Our families for the ongoing domestic support. This allowed us time and energy to focus on the book, despite the pressure of children taking GCSE exams, and all the other demands which make up normal family life. Also thank you, girls, for modelling, very brave of you: Helen, Victoria, and Venetia!

The team at Heinemann has again come up trumps. Ever professional, the support has been fantastic, even as our experience grew; we still regard their input as invaluable. Thank you Pen Gresford, for your vision, and continued faith in us. Our editors were Janine Robert and Jan Doorly: thank you for your eagle eyes, and Phebe Kynaston and Linda Mellor for your attention to detail. Photo research was carried out by Sally Smith and Bea Thomas, who gave such assistance during the photo shoots.

Gareth Boden and Tony Poole continue to make us look good, with their amazing photographs and artistic flair, combined with a sound knowledge of what would work and what wouldn't! Former student Michelle Ellis did a lovely job on the nail art photo shoot, and our thanks to all who modelled for us, too.

All our colleagues at Fareham College: Programme Manager for Beauty Therapy and Hairdressing Mary Mussell, and Head of School Joan Champion, for their support, and for providing the photo shoot location.

Tina Lawson and Sue Williams from Warrington College were of enormous help in the Key Skills development, and they were most generous in sharing good practice.

Thank you to all the professionals within the industry who have been very helpful in providing high-quality products and photographs:

Angela Barbagelata, Fabes and the team at Carlton Professional, Lancing – for providing equipment

Cherry International

Jessica The Natural Nail Company – for super manicure products

Charles Fox, London – for make-up products and brushes

Bellistas Ltd – for information

SBC (Europe) Ltd – for make-up products and photographs

We are pleased that this book has been approved by the Federation of Holistic Therapists (www.fht.org.uk).

Use of HABIA unit titles and outcome headings is by kind permission of HABIA, Fraser House, Nether Hall Road, Doncaster, South Yorkshire, DN1 2PH. Tel: 01302 380000.

Jane Hiscock and Frances Lovett

Photo acknowledgements

Alamy: pages 49 (right), 112, 135, 157 (bottom)
Beauty Professional: pages 49 (centre), 95
Beauty Salon/Jane Martin: page 106
Carlton: page 159 (bottom)
Corbis: pages 55 (left), 133, 134, 137, 138 (bottom), 140, 152 (2nd right), 157 (centre), 158, 161, 312
Cosmetics à la carte: pages 69, 78
Dermalogica: pages 159 (top), 208-10, 211 (bottom), 212, 213, 216 (top)
Fakebake: page 403 (top)
Gigi: pages 318-21
Grassé: page 15
Guinot: page 406
Harcourt Education/Gareth Boden: pages 8, 9, 19, 25-7, 44, 49 (left), 54, 55 (right), 61, 67, 79, 81, 83-5, 88, 91, 103, 107, 111, 114, 116, 119, 127, 130, 138 (top), 146, 155 (top), 156, 159 (centre), 199 (left and centre), 200, 204, 207, 215, 216 (bottom), 219, 220, 223, 225, 229, 231-7, 239, 241, 242, 244, 256-8, 260, 262 (bottom), 263, 268, 273, 275, 281, 287 (bottom), 288 (row 2, right), 304, 306-8, 309 (top left and right), 315, 327, 329, 335, 336, 338, 339, 340-4, 348, 349, 353, 354, 358, 359, 364, 365, 369, 380-6, 389-91, 401, 402, 404, 408, 410-14
Harcourt Education/Mica Brancic: pages 68, 74
Harcourt Education/Trevor Clifford: page 39
Harcourt Education/Digital Vision: page 157 (top)
Harcourt Education/Chris Honeywell: page 127
Mediphoto: page 153 (row 1, right)
MD: pages 133, 155 (centre), 211 (top)
Peter Morris: pages 252 (top), 262 (top), 285, 287 (row 1), 288 (row 1; row 2 left and centre), 376, 377, 394
Perfector: page 86
Photodisc: pages 129, 139
SBC (Europe) Ltd: pages 7 (left), 13
Science Photo Library: pages 24 (row 1, left; row 2, left), 148 (row 1, right; row 2, 2nd left), 149 (row 1, left), 152 (2nd left), 153 (row 2, left), 253 (bottom), 373 (top and bottom), 375 (centre and bottom)
Science Photo Library/Biophoto Associates: page 24 (row 2, right)
Science Photo Library/Mike Devlin: page 372 (bottom)
Science Photo Library/Alain Dex, Publiphoto Diffusion: page 148 (row 1, left)
Science Photo Library/John Radcliffe Hospital: page 153 (row 2, right)
Science Photo Library/Dr P. Marazzi: pages 24 (row 1, centre; row 2, centre; row 3), 148 (row 2, left and 2nd right), 149 (row 1, right; row 2, right), 150 (row 1, left and right; row 2, right), 151 (row 1, right; row 2, left), 152 (right), 153 (row 1, left; row 2, centre), 252 (2nd top and bottom), 253 (top), 372 (top), 374
Science Photo Library/David Parker: page 373 (centre)
Science Photo Library/Dr H.C. Robinson: page 151 (row 2, right)
Science Photo Library/Jane Shemilt: pages 149 (row 2, left), 375 (top)
Science Photo Library/St Bartholomew's Hospital: pages 24 (row 1, right), 148 (row 1, centre), 150 (row 2, left), 151 (row 1, left)
Science Photo Library/James Stevenson: page 152 (left)
Science Photo Library/Western Ophthalmic Hospital: pages 148 (row 2, right), 252 (2nd bottom)
Sothys: pages 87, 155 (bottom), 228, 293, 294, 309 (bottom), 400, 403 (bottom)
Mike Wyndham: page 153 (row 1, centre)

INTRODUCTION

How to use this book

This book has been designed with *you* in mind. It has a dual purpose:

1   To lead you through the NVQ level 2 Beauty Therapy qualification, providing background, technical guidance with possible evidence collection and key skill information.

2   To provide a reference book that you will find useful to dip into, long after you have gained your qualification. The comprehensive cross mapping within the individual chapters will guide you through the NVQ units and indicate where the information applies – and should prevent repetition!

Each of the practical units contains the same essentials – the **Professional basics**. This has been presented as a separate section that should be worked through and adapted to the unit you are taking, at the time. The anatomy required for each unit has also been separated so that it can be accessed and referred to easily. As the anatomy is a constant theme through each unit, each anatomy topic shows exactly in which unit / outcome it is required as knowledge. Remember that you only have to learn it once and apply the knowledge to the practical area you are working through.

Back to basics

If you are familiar with the NVQ system and are confident about the background to this method of gaining a qualification, then skip this section, and move on! If you are new to the NVQ system then read on!

NVQ = National Vocational Qualification

This is a different, but highly successful method of gaining a qualification.

You may not have used it before, for example if you have come straight from school, or if you have not been in a training situation for some time.

What is an NVQ?

This is not an exam, with a pass or fail outcome. NVQ uses continual assessments, in each unit, building up to a qualification. It is a fairer option for those of us who freeze at the thought of an exam room!

There are several beauty therapy awarding bodies offering NVQs. Your training establishment will be able to guide you through the particular one they use, but the standards do not vary too much, and the information within this book should cover all eventualities.

How do I gain an NVQ?

The qualification is gained by showing lots of **evidence** within each unit and is practically based, so each student gets a very good grounding in all the skill areas.

This means that when you go into a salon, you have dealt with most client requests and have lots of confidence to perform the service, which after all is what the client is paying for.

How do I get my evidence?

Many forms of evidence are acceptable and your trainer / lecturer will be able to guide you through the best options for your individual learning programme. Each of the types of evidence is valid. These are:

- observed work
- witness statements
- assessment of prior learning and experience (APL)
- oral questions
- written questions and / or assignments
- other.

These will be recorded on **evidence sheets** provided and will form **a portfolio**. A portfolio is just a collection of all the evidence together. It should be **indexed** and easy to follow.

Why index?

An **assessor** will observe or guide you through the types of evidence listed above. This person will have had special training and a specific qualification designed to help you present your evidence in a format suitable for your awarding body.

For quality control and fairness across the subject areas, an **internal verifier** will check the assessor, and the portfolio instruction. This will be performed within your section / school at your place of training and should take place on a regular basis.

The awarding body also has an **external verifier** who will visit your training establishment regularly, and check that both assessors and internal verifiers are giving the correct information to you, the candidate. Then your portfolio can be accredited with a certificate. This can be achieved a unit at a time, or applied for all at once.

So, an organised portfolio is essential to present your work in an easy-to-view format.

What evidence do I need?

You should ask your assessor about the most suitable method for the work you are doing. Most portfolios have a mixture of evidence.

If you have **external previous evidence (APL)** or recent qualifications they can also be counted. For example, if you work in a shop, part-time, and have experience using the till, dealing with customers and complaints, then a **witness statement** from your employer, that is current, valid, signed and dated is very acceptable evidence.

This evidence would cover some of the reception units, as well as some communication units and the interpersonal skills required. It also covers some of the **ranges** required in your assessment books.

Other valid evidence could be photographs, project work, videotape or client record cards.

Standards

To give the overall picture we can look at what you are going to need to do. First, your training establishment will register you with its awarding body.

The awarding body will then issue you, the candidate, with your **assessment book**. Take care of it; treat it like gold, as it is very precious. It will become your only source of evidence for all your hard work.

Blissed Out Beauty Salon
1 Burgess Road
Buxton
Derbyshire
WE1 4RP

Ref: Siobhan Taylor

To Whom it May Concern

Siobhan is one of my part time employees, and is also one of your students within the Beauty Therapy section, studying for NVQ level 2: she tells me that her salon duties can be used to help support her evidence, for her portfolio.

I am very pleased with Siobhan's client care, and her attitude towards both staff and customers is very helpful and friendly.

Her duties include:
- *greeting the clients at reception*
- *making tea and coffee and providing refreshments*
- *cleaning throughout the day where required*
- *answering the telephone and dealing with enquiries*
- *operating the till for payments and products sold*
- *supporting the staff with equipment, products or consumables required.*

Siobhan is a hard worker, and she has a good understanding of what she can and cannot do within her work role. As she is not yet qualified, she cannot take any clients for their treatments, but she does a lovely job of supporting the other therapists.

She regularly takes part in our fire evacuation procedures and health and safety training, as well as product instruction and training demonstrations.

I would be happy to offer her a therapist's job when she does qualify as she has just the right attitude to client care, which is the foundation on which my business is founded.

Yours faithfully

Victoria Daunou

Within your assessment book you will be given guidance on how to achieve each unit.

There are conditions and terms that you must follow.

Performance criteria

You must perform these in the course of your assessed treatment. They are numbered and your assessor will tick them off as they are observed. For example, Unit BT9.1 has performance criteria including: 'using consultation techniques in a polite and friendly manner to determine the client's treatment plan'.

Ranges

These must be covered through the various methods of assessment previously discussed – observed performance, oral question or simulation, written question, project or through APL; for example, different skin types for Unit BT9.

Essential knowledge

Each unit is quite specific about the knowledge and understanding supporting the practical application.

Beauty therapy pathway

The new qualifications have been designed to enhance the career path of those wishing to have an all-round qualification within NVQ Beauty Therapy level 2, or provide routes for those wishing to specialise in a make-up route.

The core units are:

- G1 Ensure your own actions reduce risks to health and safety
- G6 Promote additional products or services to clients
- G8 Develop and maintain your effectiveness at work.

These are compulsory to all students, and cover all aspects of health and safety, product promotion and how to become a good team worker for your salon. You must take these three, and then choose one of the following routes:

- General Beauty Therapy route
- Make-up route.

There are optional units as well, such as G4 'Fulfil salon reception duties', BT13 'Provide nail art service' and so on.

The object of this book is to support you by providing the units for both routes to the qualification. This will make you into a highly employable beauty therapist, as you will qualify in the units most useful to clients, salon owners and their managers. You may decide that the General route is preferable because specialising early on in your training may narrow your employability – a make-up artist is an expert in one field only, who cannot multi-task in the salon, when she is not busy.

Those who gain a good grounding of all the units may wish to further their careers by going onto NVQ level 3.

What would I want as a salon owner or employer?

I would want my employee to be skilled in all outcomes of NVQ level 2, so that I know my therapist can perform any treatment and be flexible with clients.

Your personal tutor will guide you through the best options for you to take. However, I can say that when my own daughter starts her beauty therapy training I will be recommending that she gain as many qualifications as possible: starting with the General Beauty Therapy Route of facials, waxing, eye treatments, manicure and pedicure, reception duties and make-up.

I know then she will never be out of work, as she has the options of employment in a salon, self-employment as a mobile therapist, or working from home, with a wide treatment range to suit most client needs.

Features to help your learning

The purpose of this book is to inform and guide you through your NVQ level 2 Beauty Therapy qualification. To reinforce your learning process and get you thinking, there are several features to help you.

Reality checks

These are an important feature of the book. Each reality check gives you a chance to stop and think about your practice and the safest and most effective way to carry out your treatment. Many reality checks relate to performance criteria or essential achievement and your professionalism as a therapist.

Remember

Remember points can be found within each unit to highlight specific areas we feel you need to pay particular attention to.

In the salon

These scenarios are real-life situations that you may face in an actual salon! These are designed to highlight situations with circumstances that may need to be dealt with. For example, there may be a scenario about a customer complaint, which you have to relate to your knowledge of legislation and inter-personal skills. Scenarios help you to think ahead and give an indication of what may happen in a commercial salon.

Knowledge tests

These are put at the end of a topic to test your knowledge and understanding. They will not be valid as evidence for your portfolio unless they are carried out under assessment conditions, but they are very good revision – and fun!

Your questions answered

These bring up the 'what if' questions that you may think of during your work in the practical units.

Prompts

You will find these features at the end of certain topics. They are flow diagrams, which summarise the most important things to remember. An example is shown on the outside edge of this page – it is a summary of NVQs and their structure.

Federation of Holistic Therapists

We are pleased that this book has been approved by the Federation of Holistic Therapists. You can contact them through their website at www.fht.org.uk

---

Whichever route you decide upon the way you gain your qualification is the same:

Each unit has **performance criteria** that you must do.

Ranges that you must cover.

Knowledge and understanding points that you must learn to support your practical skills.

An **assessor** will help you to put together your **evidence**.

This is a file called a **portfolio**.

The assessor is helped by an **internal verifier** who will make sure the portfolio has all the right information.

An **external verifier** comes to your college or training establishment to oversee the whole process and give information from the **awarding body**.

The application forms for your qualification can then be signed and your certificate will arrive.

professional
BASICS

Professional basics

The professional basics are all about getting you started as a beauty therapist.

Before you can decide upon the most suitable treatment for your client, or prepare treatment plans, you need to have a clear understanding of the underlying principles of what you are doing.

This section covers the basic knowledge you will need before you start working through any practical unit. You will need to refer back to this section each time you start a new practical unit.

At the end of the **Professional basics** section you will be able to:

- describe the importance of personal presentation when in the workplace
- name the various types of communication and their meaning
- describe the many salon services available and gather price lists of local salons for comparison
- compare assessment techniques and discover the right one for you
- distinguish between contra-indications and contra-actions and how this affects the client and the therapist
- relate the hygiene rules to a practical situation within the salon
- know your rights as an employee and how to protect yourself and your client within legislation
- record all treatment plans for the client and keep excellent client records
- be able to prepare in full for the treatment to be carried out.

There are three main topics in this section:

- You – the therapist
- You and your client
- You, your client and the law.

You – the therapist

You will learn about

- professional presentation
- effective communication
- salon services
- treatment planning and preparation
- effective teamwork and relationships
- record keeping.

Professional presentation

As required by your awarding body, a professional appearance is expected not only to achieve your assessments but also to set the standards within your working life as a fully qualified therapist.

A professional appearance gives the client confidence in your ability as a therapist. This presentation should include:

Hair

Hair should be tied back and kept away from the face. The style should not interfere with the treatment. It is very distracting for the client if you have to keep flicking hair out of the eyes, and hygiene rules are broken if you keep touching your hair.

Nails

Nails should be clean, short and unvarnished (unless the employer states that, as a nail technician, you can have varnish on). Clients may develop an allergy to varnish, and chipped nail varnish is not a good advert for your trade! Unvarnished nails can also be seen to be clean. Long nails may scratch the client's skin when performing massage.

Jewellery

Most awarding bodies state that the only jewellery permitted is a plain wedding band and small unobtrusive earrings. Rings could scratch the client and carry germs. Remember that other body piercing may cause offence to some clients and does not reflect a professional image.

Uniforms

Most salons and training establishments require a professional uniform to be worn. This should be clean, pressed, and of a suitable length to work in. It is advisable to go up a size to allow free movement, or at least try it on with arm movements tested!

It is also wise to have several uniforms in order to allow one to be in the wash, and to prevent one uniform getting too soiled. Regular washing is essential to prevent body odour build-up as this can give off an unpleasant stale smell to the client.

Make-up

Subtle make-up may be worn, but heavy make-up or stale-make-up (e.g. left over from last night) is not professional. If the skin is clear and the eyebrows tidy the therapist may decide not to wear make-up at all – this is personal choice. The key should be how the therapist feels and looks on the day! Light make-up can hide minor blemishes and help tired eyes. If you need a 'pick me up', use it wisely.

Perfume

Remember that strong perfume may be as unpleasant to the client as body odour. Choose a light fragrance that does not overpower, and remember that stale perfume can be very unpleasant.

Also bear in mind that perfume cannot hide body odour, so the use of anti-perspirants and deodorants is recommended, as well as daily bathing to prevent an accumulation of smells. An anti-perspirant will prevent perspiration building up, and a deodorant will help prevent odour. Most of the products available do both jobs.

Shoes

Your shoes should be clean and comfortable for a full day's work. If your shoes do not fit securely, you could have or cause an accident.

Open shoes do not provide enough support for the feet, and high heels can damage your posture. Leather shoes allow the feet to breathe and are therefore more hygienic, preventing a build-up of bacteria, which may cause odour problems and lead to athletes' foot.

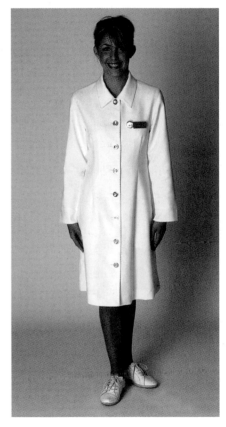

A clean uniform is part of your professional appearance

Oral hygiene

Regular dental care will prevent decay in the teeth, and so stop bad breath forming. Regular brushing, mouth sprays, mints and breath fresheners are also advisable to prevent stale breath being passed over the client. Remember that bad breath can be a sign of illness, so it may be worthwhile getting a dental or medical check-up if you think you may have a problem. It is only polite and courteous to your client to avoid strongly flavoured foods, such as curry, garlic and onions, especially at lunchtime. Smoking can also cause odours to cling to the breath and the clothing – a good excuse to give up smoking, even if only at work.

Professional presentation: preparing to work

It is not only personal presentation that makes a professional beauty therapist but your attitude, too. Beauty therapy is a service industry. The general public are our clients and they pay for our service and our expertise. Therefore they should also be entitled to our full attention and care.

It is not just the décor of a salon that creates atmosphere, it is the ambience created by the people within it. How the therapist mentally prepares for work goes a long way to producing the calm, relaxed feeling of a salon which allows the client to gain maximum benefit from the treatment.

Put on a smiling, caring expression when you are working – you may have lots of your own personal problems, but passing them onto your client is not acceptable. Never gossip to your client about others: either staff or clients. Do not shout, swear or curse at work – you will develop the habit and not even realise when or to whom you are doing it.

It is said that you get out of life what you put in – and that is also true about a beauty therapy treatment. A quiet, relaxing facial should be as pleasurable to give as it is to receive – make sure that it is. A good therapist will gain satisfaction from a tranquil hour and you will find that giving a facial massage is very soothing to both of you.

As a quality check after a treatment a good therapist should ask herself:

- Would I like to be treated as I have just cared for that client?
- Would I pay for the treatment I have just given to that client?
- Could I have improved upon the quality of my service?
- Was it as restful and as peaceful as it could have been?
- Has the client re-booked?

Effective communication

Whatever your position at work you will need to communicate with others. If your business is to be successful you will need to communicate effectively with a variety of different people, as can be seen in the diagram. This communication can be verbal, non-verbal or written.

Verbal communication

This is what you say and so it must be:

- clear
- to the point
- easily understood, using everyday language – technical terms should be put into easy terms, where possible
- spoken in a friendly manner.

Communication at work will be with many different people

Remember those who may be hard of hearing – eye contact reinforces the message.

Non-verbal communication

This is another term for **body language**. Your body conveys messages through your:

- posture
- facial expressions
- gestures.

These unconscious gestures tell you a lot more about your client than verbal communication can. The therapist should be aware of body language and learn how to interpret it.

Watch for signs that understanding is not clear, or the client is not satisfied or following what you are saying.

- **Positive body language** – expressions and gestures such as smiling, nodding in agreement, lots of eye contact and open gestures, such as arms uncrossed.
- **Negative body language** – frowning, tension, no eye contact, and closed gestures, such as the arms crossed.

Communicating and working together

When you work in a salon you may have a manager who supervises what you do, or you may have junior staff whom you guide through the working day. Good communication means being understood: the message sent out is the message received.

Working under supervision

This means that you:

- accept that someone is in charge
- should take instructions and act upon them
- communicate effectively
- take responsibility for your job role and do it to the very best of your ability.

Working together

Good teamwork means:

- supporting each other, not being in conflict with one another
- giving the salon a good atmosphere, which the client senses
- providing a reliable service
- giving effective results.

The ability to listen

Communication is a two-way process and having effective listening skills means:

- knowing when to stop talking and listen to what is being communicated
- listening with interest and understanding
- providing encouragement and confirming you have understood what has been said – nodding or agreeing with the point raised.

Written communication

Communication that is written down must be:

- **clear** and easy to understand
- **concise** – only information that is required should be given
- **legible** and easy to read
- **well presented** – handwritten or word processed
- **correct** – *all* the information should be included.

Body language can give you a lot of information – what can you tell from the body language of the client, on the left?

Check it out 🔍

Observe those around you, and analyse their communication skills. If you have part-time employment, quietly observe people in various skill areas, and in different positions, e.g. managers, and make some notes on this. How does your direct boss communicate with you?

memo

to	*Rasheda - Senior Therapist*
from	*Mrs Makowska*
time	*9.30am*
memo	*Mrs Makowska has phoned to cancel her appointment tomorrow, she has been signed off sick by her doctor - Possible Chicken Pox!*
message taken by	*Judy on Reception*

Written communication must be clear and concise

Clear written communication is important for many aspects of work within the busy salon environment, including health and safety, accident reports and record cards. For example, the client could be placed in danger if an allergic reaction warning on her record card is not readable.

Salon services

A good therapist is pleasant, patient, and helpful to everyone who comes into the salon. The needs of each person will vary and you must be able to give correct information. If you do not know, you must be professional enough to admit your knowledge is not sufficient, and get a salon manager to help – rather than making something up.

Treatments offered

Even if you personally cannot perform the entire treatment list, it is important to be aware of all the treatments and sell them. A professional therapist will have a thorough knowledge of the treatment process, the advantages or disadvantages of each, and each of the topics mentioned below. The salon will lose business if you just shrug and say you don't know.

Suitability of treatment

Not all treatments are suitable for all clients. Some treatments require a patch test, prior to the appointment, in order to assess the sensitivity of the skin or eyes. If a client has a treatment that was not entirely suitable for her, she will not be pleased. A dissatisfied customer will not return to the salon and may spread bad advertising instead.

Treatment timings

The timings of treatments should be accurately given. Do not mislead the client or underestimate how long a treatment may take or your credibility will be undermined. In addition to this, the smooth running of the salon will be disturbed if timings are not given correctly.

> **Reality Check!**
>
> Sales-related bonuses are common in the beauty therapy industry: a basic salary is boosted by commission on sales of products and of services – especially if you work on cruise liners. Linking treatments and products, and selling them to your client, should become second nature. With confidence and knowledge of products and services, selling is very straightforward. Remember that the client will want your products.

TIME	(1) SUSAN	(2) YASMIN	(3) LOUISE	(4) HAYLEIGH	(5)
9.00	MRS AUSTIN PHONE 823181 ½ LEG WAX	MISS ALLEN PHONE 631212 ACRYLIC NAILS FULL SET	MISS BROWN PHONE 761047 WEDDING PAMPER	MR SIMONS PHONE 471151 FULL BODY MASSAGE	
9.30	MRS WOOLFORD PHONE 621148				
10.00	FULL BODY MASSAGE			MRS SINGH PHONE 821356	
10.30	MRS J STREET PHONE 521683 EYELASH PERM			EYELASH & BROW TINT	
11.00	MRS K GAROGHAN PHONE 356987 AROMATHERAPY CANCELLED BACK MASSAGE	MISS COLLINS PHONE 712185 BRIDAL MAKE-UP			

Accurate treatment timings are helpful for both the client and the therapist

Time is money and in order to be cost effective the timing of treatments must be accurate. Standard timings also help maintain the quality in the salon, so that all therapists offer the same time for each treatment. Clients are then all treated equally and get the same value for money.

The frequency of treatments given should also be negotiated with the client and will be dependent upon:

- the time available
- financial considerations of the client
- the condition or suitability of the area of the body to be treated.

Prices

Prices will vary from salon to salon, and area to area. Price lists should always be on display. This allows the client to view the costs for herself and is also additional advertising.

Costings given should be truthful, with no hidden extras – no one likes to be conned.

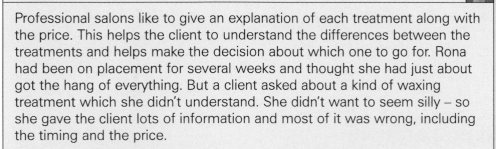

In the salon

Professional salons like to give an explanation of each treatment along with the price. This helps the client to understand the differences between the treatments and helps make the decision about which one to go for. Rona had been on placement for several weeks and thought she had just about got the hang of everything. But a client asked about a kind of waxing treatment which she didn't understand. She didn't want to seem silly – so she gave the client lots of information and most of it was wrong, including the timing and the price.

In your group discuss all the effects that might have had:

a on the salon
b on Rona's colleagues
c on Rona.

Special offers

If the salon has any offers to pass on to the client then you need to be aware of them. This helps to promote the offer and provides a chance to sell additional treatments that your client may not be aware of.

Most people like a bargain, or offer, and if they get to hear about it after the offer closes they will be very cross.

Remember that there is legislation in place regarding sale prices (refer to the Sale of Goods Act, page 38, in the legislation section) so be careful when advertising a sale in your window.

Retail sales

As mentioned earlier, retail sales form an important part of any busy salon, and can help boost your wage packet at the end of the week.

Many salons offer a full retail sales service to complement the products used in the treatment. You need to be aware of what your salon sells, whether it is in stock, and what its benefits and selling points are.

Reality Check!

A manicure should have a time of about 45 minutes, but if the receptionist has only allowed half an hour, and it is the first appointment of the day, you will be at least a quarter of an hour behind all day. If you then over-run by ten minutes with every client, your last client of the day may be kept waiting for nearly an hour.

Body Treatments

We offer a comprehensive range of treatments designed to relax, invigorate and revitalise you.

Body Massage

In a relaxing atmosphere, tired muscles, aches and pains are revived reducing tension, easing away stress; skin, blood and lymph are improved, helping remove toxins and increasing metabolism.

Full body massage: £22.50
Back, neck and shoulder massage: £12.50

G5 Massage

The ultimate stress buster ....
A mechanical massage designed to reduce tension, soften fatty deposits and detoxify problem areas. £18.00

Clients need to know what the different treatments involve and how much they cost

Retail sales can be an important part of a salon's business

Money will be lost if you ignore the customer who wants to buy the product that has just been used within the treatment. Most suppliers provide large sizes of product for use in the treatment room, with a smaller retail size for the client. In the course of conversation you will be asking about your client's homecare routine and which products she uses. Continuous care at home with the right products boosts the benefits of a salon treatment and good results can be seen.

Complaints

Realistically, a busy salon will encounter complaints sometimes. It is therefore important for salons to have a complaints procedure, which staff are aware of and have been trained to follow. This will mean that when a complaint does arise, however minor, the correct salon policy can be followed. An example of a complaints procedure follows.

- Deal with any complaints pleasantly in a professional manner.
- Calm the client and remove her from the reception desk to a more private area.
- Listen to her. Be objective and not defensive – the complaint may be valid.
- Be prepared to apologise if you are in the wrong and offer some form of compensation – a free treatment perhaps.
- Try to reach a mutually satisfactory outcome. This will minimise the damage that a complaint may have on other customers, and prevent further legal action being taken.
- Should the complaint be about another person, ask the staff member later in a calm manner. Do not blame the others in front of the customer.
- Record the complaint in the customer comments book.
- Be aware of the legal implications of further action – check out the insurance topic on page 40.

Treatment planning and preparation

Treatment planning is essential for the smooth organisation of a salon with more than one therapist working. Through good organisation, the relaxed, calm atmosphere that a salon should have will be in place, and that will be reflected in the mood of both customers and staff. Even if there is only one therapist employed, treatment planning will help with time management in order to ensure that money is not lost.

Remember the old saying:

Time = money

Treatment planning should be viewed as an investment. The more planning carried out 'behind the scenes' the more professional the treatment becomes. The key is to be organised.

The receptionist

A great deal of planning for the treatment starts with the receptionist and the initial booking of treatments. The receptionist needs to be aware of:

- what treatments are being offered through the day and therefore which preparations can begin early, e.g. turning on the wax heaters
- what any treatment involves and therefore how much time should be booked out
- if this is a first treatment for the client or the middle of a course
- if a full consultation is needed, therefore needing more time
- the 'before and after' of the treatment – undressing / dressing / shoes etc.

A safety net of time should be included so that a client relationship can be built up.

Check it out

1 If you are employed in a salon, put in your portfolio the salon price list and all the advertising material the salon may have. Regardless of whether you can perform the treatments, you need to be aware of the salon services available. If you do not understand some of the treatments in the price list, ask your manager for a demonstration during staff training, or ask a beauty therapist for a full explanation.

2 Do an analysis of the services available in two local salons and compare their services and prices. Are they similar? Do they cater for different client types? Are their prices competitive with one another?

How would you improve upon their price lists? What would you introduce?

Discuss in your group the differing services and why they may be different.

Treatment and planning should include these tasks

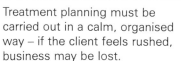

Reality Check!

Treatment planning must be carried out in a calm, organised way – if the client feels rushed, business may be lost.

Unexpected occurrences

An organised therapist will make the receptionist aware of any alterations to the day, any time out of the salon, and any change of plans, well in advance.

Obviously the uncontrollable factor is **sickness**. If you have a full column of clients booked in and are unable to attend work because of illness there is very little that can be done. Therefore, the earlier you notify the salon, the better.

The receptionist should be able to rearrange some clients for another day, or at least notify them, as they may wish to cancel. The other therapists in the salon then have the task of covering all the clients who cannot be contacted. This is dependent upon the goodwill of the other staff members, and a good relationship is vital for the health, growth and atmosphere of the salon.

You should discuss at the initial job interview what the establishment policy is regarding illness and sick cover, as well as sick pay.

Good working relationships between staff should also be part of the planning for the salon manager or owner. **Teamwork** is very important and regular training and team building is essential.

If you as a therapist are continually unreliable and dependent upon the goodwill of others, then resentment will soon start to build up. The good atmosphere of the salon is lost, tensions will rise and arguments may occur – not very good public relations.

Develop and improve personal effectiveness within the job role

You must prepare for the working day ahead and contribute to the planning of the salon. Look back to the 'Professional presentation' section (pages 8–10), which deals with your expected appearance and presentation.

Remember, however, that treatment planning is not just about appearance and personal presentation. Just as important is your approach or mind-set. Most organisational skills develop from having the right attitude.

Being organised and planning ahead can become second nature and almost part of your personality at work. Being prepared, tidy and forward thinking are very good habits to cultivate!

You should ask yourself these questions:

Treatment planning starts at the booking-in stage

Reality Check!

As part of your evidence for Unit G8 you may be asked to be the salon manager for the practical workshop session, when practical assessments are taking place. This puts *you* in charge of your fellow trainees and you may face the problem of having clients in reception, with no therapist to treat them because of sickness. You will see the other side of the coin.

Reality Check!

Treatment planning should begin right at the start of the day, as you get out of bed. As evidence for Unit G8 you will be expected to analyse your own performance within your job role and set your own targets for improvements. Self-evaluation really helps with the development of organising skills.

At home
- Is my overall ready?
- Will I be early enough to organise my day?
- Is my personal presentation professional?
- Enough time for the journey to work?
- Money, keys and lunch organised?
- Am I prepared for minor accidents eg laddered tights?

At home

Arriving at work
- What treatments do I have today?
- Am I organised and calm?
- What preparation do I need to begin?
- How can I help anyone else?
- What products, stock or equipment do I need?
- When is my first appointment?

Arriving at work

During the day

By continually evaluating these questions you can recognise and improve upon your working pattern. If being disorganised is a habit that you have fallen into, with the attitude that 'it really doesn't matter, because someone else will do it', then bad habits need breaking.

How will disorganisation be recognised? By:

- clutter in the salon
- complaints from customers
- grumbles from other members of staff regarding extra workload
- continual poor time keeping
- confusion regarding treatments and equipment.

Effective teamwork and relationships

The salon manager plays a vital role and it is important that you understand how what he or she does affects how the salon operates.

The manager

The role of the salon manager is vital to the treatment planning and preparation of the working day. A good manager should:

- have a set salon system in place for morning and evening preparation and jobs to be done (these should be on a rota basis for all to do)
- have procedures and rules for everyone to follow – this will provide a consistent standard of service
- have clear guidelines on treatment times and expected preparation time
- provide realistic times for specific treatments
- hold regular training sessions for everyone so that all members of staff know what is expected of them
- praise and reward those who perform well
- appraise and direct those who are not organised
- instruct clearly and without favour
- instruct clearly with regard to being cost effective, not wasting products and being uneconomical
- lead by example and be professional at all times.

Reality Check!

Poor treatment preparation and planning ultimately lead to stress. This is the feeling of not coping and always being in a muddle.
If you feel stressed, ask yourself why.

You – the therapist – should reflect upon the following.

Would I like to be a client of mine?

Did I offer the very best of service?

Would I pay for the treatment I have just given?

If the answers are No then a review of planning and preparation could make a big difference.

Record keeping

Good record keeping is absolutely essential to any beauty salon. You should create and use good systems in order to keep track of your work and your clients.

Record cards

The functions of a record card are:

- to record relevant details so as to be able to contact the client if necessary
- to provide full and accurate information which will ensure client safety
- to ensure consistency of treatment – regardless of who performs the treatment
- to record the number of treatments in a course and the date of each
- to note changes to the treatment programme or contra-actions if they occur
- to record the progress of the condition or treatment success
- to safeguard the salon and the therapists – to prevent clients taking legal action for damages or negligence.

The record card should be filled out in full for every treatment the client has. It should be written accurately, neatly and legibly.

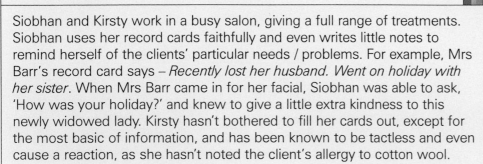

In the salon

Siobhan and Kirsty work in a busy salon, giving a full range of treatments. Siobhan uses her record cards faithfully and even writes little notes to remind herself of the clients' particular needs / problems. For example, Mrs Barr's record card says – *Recently lost her husband. Went on holiday with her sister.* When Mrs Barr came in for her facial, Siobhan was able to ask, 'How was your holiday?' and knew to give a little extra kindness to this newly widowed lady. Kirsty hasn't bothered to fill her cards out, except for the most basic of information, and has been known to be tactless and even cause a reaction, as she hasn't noted the client's allergy to cotton wool.

Would you rather be treated by Siobhan or Kirsty?

Record systems

Most salons have a number system in place, or keep records on computer. This is both for safekeeping and for easy retrieval. Most software packages for computers have a database system for easy recovery of names and storage. A computer system is a large cost to start with, but can be very easy to use, with the correct training. It is ideal for use in a larger salon, with a wide client base. However, the **Data Protection Act** needs to be upheld. Please go to the section on legislation (page 39) for more details.

The storage of record cards should be given consideration. They need to be accessible to the receptionist or therapist, but not so open that others can view them. A locked filing cabinet or drawer is most common, with limited access to the keys.

The two most common ways of filing names are:

- a number system i.e. client 1, client 2, etc.
- an alphabetical system i.e. A, B, C, etc.

Alphabetical systems tend to use the first letter of the surname and if two names begin with the same letter then the second letter is used and so on.

Reality Check!

The information on record cards should be kept private and confidential. If confidentiality is broken it is an offence to the client, leading to loss of clientele and revenue. If confidentiality of client records is broken, it is an offence under the Data Protection Act and the salon or therapist can be liable to prosecution.

Remember

Be safe – check for clients with nut or wheat allergies as these ingredients can be used in oils, creams and masks.

FACIAL TREATMENT	NAME		TEL	HOME			
				OFFICE			

ADDRESS			AGE	

DOCTOR Name:		TEL :		SMOKE		DRINK		MEDICATION:	

MEDICAL HISTORY	ASTHMA		HEPATITIS		DIABETES		ALLERGIES:				

GENERAL HEALTH	GOOD		POOR		CONSTIPATION		BLOOD PRESSURE	NORMAL		HIGH		LOW	

SKIN ASSESSMENT	A	B	C			A	B	C			A	B	C
SEBORRHOEA				DELICATE					SUNTAN				
OPEN PORES				DRY					PIGMENTATION				
BLOCKED PORES				DEHYDRATED					DILATED CAPILLARIES				
BLACKHEADS				MATURE					SKINTAGS				
ACNE				AGEING					MOLES				
SCARS				SLACK					SUPERFLUOUS HAIR				

	TREATMENT	MACHINE SETTINGS	PRODUCTS	AMPOULES	ADVISED FOR FOR HOME USE	THERAPIST	AMOUNT £	DATE
1								
2								
3								
4								
5								
6								

HOMECARE ROUTINE: ADVICE FOLLOWED   YES ☐   NO ☐   REGULAR HOME USE ☐   IRREGULAR HOME USE ☐

NOTES

INDEMNITY: I confirm that to the best of my knowledge the answers that I have given are correct and that I have not withheld any information that may be relevant to my treatment.

Signature .... *Date* ....

A facial treatment record card

However it would be unrealistic to assume that there is only one Mrs Thomas in the area! This is how confusion can occur.

Be very careful about which client is which. Always take the client's full name and initial, along with address details. Repeat them back to the client as a double check so that there is no confusion with clients of the same name.

Subject-specific record cards

Obviously each client will have a slightly different record card, depending upon the treatment needs. The more detailed the record card is, the better picture will be drawn of the client, so that each therapist who treats that client is aware of all possible details that may affect the treatment outcome.

Many manufacturers of beauty therapy products supply record cards to salons, and they can be purchased in bulk for ease of use. Many have an area for illustration for both face and body treatments. This is especially useful with make-up charts and skin diagnosis, and will save the therapist writing a lengthy description.

Both skin problems and make-up application can be recorded on a simple diagram. Most record cards will provide this facility.

Remember

The more detailed the card the easier the treatment will be, and the safer the salon will be.

You and your client

Assessment techniques and questioning the client

This is a vital part of your role as a successful therapist. All treatments are based upon what you discover within the initial consultation. The only way to make a correct diagnosis of the client's needs is through questioning and then tailoring your plan to the information you receive. All practical assessments are based upon successful client consultations and recognising your client's needs.

All successful salons earn their reputation by providing an excellent personal service. Care and attention to your client is the key to good business. Your consultation should be carried out in privacy, and the service should be free. It is standard practice to link a consultation with a treatment plan.

A good therapist will use all the skills mentioned and follow the client's body language to help obtain the information required for a good effective treatment plan. It must be agreed mutually that the time and money involved and the results suit both your client and yourself. If the plan is unrealistic your client will not stay with your salon. She will go elsewhere.

Questioning techniques

Asking questions is a skilled task. If you really want to find out what your client thinks and needs from you, you need to ask her. How you ask, what you ask and the type of question will dictate the reply you get. So, it is important that you give some care to your questioning technique. This information should be included on the record card, which you will be filling out as you discuss details in your consultation. Use your record card as your guide. As already stated, verbal questioning will determine all the personal details – refresh your memory by looking at record cards, pages 17-18. There are two types of questions – open and closed.

Open questions

Open questions are much better for making the conversation flow, as they require a response. For example: 'How are you today?' The client cannot respond with just a 'yes' or a 'no'. A more detailed answer is needed and so these questions are good to break the ice.

Closed questions

Closed questions usually need only one-word answers. For example: 'Have you ever had high blood pressure?' These questions confirm or eliminate information: 'Yes I have' or 'No, I have not'. Sometimes you have to use a closed question if you just require facts, but try to keep them to a minimum.

A professional therapist will use open or leading questions to help put her new client at ease. For example, the following open questions could be asked as she greets the client at the door.

A successful consultation leads to a good treatment

Your professional consultation will include all this

- What's the weather doing out there now?
- Where did you manage to park the car?
- How far have you come?
- How did you hear about us?

It is better to use open questions than closed questions, such as the following.

- Is it still raining?
- Did you get the bus?
- Have you been here before?
- Is this your lunch hour?

Can you spot the differences? Try making up some of your own open and closed questions and try them out within your group.

Listening skills

Communication is a two-way process and the ability to be effective in listening skills means:

- knowing when to stop talking and *listen* to what is being communicated
- listening with interest and understanding
- providing encouragement and confirming you have taken in the conversation: nodding or agreeing with point raised.

Listening is a good skill to develop and is different from hearing. It is so easy to talk and not really listen. So:

- always maintain eye contact with the person who is speaking, and let them finish their sentence – never interrupt
- remember that really understanding what the client is trying to say may mean you also pick up on what she is *not* telling you
- do not formulate your reply whilst you are being spoken to – you will not have all the facts until the client has finished.

Observation skills

Diagnosis of the client's well-being is not only discovered by the consultation questions but also through observation. It can reveal as much as, and sometimes more than, questioning alone. The unconscious body language of the client can speak volumes about her general attitude and state of mind.

A dropped pair of shoulders and dragging feet will indicate that she is nervous, a bit low in self esteem or worried or anxious about something. A confident client will have more direct body language, more eye contact, with a spring in the step and an upright posture. So, when your client arrives it is important to observe:

- how she walks
- how she stands
- how she sits
- your client's body language generally
- whether there is a mobility or handicap problem to be aware of.

In addition to this, you may be able to view the area to be treated (if on the face), the condition of the client's skin, the amount of care and attention previously given to the area as well as, of course, your client's reactions to you.

Clarification techniques

Clarification means checking the details given by the client to ensure the information that she gives you is recorded correctly. You need to do this whenever information is being passed on to you. It will happen at all stages of client contact. The following are examples.

1   When the client makes a **telephone booking**, all information regarding date, time, the nature of treatment, and the client's name and number should be repeated back as confirmation. Avoid saying what the treatment is too loudly, as it

could be of a sensitive nature e.g. if the client is booked in to have a bikini wax she may not appreciate everyone in reception knowing about it!

2   When the client arrives at reception for the appointment, the time of the booking and the name of the therapist can be repeated to the client.

3   When the client is having the consultation.

Repetition of details will enable the correct treatment plan to be prescribed and reinforces what the therapist may already know. For instance: 'So, Mrs Gupta, your skin has been dry for most of the winter months. What products are you using?' This also gives the client lots of opportunities to respond to your open questioning techniques and therefore rapport builds up between you.

Technical knowledge

It is very important that you fully understand the treatments you are talking about. Do not make anything up – this is very unprofessional. Always refer to the manufacturer's instructions and product information if you are unsure.

You should always have a copy of your salon's price list at hand to refer to. A good price list should have the treatment description, time of the treatment and the cost.

Be straightforward and use words that your client will recognise. For example, she may not know what a comedone is – but she is sure to understand blackhead!

Product knowledge

Products, like treatments, require some time and effort so that you fully understand what they can do and how to use them properly. Be sure the information, benefits and effects you are claiming are true. It is also professional to ensure that the product you wish to sell to your client is appropriate and in stock. Selling an unsuitable product just to close the sale is very bad practice.

Regular training and visits from manufacturers will ensure that your information is up to date and accurate. Many companies are happy to visit training establishments to introduce their product knowledge.

Treatment and product advice

The client has come to you (and is paying) for your skill and expertise. Some of her issues may be of a personal or sensitive nature. Be gentle with her and treat her kindly.

When giving advice remember never to patronise or talk down to your client. All clients should be treated with the same respect and courtesy, regardless of how trivial their problems or questions may seem. Be both honest and realistic with aims and objectives in the treatment plan, especially with courses of treatment.

Make sure your client realises that results may take some time and are often not instant. Perhaps some small treatments that do have instantly visible results could be used as a morale booster, such as a pretty nail varnish with a manicure, or an eyebrow tidy.

⚠ Contra-indications

A contra-indication is the presence of a condition which makes the client unsuitable for treatment. A contra-indication means that treatment should not take place at all or that the treatment needs adapting. A treatment is normally unsuitable because the client has a medical condition which may be external and/or visible, or it may be 'hidden' and discovered during the consultation.

Remember

Clarification of information gives you the chance to help the client examine her lifestyle, health and homecare routine. It is also extremely flattering for the client when you take such an interest in her. After all, we all like to talk about ourselves. Having a loyal therapist who takes notice, with genuine concern, is very good for the ego and helps to boost the feel-good factor in the salon.

Reality Check!

Be careful when talking to your client of using technical terms that could cause confusion. It may be thought that you are showing off!

Accurate knowledge of your products is essential

Reality Check!

Under the Trades Descriptions Act 1968 it is a crime to describe goods falsely and to sell, or offer for sale, goods which have false claims about them. So, you cannot claim that a cream will make your client look twenty years younger, or that a treatment will make all her facial lines disappear. It is much better to say that the product will help replace lost moisture within the skin.

It is important that you do not treat the client because:

- the disease could be contagious and therefore there is a risk of cross-infection to both therapist and other clients
- the condition may be made worse by a treatment
- there may be a reaction later, which puts the client's health at risk.

This is why it is essential to complete a thorough consultation, prior to any treatment being given.

If the contra-indication is small and localised in one area, treatment **may** take place with some adaptation. For example, a minor cut would be covered with a plaster.

But a larger problem, such as a leg with open, weeping eczema, would be a definite contra-indication and further advice should be sought from the client's GP.

Be warned that some doctors' surgeries do demand a small fee for administration costs. However, this is preferable to risking a reaction to drugs taken, and a possible court case for negligence.

The GP permission slip could then be placed in the client's record card so that all therapists are aware of medical problems for that client and therefore all therapists are protected.

General contra-indications

To help you remember different contra-indications, try to visualise looking from the outside of the body and work inwards. What you may see on the skin comes first, then muscles, bone, blood and so on.

> **Reality Check!**
>
> A therapist should not name specific contra-indications when referring a client to a GP. This is because, as a therapist, you do not have medical qualifications with which to make a diagnosis, and it is unacceptable to cause the client any concern, which may be unfounded.

> **Reality Check!**
>
> It is important that the contra-indications are discovered prior to the treatment taking place, rather than half-way thorough the treatment. This is fundamental to both your clients' safety and to your professionalism.

Skin	Muscles	Bones	Body systems
Skin infections, diseases and disorders	Dysfunctional muscular conditions (such as Parkinson's disease or multiple sclerosis)	Broken bones	High or low blood pressure
Cuts, bruises and abrasions			Heart conditions
Thin papery skin			Diabetes
Raised and hairy moles	Loss of sensation in the area		Epilepsy
Unknown swellings	Dysfunction of the nervous system (such as motor neurone disease)		Severe asthma
Recent scar tissue			High fever, colds and flu
Varicose veins and phlebitis			

Contra-indications

Specific contra-indications are listed at the beginning of each unit. Please refer to them prior to commencing your treatment.

Contra-actions

A contra-action is the unfavourable reaction of a client to a treatment. Some treatments do cause some slight reaction, which is normal and to be expected, e.g. a waxing treatment will cause the skin to go red, and there may be some blood spotting. It is a normal reaction to the slight trauma that the skin has undergone. However, an abnormal reaction to a treatment would be a severe response, as shown in the diagram opposite.

> **Remember**
>
> Some of these contra-indications will not prevent treatment from taking place if the treatment is adapted or a doctor gives written permission. It may be that the condition is slight and not serious. Some clients find that treatments do help them, but it is not a therapist's job role to decide that. A GP must recommend it.

It is up to the therapist to respond quickly to any adverse reaction that happens within the salon, in order to minimise the problem and not make it worse. The client must also be informed of what to look for *after* the treatment has finished and what action to take at home.

Contra-actions can occur with the application of any product – even one your client has used for years can suddenly produce a reaction not seen before.

For specific contra-actions please refer to the individual units.

Hygiene and avoiding cross-infection

A dictionary definition of hygiene is: 'The science concerned with the maintenance of health; clean or healthy practices or thinking.' So for you, as a professional therapist, hygiene could be described as good practice to maintain:

- your own health
- your clients' health
- your colleagues' health.

However, there is no such thing as a completely sterile environment; perhaps the closest to it would be an operating theatre within a hospital. Germs are all around us and, while some are beneficial to humans, many of them are not. Beauty therapy treatments demand close human contact, so care must be taken to provide the maximum protection against cross-infection.

Expert advice on hygiene can be confusing. Conflicting reports have been seen in the media with regard to AIDS and hepatitis. The most valuable information can be gained from the professional body's code of ethics or practice. (Refer to your own awarding body for more details.) These guidelines have been established after a great deal of research on behalf of the beauty industry, and are most likely to be current.

It is important to understand the responsibilities we each have under the Health and Safety at Work Act, and under COSHH (Control of Substances Hazardous to Health), so please also refer closely to the legislation section for extra guidelines (pages 31–40).

Micro-organisms

In order to understand how to maintain the highest hygiene standards it is important to know how infection can occur. Micro-organisms are organisms that are too small to be seen by the naked eye. These micro-organisms are ever-present in the environment and can cause different types of infection.

An abnormal reaction to a treatment can lead to unpleasant contra-actions

Micro-organism	Disease
Bacteria	Boils, impetigo, sore throats, meningitis, pneumonia, diphtheria, tuberculosis, typhoid fever, tetanus (or lockjaw), whooping cough
Viruses	The common cold, flu, cold sores (herpes simplex), warts, measles, rubella (German measles), mumps, chickenpox, hepatitis A, B and C and HIV
Fungi / yeast	Ringworm of the foot, body, head and nail, thrush, infection to the heart and lungs, which may prove fatal
Protozoa	Diarrhoea, malaria and amoebic dysentery

Type of micro-organism and the diseases they can cause

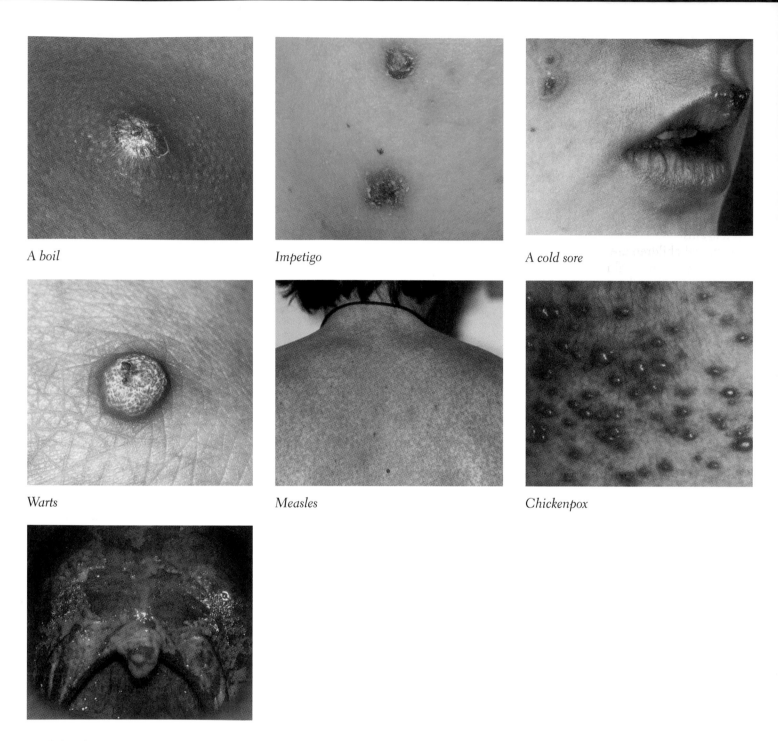

A *boil*

Impetigo

A *cold sore*

Warts

Measles

Chickenpox

Oral thrush

Micro-organisms enter the body through any route they can:

- through damaged, broken skin
- through the ears, nose, mouth and genitals
- into hair follicles
- into the blood stream via a bite from blood-sucking insects (e.g. malaria).

The symptoms and severity of the infection or disease will depend on the type of invasion, the person's immunity system being able to defend the body and general health. If a person is run-down then the micro-organisms have more chance of multiplying rapidly. They also thrive in poor hygiene. The best methods of avoiding these are prevention – through good hygiene practices.

Obviously some of these diseases are life threatening, but many are not and can be prevented by good hygiene. For example, protozoa can be transmitted from contaminated food and water, which grow and infect the bowel, causing ill health with diarrhoea.

Many of these diseases are also radically reduced by vaccination. Precautions can be taken against both Hepatitis B and tetanus – recommended for beauty therapists. Most school children are given immunisation against measles, mumps and rubella, unless there are medical reasons not to have the injections. Whooping cough has been dramatically reduced by the same method of immunisation.

Please refer to the contra-indication section (pages 21–22) for recognition of the common diseases that may prevent the treatment from taking place.

Good hygiene practices

How do you maintain good hygiene practices in a beauty salon?

A guide to controlling micro-organisms

Ammonia

Ammonia is commonly used as a base for trade liquids used to kill bacteria, e.g. barbicide that is used to soak suitable instruments in salons.

Antibiotics

An antibiotic is a chemical substance that destroys or inhibits the growth of micro-organisms. They are usually used to treat infections that will respond well to them, such as fungal or bacterial infections, and are given to humans and some animals for treatment.

Antiseptic

An antiseptic is a chemical agent which destroys or inhibits the growth of micro-organisms on living tissues, thus helping to prevent infection when placed onto open cuts and wounds.

Autoclave

An autoclave is a piece of equipment rather like a pressure cooker, used to sterilise equipment. It works by heating water under pressure to a higher temperature than 100°C, therefore creating an environment where germs cannot survive. It is most suitable for small metal equipment, such as eyebrow tweezers and manicure items.

Refer to individual manufacturers' instructions for use.

Bactericide

A bactericide is a chemical that will kill bacteria but not necessarily the spores, so reproduction may still take place. It can also be called biocide, fungicide, virucide or sporicide.

Be wise – immunise

Good hygiene practices must include these aspects

Remember

All good hygiene practices should be continuously carried out to ensure that no cross-infection takes place, that the client has total confidence in the salon and to ensure the best results are gained from each treatment carried out.

An autoclave   *A bactericide jar*

Chlorhexidine

Trade names for chlorhexidine include Savlon and Hibitane. Chlorhexidine is widely used for skin and surface cleaning and some sunbed canopies. Check individual manufacturers' instructions for cleaning.

Detergent

A detergent is a synthetic cleaning agent that removes all impurities from a surface by reacting with grease and suspended particles, including bacteria and other micro-organisms. Detergents need to be used with water, but are ideal for cleansing large surface areas.

Disinfectant

This is a chemical that kills micro-organisms but not spores – most commonly used to wash surfaces and to clean drains.

Phenol compounds

Phenol compounds are ideal for large areas that need cleaning but phenol does have a chlorine base and should not be used on the skin. It is used in industrial cleaning preparations and the old-fashioned carbolic soap.

Sanitation

This is the term used to describe conditions that are favourable to good health and preventing the spread of disease.

Sterilisation

Sterilisation is the complete destruction of all living micro-organisms and their spores.

Surgical spirit

Surgical spirit is widely used and easy to purchase from chemists. It can be used for skin cleansing, and the removal of grease on the skin. Surgical spirit comes in varying strengths of dilution. A 70% alcohol base concentration is acceptable for cleansing.

There are a great many commercial products on the market for cleaning and sterilisation – with lots of different trade names. This is merely a general guide. Please consult with the manufacturer's instructions for each individual piece of equipment. Most companies have their own particular favourites that they recommend. Also investigate the recommendations from beauty wholesalers and suppliers.

Your personal hygiene

- Always wash your hands – ideally with bactericidal gel – before and after every treatment.
- Wear disposable gloves for treatments if there is a possibility of an exchange of body fluids, e.g. waxing.
- Wear protective clothing for protection and to sustain a professional appearance, i.e. an apron for waxing.
- Cover cuts or broken skin with a waterproof plaster.
- Keep nails short and scrub under them with a nail brush.
- Do not come into work if you know you have an infection or disease likely to put anyone else at risk, e.g. impetigo.
- Wash hands thoroughly after every visit to the toilet.
- Follow the guidelines given in the 'Professional presentation' section (pages 8–10) for clean overalls etc.

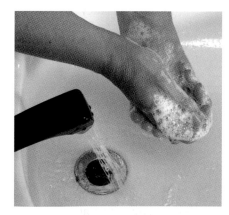

Thorough handwashing is essential to good hygiene

- Attend training programmes about hygiene and the use of sterilising equipment.
- Do not use equipment that is cracked or broken, as germs will be present. This includes chipped cups, plates or glasses.

Salon hygiene

- Sanitise used equipment, as fully as possible. This means following the manufacturer's instructions for individual equipment, such as using the recommended cleaner for make-up brushes so that the bristles do not fall out. Some cleaners will dissolve the glue that holds them in place.
- Invest time and correct training in the use of sterilisation equipment, such as an autoclave or sanitising unit.
- Clean the treatment area or room thoroughly. Clean daily and also wipe generally after each treatment has taken place. There are many preparations on the market for use on walls, floors and work surfaces, trolleys and couch and stool.
- All work surfaces should be cleaned regularly with hot water and detergent.
- Couch roll and towels can be used as a barrier between blankets and the clients – these can then be disposed of, and fresh ones put on for each client.
- Tissues tucked into the headband or turban can be disposed of after use, so keeping the headband / turban looking fresh.
- Towels should be washed after use – so your salon needs to invest in plenty of towels to ensure you do not run out.
- The same applies to towelling robes for clients. Big fluffy robes are very luxurious, but the image would soon be spoilt if dirty ones were given to clients.
- Disposable brushes for applying make-up will prevent cross-infection from lips and eyes.
- Make-up pencils should be wiped clean with spirit and resharpened to get rid of any contamination.
- Powder eye shadows and blushers need to be scraped onto a palette and then applied to the client, to avoid contamination.
- Creams and oils need to be decanted into a smaller bowl, using a spatula, and any excess should be thrown away. Never pour back into the original container any product that has been in contact with your hands or the client. In order to be cost-effective, be careful not to pour out too much, as it may be wasted.
- Disposable spatulas should be used for waxing, i.e. one use from pot to client, to avoid contamination.

Client hygiene

- It is a good idea to have some form of notice in the reception area asking clients to inform staff if they are suffering from any contagious diseases.
- Always carry out a full consultation to discover any contra-indications.
- Always perform a physical check of the area to be treated for infection etc.
- Do not treat if any unrecognised problems are present.
- Ask the client to sign the declaration on the record card stating that all medical and other information is correct to date, to avoid possible repercussions later.
- Before you start, always wipe the area to be treated with the appropriate lotion e.g. surgical spirit, Hibitane or the recommended choice of your establishment.
- Provide all possible protection for the client and insist that clients use the recommended procedure, for example: treading on the couch roll with bare feet to avoid touching the floor surface.
- Discourage the client from having a treatment if she has the beginnings of an illness – she may really want the treatment but spreading a cold or flu to you and to other clients is not fair.

Client modesty

Whatever treatment your client is having, remember to preserve her modesty and dignity. This is especially important on the first treatment, as the client may be very unsure of the procedures.

- Explain fully to clients how they will be positioned and how much clothing they will need to take off – a facial would not require the removal of the lower garments, but a wax treatment would. Make sure clients understand this.
- Always allow clients to get undressed and into a robe in privacy behind the curtains.
- Cocoon the client in a blanket and towels, with couch roll if required for treatment, and only expose the area of the body being treated. This will not only ensure the client is cosy and secure, but will also preserve modesty and provide warmth.
- Provide full instructions and a modesty towel if carrying out a more intimate treatment, such as a bikini wax. Ask the client to place protective couch roll in the pantie line rather than just assuming she won't mind you doing it.
- Ensure your working area or cubicle is private and that others are not able to see in. No one having a bikini or leg wax wants to feel the general public can see in. Even a facial is not a very relaxing treatment if the client feels exposed.
- Respect clients' modesty by keeping personal details, information and record cards confidential and private. It is a privilege to be a party to certain information – do not abuse the clients' trust by sharing information with others unless it is necessary for a professional referral.
- Allow the client time and personal space to dress and prepare to meet the outside world after the treatment. Do not pull back the curtains and tell her to get up as your next client is waiting – this is very bad form.
- Finally, treat your client as you yourself would wish to be treated – with dignity, respect and as a valued customer.

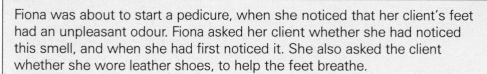

In the salon

Fiona was about to start a pedicure, when she noticed that her client's feet had an unpleasant odour. Fiona asked her client whether she had noticed this smell, and when she had first noticed it. She also asked the client whether she wore leather shoes, to help the feet breathe.

On discovering that the client's hygiene was good, and that the problem had only just started, Fiona examined the feet in close detail. She found between the toes the beginnings of an infection called athlete's foot.

Fiona is not a doctor, and is not qualified to suggest what might have caused this problem, but she was able to suggest tactfully that her client seek advice from her doctor.

The treatment had to stop, as athlete's foot is highly contagious, and could be spread to both clients and therapists. Fiona's tact and diplomacy stopped an infection from spreading, safeguarded herself and her salon, and helped her client, who was very grateful and returned for further treatments.

Remember

Ensure your client is fully aware of homecare routines and how to treat a possible contra-action to avoid infection. If the skin is broken or there is blood spotting, such as after waxing, this is especially important.

Treatment and client expectations

It is important to explain the treatment thoroughly to the client, and it is important that the client understands what the treatment involves.

This will help to:

- ensure client satisfaction
- avoid misunderstandings
- dispel any unrealistic expectations
- give the client confidence in the salon and the therapist.

Honesty between therapist and client is part of the ethical conduct expected to maintain the high professional standards for all beauty therapists. The table opposite gives some examples of unrealistic and realistic expectations.

The client must also be aware of:

- the time involved in a treatment
- the total cost of the treatment or course of treatments
- the position to be in – on the couch, sitting etc.
- the expected outcomes
- the length of time the treatment should last
- the possible contra-actions to the treatment
- the aftercare and homecare for the treatment
- the cost of items that may be purchased
- the cost of maintenance, e.g. for artificial nail structures
- how often the treatment should be given for maximum effect
- the reasons for a patch test, consultation and record cards.

The entire list above has a part to play in creating the complete picture for the client, so that the therapist gains the client's full trust and confidence.

The employer's duty to other persons not in employment includes not exposing them to health and safety risks – this includes contractors, employees, and self-employed people.

The **employee** has a responsibility to:

- take care during time at work to avoid personal injury
- assist the employer in meeting requirements under the Health and Safety at Work Act
- not misuse or change anything that has been provided for safety.

The employee has a duty to herself / himself, to other employees, and to the public.

The Act allows various regulations to be made, which control the workplace. The Act also covers self-employed persons who work alone, away from the employer's premises.

In 1992 EU directives updated legislation on health and safety management and widened the existing Acts. These came into force in 1993. There are six main areas:

- provision and use of work equipment
- manual handling operations
- workplace health, safety and welfare
- personal protective equipment at work
- health and safety (display screen equipment)
- management of health and safety at work.

Some provisions of the EU directives are:

- the protection of non-smokers from tobacco smoke
- the provision of rest facilities for pregnant and nursing mothers
- safe cleaning of windows.

Workplace (Health, Safety and Welfare) regulations 1992

Your employer should ensure your workplace complies with the requirements of these regulations by:

- maintaining the workplace and all equipment and systems used there
- ensuring adequate ventilation
- keeping the workplace at a reasonable temperature (minimum 16°C)
- making sure you have sufficient light to work comfortably
- keeping your workplace clean and tidy
- ensuring you have enough room to work comfortably
- keeping floor and 'traffic routes' in a reasonable condition (no holes, slopes or uneven surfaces)
- ensuring the workstations and seating are suitable
- providing you with suitable washing and toilet facilities (with soap and a means of drying your hands)
- making sure you have accommodation for clothing (worn at work) and changing facilities
- providing you with facilities for resting and eating (if meals are to be eaten on the premises)
- providing you with clean drinking water and cups
- removing waste materials on a regular basis
- keeping you safe from falling objects
- making sure all doors and gates are suitably constructed and fitted with any necessary safety devices

- making sure windows are protected against breakage and signs (or similar) are incorporated where there is a danger of someone walking into them
- making sure escalators and moving walkways have safety devices fitted so they can be stopped in an emergency

Manual Handling Operations Regulations 1992

The Health and Safety Executive (HSE) has drawn attention to skeletal and muscular disorders caused by manual handling and lifting, repetitive strain disorders and unsuitable posture causing low back pain. The regulations require certain measures to be taken to avoid these types of injuries occurring.

1 Think about the lift. Where is the load to be placed? Do you need help? Are handling aids available?

2 Get ready to lift. Stand with your feet apart.

3 Bend the knees. Keep the back straight. Tuck in your chin. Lean slightly forward over the load to get a good grip.

4 Get a good grip on the load and lift smoothly.

Safe lifting procedures must be observed

Think of all the situations that may apply in the salon:

- stock unpacking and storage – lifting heavy objects
- couch height adjustable for individual therapists
- chairs or stools used in the treatment rooms
- trolley height
- reception desk and chair
- rotation of job roles so that the therapist is not in the same position for every treatment
- height and size of nail art desk.

It is worth considering all of these factors when purchasing your equipment, as you then have to work with the consequences!

When purchasing a couch for home or mobile use, it is well worth pretending to carry out a body massage, complete with client lying on the couch, to find the right height. Working at a couch at the wrong height is very bad for the back in the long term, and may cause considerable discomfort.

Heat stress

The Health and Safety Executive draws attention to heat stress at work. The best working temperature in beauty therapy is between 15.5 and 20 °C.

Humidity (the amount of moisture in the air) should be within the range of 30 to 70 per cent, although this will vary if your salon has a sauna and steam area. They should be in a well-ventilated area away from the main workrooms, whilst still being accessible to clients. There should also be sufficient air exchange and air movement, which must be increased in special circumstances, such as chemical usage. Treatment rooms used for nail art, aromatherapy, bleaching or eyelash perming will need specialist ventilation methods.

Remember

Follow the golden rule: always lift with the back straight and the knees bent. If in doubt – don't lift at all!

Mechanical ventilation: extractor fans, which can be adjusted at various speeds.

Natural ventilation: open windows are fine, but be careful of a draught on the client.

Air-conditioned ventilation: passing air over filters and coolers brings about the desired condition, but of course this is the most expensive method!

A build-up of fumes, or of strong smells (for example, from manicure preparations), will cause both physical and psychological problems, which affect not only clients but staff, too!

Physical effects	Psychological effects
Headaches	Irritability
Sweating	Aggressive behaviour
Palpitations	Nervous fatigue, which may result in mistakes being made
Dizziness	
Nausea or fainting	Lethargy

The effects of heat stress

Protective clothing

This covers both equipment and protective clothing provisions to ensure safety for all those in the workplace. The regulations also provide that workplace personnel must have appropriate training in equipment use. Protective clothing, such as white overalls for work wear, ensures cleanliness, freshness, and professionalism. For certain treatments it may be advisable to wear extra disposable coverings. The client's clothing must also be protected.

Protection against infectious diseases

Caution: It is important to protect against all diseases, which are carried in the blood or tissue fluids. Protective gloves should be worn whenever there is a possibility of blood or tissue fluid being passed from one person to another i.e. through an open cut or broken skin. Two specific infectious diseases to mention are:

• AIDS

Acquired Immune Deficiency Syndrome (AIDS) is a disease caused by the Human Immuno-deficiency Virus (HIV). The virus is transmitted through body tissue. Most people are aware of AIDS because of media coverage. The virus attacks the natural immune system, and therefore carries a strong risk of secondary infection, such as pneumonia, which could be life threatening. As there is no known cure, prevention through protection is vital.

• Hepatitis variants (A, B and C)

Hepatitis is an inflammation of the liver. It is caused by a very strong virus also transmitted through blood and tissue fluids. This can survive outside the body, and can make a person very ill indeed; it can even be fatal. The most serious form is Hepatitis B and you can be immunised against this disease by a GP. For those who can prove they need this protection for their employment there is no cost involved. Most training establishments will recommend this.

> **Remember**
>
> It is very good practice to investigate what your professional body states about protective clothing. It may invalidate your insurance if you do not follow these directives.

> **Remember**
>
> Always cover cuts with a plaster.

Dust   Toxic   Flammable

Irritant   Corrosive   Oxidising Agent

Symbols showing types of hazardous substances

Personal Protective Equipment at Work Regulations 1992

Every employer and self-employed person must ensure that suitable personal protective equipment is provided both for themselves and for their employees in situations where they may be exposed to a risk to their health or safety while at work. This is particularly relevant to waxing (refer to BT6 'Remove hair using waxing techniques') and where there is a risk of contamination by body fluids (see also Environmental Protection Act 1990, Controlled Waste Regulations 1992 and Special Waste Regulations 1996, page 36).

Control of Substances Hazardous to Health Regulations 1999 (COSHH)

This law requires employers to control exposure to hazardous substances in the workplace.

Most of the products used in the salon are perfectly safe, but some products could become hazardous under certain conditions or if used inappropriately. All salons should be aware of how to use and store these products.

Employers are responsible for assessing the risks from hazardous substances and must decide upon an action to reduce those risks. Proper training should be given and employees should always follow safety guidelines and take the precautions identified by the employer.

The COSHH regulations require that the containers of hazardous substances are labelled with warning symbols. These symbols are shown on the left.

Here are some examples of potential hazards:

- **highly flammable substances**, such as solvents, nail varnish remover or alcohol steriliser are hazardous because their fumes will ignite if exposed to a naked flame
- **explosive materials**, such as hairspray, air freshener or other pressurised cans, are also highly flammable and will explode with force if placed in heat, such as an open fire, or even on top of a hot radiator
- **chemicals** can cause severe reactions and skin damage – vomiting, respiratory problems and burning could be the result if chemicals are misused.

COSHH precautions

Employers must, by law, identify, list and assess in writing any substance in the workplace. This applies not only to products used for treatments in the salon, but also to products that are used in cleaning e.g. bleach or polish. Potentially hazardous substances must be given a hazard rating, or risk assessment, even if it is zero.

Finally, you should read all of the COSHH sheets used in the salon, and be safe: follow what they say, never abuse manufacturers' instructions and attend regular staff training for product use. You never know when you might need it!

TIPS

Manufacturers **have** to supply COSHH data sheets for all their products. Get one for each product.

Remember that a reaction can happen if the client is using products at home that may not mix well with salon preparations, eg home hair colorants.

Clients may be more susceptible to reactions if they are taking long-term medication, such as HRT or the contraceptive pill. This must be included on the client record card.

Obtain all the leaflets and latest information regarding COSHH from your local Health and Safety Executive office. **Keep up to date and keep safe**.

Remember these COSHH tips

Gas Safety (Installation and Use) Regulations 1994

These relate to the use and maintenance of gas appliances. You may think that this does not apply to you as a therapist, but read on! The **Rights to Entry Regulations** 1996 give gas and HSE inspectors the right to enter premises and order the disconnection of any dangerous appliances. The inspectors themselves are not normally trained gas fitters, so they will instruct you to contact your local service engineer. Gas fumes are silent, with no smell, and very, very deadly.

Cosmetic Products (Safety) Regulations 2003

These regulations are all part of consumer protection legislation. The EU has laid down strict regulations about the composition of products, labelling of ingredients, how the product is described and how it is marketed. American cosmetic companies have had to list all ingredients on their labels for years, and Europe is now following suit. This is ideal for the easy identification of products that some clients may be allergic to, such as lanolin.

Medicines Act 1968

This Act deals with the supply and use of topical anaesthetics and is enforced by the police and the medicines control agency. Product licence conditions are for medical application only and not for cosmetic use, therefore their use by a beauty therapist can be unlawful.

Trade Descriptions Act 1968

This Act is concerned with the false description of goods. It is important to realise the relevance of this Act.

It is illegal to mislead the general public. This also applies to verbal descriptions given by a third party and repeated. So, if a manufacturer's false description of a product is repeated you are liable to prosecution. The law states that the retailer must not:

- supply information that is in any way misleading
- falsely describe or make false statements about either a product or a service on offer.

The retailer may not:

- make false contrasts between present and previous prices
- claim to offer products at half price unless they have already been offered at the full price for at least 28 days prior to the sale.

Be mindful of using statements saying something is 'our price'. Comparison of prices can be misleading and can be illegal – be sure that the product is identical in every way. You should also check that products are labelled with their country of origin.

Sale of Goods Act 1979 and Sale and Supply of Goods Act 1994

This Act has several others under its umbrella of protection:

- the Supply of Goods and Services Act 1982
- the Unfair Contract Terms Act 1977
- the Supply of Goods (Implied Terms) Act 1973.

The Sale of Goods Act recognises the contract of a sale between the retailer and the consumer when purchasing a product, which applies when the salon sells a product to a client. Of course, it can also apply to us all as consumers when we purchase any goods (this Act is a good one to quote when returning something to a shop!).

The Act states that the retailer:

- has a responsibility to sell goods of the very best quality, which are not defective in any way
- must refund the money for the purchase if it is found to be defective (some retailers will only offer an exchange of goods, if there is no receipt)
- must then make a complaint to the supplier.

The Trade Descriptions Act covers several different areas

The Supply of Goods and Services Act 1982

This Act also deals with rights for the consumer and the trader's obligations towards the consumer. It has two branches: goods and services.

- **Goods** When we buy something in good faith we expect it to be:

  – of merchantable quality
  – fit for the purpose for which it was sold
  – as described in the advertising.

  If it is not, some or all of the money paid can be claimed back. This applies to all goods, regardless of whether they are on hire, in part exchange, or as part of a service.

- **Services** A person or trader providing a service (such as a beauty therapist) must:

  – charge a reasonable price
  – provide the service within a reasonable time
  – give the service with reasonable care and skill.

  This means no two-hour manicures, no charging outrageous prices, and no slapdash treatments! Your customer can complain and contact the Trading Standards Office, if she feels she has a case against you. Be careful!

Performing Rights – within Copyright, Design and Patents Act 1988

This Act is designed to protect the people who write music but then do not get the royalty payments they should when the music is played! Any use of music in the treatment room, reception or in exercise groups is classed as a public performance.

Phonograph Performance Ltd (PPL) collects licence payments from people wishing to use music on behalf of artists and record companies. Under the **Copyright Designs and Patent Act 1988** PPL can take legal action against persons who do not pay a licence fee to use music – and they do! This can mean a considerable fine for those who try to avoid paying. So all salons and exercise/aerobic instructors need to purchase music that has a built-in licence. Although more expensive to purchase in the first place (a CD can cost about £30) it does save all the worry of a heavy fine, if caught!

Most good specialist music shops have a section of licensed music – just ask.

Salons should purchase music with a built-in licence

Data Protection Act 1998

Businesses that use computers or paper-based filing systems to hold personal details about their staff and clients may be required to register with the Data Protection Registrar.

The Data Protection Registrar will place your business on a public register of data users and issue you with a code of practice which you must comply with, stating:

- you must keep information secure
- you must ensure information is accurate and relevant to your needs
- you must comply with individuals' requests for information that you are holding on them.

Contact: Data Protection Registrar, Springfield House, Water Lane, Wilmslow, Cheshire. SK9 5AX. (tel. 01625 545745).

Any person can ask to see the information held by an organisation about him or her within 40 days for a fee not greater than £10. It is possible to gain compensation through a civil court action if you feel there has been any infringement of rights, in which information that was given for a specific purpose has been abused.

Test your knowledge

1 List five points that you think contribute towards a professional consultation.

2 a Give three examples of open questions.
   b Give three examples of closed questions.

3 As a student, what would your responsibilities be regarding the following pieces of legislation?
   a The Health & Safety At Work Act
   b The Consumer Protection Act
   c COSHH

4 a How do the Electricity at Work Regulations affect the use of electrical equipment in the salon, clinic or health club?
   b If electrical apparatus is found to be faulty, what action must be taken?

5 Why should you be insured?

6 When would you need to wear protective clothing? Why?

7 What are your salon guidelines regarding client safety?

8 If a face cream states on its label that it can guarantee loss of wrinkles, under which Act would you be liable to prosecution?

9 Which body provides a code of practice or ethics that you have to follow as a beauty therapist?

10 Which regulations require the small business owner to adequately assess fire risks in the workplace?

11 Name the three Acts which require all clinical waste to be kept apart from general waste and be disposed of to a licensed incinerator or landfill site, by a licensed company.

12 Which Act requires all premises in London that carry out treatments to be licensed by their local authorities?

13 Which Act states 'Every employer and self-employed person shall ensure that suitable personal protective equipment is provided for themselves and employees where they may be exposed to a risk to their health or safety while at work'?

the workplace
ENVIRONMENT

- acting as a spokesperson for the salon
- writing a report on the benefits of a treatment
- learning or designing a price list
- visiting a supplier
- spending the day with the salesperson
- showing people around the salon
- stock taking.

Learning opportunities to be gained by extending your job role include:

- standing in for a receptionist/senior therapist
- shadowing/work experience
- job sharing
- job rotation
- modelling for treatments at demonstrations
- taking part in open evenings at your salon
- attending open evenings at other salons
- watching the experts in action
- applying for extra training courses.

Seeking help and asking questions of others with more experience than you should never be seen as a weakness – quite the opposite. Within the salon there is a wealth of experience and knowledge. Checking with others will ensure your information is correct and give you wisdom, which you, in turn, can pass on. (Refer to G8 'Develop and maintain your effectiveness at work', page 91, for other ideas on how to increase your knowledge base and how to learn from others.)

Factors that influence clients when choosing products or services

Matching products to clients' needs

With a little experience and knowledge of the products and salon treatments, you will be able to match clients' needs to the correct product or service. Use your intuition when discussing additional treatments or products, just as if you were talking to an old friend. Develop an insight into what to mention to different clients and which treatment or product would be most beneficial. Tread carefully – going through the whole price list and reciting every single treatment the client could have can be overwhelming and put her off. If the choice is too large she may become confused, or deterred by the costs or time involved. Being aware of her constraints, such as time and finances, will help you make an informed choice about what to recommend. The client may not have the time to come in every week for a manicure, or she may only be able to afford a monthly manicure. However, her contribution to keeping her nails in good condition may be as simple as wearing gloves to do the housework and using a basecoat and a hand cream nightly.

Natural links to products and services

In the salon

At this stage of your career as a beauty therapist you are being trained in level 2 treatments. When qualified, you will be able to carry out all practical skills with confidence. Hopefully, you will further your training by gaining additional qualifications and ideally, gain valuable experience in a part-time position within a salon local to you.

Imagine, in your first few weeks in a new salon, that you are waxing the legs of a client. Your client starts to ask about nail extensions as she is getting married later in the summer and is considering having her nails done. The scenario could go two ways:

 What do you say?

Sorry, I don't know anything about that treatment – I haven't trained in that area yet, so I don't know how long they last.

I've seen the treatment being done by our senior nail technician and she is excellent. The nails look very natural and last as long as your nail growth allows. I will get you a price list and see if the nail technician is available to talk to you. Now, have you thought about a pedicure and eyelash tint for your big day? Very convenient on your honeymoon if you are swimming …

Remember

Giving the client good aftercare advice and recommending the correct products to use at home will reinforce the benefits of your salon treatments and continue your good work. For example, if the client is not cleansing her face properly at home, or if she is using an incorrect product, then all the improvements of a good facial treatment will be lost. If, however, you have recommended the correct skin care routine, she has purchased the products and you have instructed her on the correct usage, then her skin will improve enormously, and she will be thrilled.

Spotting opportunities to offer additional treatments

The above scenario is a golden opportunity to exercise your knowledge and to give the client all the information you can. Link the treatments that would be most suitable to enhance her wedding day appearance, both within your own area of expertise and within the expertise of the salon as a whole. The client has already provided the lead, you just have to follow.

Discuss the benefits and possible drawbacks of each treatment as you are waxing her legs. This makes the whole approach more of a conversation than a sales pitch. For example, nail extensions and eyelash tinting are ideal treatments for a bride, but a series of electrical facials may not be. The client may find her skin breaks out in spots just at the wrong time!

As waxing may produce blood spotting, it would be done in the previous week rather than on the day before the wedding. Facials should also be timed to gain maximum benefit for the skin. If they are too stimulating they may cause blotchiness or other unwanted blemishes at this vital time.

Other opportunities may arise from:

- the client looking at the product stand at reception
- the client asking after a particular product that she has heard about or seen in the press

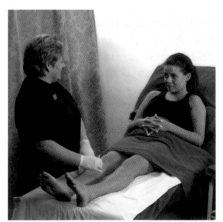

You could discuss the benefits of other treatments while waxing

- the client observing another treatment as she is walking through the salon, e.g. nail extensions
- the client asking for a price list
- a friend recommending a particular treatment
- an open evening or promotional demonstration creating interest
- a commercial company holding a training day for which you request your favourite clients to model.

Use all of these openings as a chance to inform, educate and offer your clients the best products and services for their needs.

Inform clients about additional products or services

G6.2

In this outcome you will learn about

- good communication to introduce products and services
- giving accurate information
- salon and legal requirements
- timing your discussion.

Good communication to introduce products and services

Spotting opportunities for offering clients additional products or services is easy if you are receptive and have your ears and eyes open. Very often they will ask. Either they have heard about a treatment from another client, or they see something going on that they want to know more about. A special day or occasion will trigger extra interest, for example a wedding, a party, a holiday or a Christmas function. (Refer to the **Professional basics** section, pages 19–21, for further questioning techniques to use during your consultation.)

Open questions will help draw out the client's needs. These could include:

- How long is it until the wedding/party/holiday? Do you feel ready?
- Have you read about our special bridal top to toe package? / How do you want to look on your big day?
- What are your worries about your party? How can we help you?
- Have you seen any pictures of how you would like to look, as a guide for make-up, eyebrow shape and nails?

Pointing out options

If the client does not ask directly, it could be she is shy about asking, or does not know you offer a certain treatment. Tell her all about it – and use the current treatment to start the discussion. The consultation always provides a good opening to talk through alternative options to the client's normal treatments, for example:

'Did you know that an eyebrow wax is great for giving a clean finish to the shape and lasts a long time? I know you have booked in for an eyebrow tidy with tweezers next week.'

Your role is to point out options to the client

'I notice your skin is very dry on your feet. How about a pedicure and warm paraffin treatment to soften and moisturise the skin? We have a special offer on at the moment.'

'For your honeymoon why not have a French manicure finish on your toes to match your manicure. It looks lovely with brown feet and open-toed sandals.'

By providing the link to additional treatments you are not introducing lots of different options all at once. The client will be pleased to receive any suggestions related to her big event. She will be pleased you are taking such an interest (which you are) and will not view it as an intrusion or a hard selling technique (which it is not).

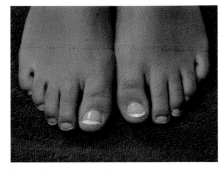

French manicure finish on toes

Giving accurate information

Do try to be as accurate as you can when giving information. Not only is your professional reputation at stake, but you also have a legal obligation not to give any false or misleading information to the client. As a consumer, your client has legal rights to protect her, and you, or your salon, will be liable for prosecution if found to be in breach of the law.

Not only that, you will lose your clients very quickly if they have no faith in the information you are giving them, and if the products you recommend are unsuitable for their needs.

Salon and legal requirements

Underpinning all the product knowledge and treatment skills you have to pass onto your clients are the legal aspects of promotion, selling and client and consumer rights. (Refer to the **Professional basics** section, 'You, your client and the law', pages 37–39.)

The specific laws relevant to this unit are:

- the Health and Safety at Work Act 1974
- the Consumer Protection Act 1987
- the Cosmetic Products (Safety) Regulations 2003
- the Trades Description Act 1968
- the Sale of Goods Act 1979
- the Sale and Supply of Goods Act 1994
- the Supply of Goods and Services Act 1982

Refer to G4 'Fulfil salon reception duties' (page 111) for information on dealing with clients with special needs.

As a professional you need to work within the guidelines of your industry and code of practice. (Refer to the Professional basics section, pages 41–3.)

> ### Remember
>
>
> It is essential that you do not give misleading information, directly or by implication. In all your promotional activities you must always protect your client, yourself and the salon's reputation.

Timing your discussion

It is important to give the client the time to ask questions, so choose an appropriate moment to discuss her queries. During a treatment is fine if it is one where you can maintain a conversation and have lots of eye contact. A manicure, pedicure or waxing is ideal for this, as the client is awake, upright and alert. Talking during a facial will detract from the quality of the treatment and all relaxation properties will be lost. Do not pick moments when the client is distracted, i.e. when she is trying to get dressed or pay for her treatment. Where possible, keep the question and answer session quiet and confidential – not everyone in the salon should hear about her future bikini wax! It is important to hold the client's attention and focus entirely on her questions. This will give her the confidence of knowing that your suggestions really are in her best interests.

Gain client commitment to using additional products or services

G6.3

In this outcome you will learn about

- moving the situation forward when the client shows interest
- promoting existing treatments and products
- closing the discussion if the client shows no interest
- not judging your client
- checking client understanding of product use
- ensuring prompt delivery of goods
- referring clients to alternative sources.

Moving the situation forward when the client shows interest

A client will indicate that she agrees with your recommendations in several ways. She may:

- book an appointment for the recommended treatments
- purchase the suggested products
- book a consultation with the nail technician/tanning consultant
- order the delivery of the product if not in stock
- put a deposit on a course of treatments
- buy a gift voucher to give as a present.

Once she has made up her mind, the client will clearly indicate the route you should take: escort her to the till or to the receptionist who will book her follow-up appointment, or fill out the purchase order for whatever product she is having. If the item is not in stock, make it quite clear at the beginning – this will avoid disappointment and she will keep her faith in you. Try not to recommend a product and then backtrack and suggest an alternative once you realise that you do not have the item in stock. That is not fair to the client and it will put you in a bad light – it looks as though you are only after her money, rather than providing the best possible product for her.

When you recommend a product, be clear whether it is in stock

Promoting existing treatments and products

New treatments and products are always easy to recommend to the client. You may have had training in their use, had the treatment yourself, seen the excellent results and be brimming over with excitement and enthusiasm. This becomes infectious and soon the cash registers are ringing and stock is moving very quickly.

But what about the existing services and products? They may be seen as old hat, or just boring and regular, and your excitement for all the new products only reinforces that. There is a danger that the standard treatments, which are still very trustworthy and beneficial, get overlooked.

It is worth revisiting the price list to see what treatments or products have not been recommended very often recently. The old faithful such as a paraffin wax incorporated into a manicure and pedicure has lots of pamper appeal to someone who has never had one before, but can easily be overlooked as for you it may be bordering on the mundane.

Least-used treatments and products

A very useful exercise is to do a 'Top of the Pops' chart of treatments carried out in the last month. Often a pattern emerges – a therapist may have a favourite treatment or product and always recommend that, rather than other options. Does the top therapist's pattern on the chart match her passion for waxing or facials and show her least favourite treatments less frequently?

A chart will clearly show the most common and the least-used treatments and products. A promotional period of a month could be used to generate interest in those trailing behind. Remember, stock sitting in the cupboard is dead money, generating neither income nor interest if the client does not know it exists.

The same applies to machines and equipment. A client will not ask what a brush cleanse machine does if it is sitting on the top shelf of the storeroom, with all its related creams and washes, so she can't see it. Dust it off, do a demonstration of its use, revisit the manufacturer's instructions and offer it to clients to enhance their facial. Or think laterally and offer alternatives – have a back treatment promotion at the beginning of the summer when clients are coming out of winter woollies and showing off their backs in swimming costumes.

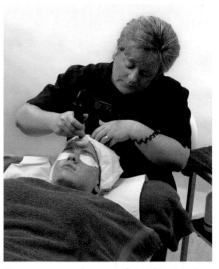

Demonstrate the use of machines and equipment

This is how many salons improve their business: through analysis of turnover and ensuring movement of static items. Most salons set targets, either within sales or treatments. It is important, through regular meetings and agreed personal goals, that you understand what is expected of you. It should be agreed at the time of your interview what your personal goals are, what incentives there are for achieving those goals, and what happens if you do not achieve them. (Please refer to G8 'Develop and maintain your effectiveness at work', page 91, for information on personal goal setting, how to work with your manager and how to develop your job role for personal satisfaction.)

Closing the discussion if the client shows no interest

Just as important as giving time and enthusiasm to the client's enquiries is knowing when to stop if she shows no interest. If the feedback from the client is minimal, or she says 'no thanks, not just at this moment', then take your cue and stop. Nothing is more irritating to the client than a hard sales pitch; you will lose her altogether if you come over as pushy and forceful.

As a double check, ask yourself the following questions.

- Am I giving the relevant information for my client's particular needs?
- Am I explaining myself clearly, or am I confusing the client?
- Am I being too technical in my explanation?
- Have I chosen a good time to give advice?

Review your techniques to answer the above questions satisfactorily.

- Try to make the information relevant to the client's needs.
- Make your explanation of the treatment or product crystal clear.
- Avoid being too technical – explain the benefits of the product, not the way it works.
- Stop the conversation if necessary and choose a better time to discuss the client's needs – this will show her that you are aware of her time constraints.

> **Reality Check!**
>
> Revenue may be lost and the client may take her business elsewhere if you are not offering a full service and are hesitant in your approach to promoting your products and services.

The way to close the discussion is to offer some literature, a price list, or a leaflet on the subject and allow her to read it at leisure. If a client is not interested in a treatment, it may be because she does not have the time to discuss it, because she cannot afford it or because the treatment just does not appeal to her. Knowing when to back off and stop giving information is essential to maintaining good communication.

Be ready to show clients a range of products and/or leaflets

Not judging your client

Do not prejudge what your client may want or what she can afford. Until you open up clear lines of communication and discuss this with her, you don't know how best to help her, whether she can afford a course of treatment or how much she already knows. Whilst we all tend to judge one another within three seconds of meeting, it is certainly not up to you to judge a client's financial state and decide what she can or cannot afford. Do not underestimate a client's commitment to the treatments – it is not up to you to decide that your client does or does not have the time, money or inclination to attend her appointments.

Remember

Beauty therapists are just as likely to have a treatment as anyone else. It has been known for salon owners to either check out the opposition by booking in under an assumed name, or just to have a treatment anonymously as it is more relaxing than being in their own working environment. They will soon spot an insincere therapist or one who doesn't know what she is talking about. Customers, too, read the beauty reviews in the press and are very aware of salon treatments. If you lie or try to fob them off with information that is not accurate you will soon be spotted.

In the salon

Sangita was at the reception desk when a lady walked in who was rather scruffy, in old clothes and with very bad hands – torn cuticles, cuts and very dry skin. The lady wanted some products to help her hands look 'a little more decent, as I have a lunch in London to attend and I have been doing a lot of gardening'. Sangita was a bit sniffy about this as the client didn't look as well groomed as her regular clientele. Dubiously, she offered the client hand cream and cuticle oil, but did not suggest a manicure later in the week when the cuts had healed over. She showed little real interest in the client as she was sure she couldn't afford very much.

The client agreed to pay for the recommended items and handed over her gold Visa card. The client turned out to be the owner of a large estate, and had been getting her acres of garden ready to receive the summer crowds who visit the estate. She also dropped into the conversation that her lunch was at Buckingham Palace! Needless to say, Sangita soon realised her mistake and tried to rectify her flawed attitude. The lady was very gracious and did become a regular client in the salon.

What is the lesson to learn here? What did Sangita do that was fundamentally wrong? How could this situation have been handled differently? What might the outcome have been?

Discuss in class and with your lecturer.

Checking client understanding of product use

To get the best from the product, the client should fully understand how to use it, when to apply it, and its benefits and advantages. For example, a rich eye cream needs a delicate application using the ring fingers of both hands. A tiny amount of product should be warmed between the fingers before it is patted on, starting from the outer eye and working inwards. If too much product is applied, the eye area absorbs it and becomes puffy. Using heavy strokes to apply it will pull the fragile skin around the eyes causing damage. Little is definitely more in this case!

When talking through the method of application with the client, and possibly demonstrating, look for lots of eye contact and nodding, which the client will do if she has understood. If the client looks confused, bored or distant, you have lost her interest. She will not use the product and may even return it.

Ask her to repeat back to you what you have said. Ask her questions such as the following.

- When do you apply it?
- How is it put on?
- How regularly should you apply it?

Check that clients understand correct use of the products they purchase

This will affirm her information and show you she fully understands how and when she is to use her product. Write in her record card that she has purchased the product. The next time you treat her, ask her how she found it and if she is pleased with the results. Be interested in her efforts and comment on the effects of her product use. This will confirm your recommendations were correct.

Ensuring prompt delivery of goods

If, following your advice, the client wishes to purchase either a product or treatments, you need to ensure she understands the time restraints or delivery expectations. The client will get very enthusiastic and if she has to wait, perhaps because it needs to be ordered, you should keep her fully informed to avoid misunderstandings.

Delivery dates vary considerably. They are dependent upon the company, its resources and stock levels, and how local they are to you. It may be a next-day delivery if the supplier is on the doorstep, or there may be a wait of several weeks if the suppliers are awaiting a shipment themselves. Problems arise when the client is not kept fully in the picture and is kept waiting. She will not be happy if she thinks she is being 'fobbed off' with poor excuses. Honesty is the best policy – if the client is told she has to wait two weeks, then at least she knows and is not irritated by what she would see as a late delivery.

If the client has booked an additional or new treatment, ensure she understands the time restraints there too. The nail technician may be fully booked for a week in advance, so the treatment is not instant. Match up the appointment booking to suit both your client's needs and the therapist's column. Squeezing a client in late on a Friday evening because you promised her that week will not make you popular with the therapist, and there is no guarantee of a quality treatment.

In both instances take responsibility for your actions. Ensure you know how to order the correct goods, or give the task to someone who does, and take a little effort to juggle the appointment system to suit everyone. A little consideration and kindness goes a long way and is always appreciated.

Referring clients to alternative sources

There are times when you cannot recommend or offer the client what she needs. This may be because you are not yet trained in the particular treatment or because your salon does not offer that treatment. Should she require a sunbed session and you do not have one, or want a specialist epilation treatment (hair removal) and you do not offer it, then recommend somewhere else, but only if you know of a reputable therapist.

There is always the danger that you will lose the client altogether of course, but she may approve of your professionalism and remain loyal to you for all other treatments. That should be viewed as the best of compliments to your customer relationship.

If there is sufficient demand and the salon is losing clientele by not offering the required treatment, this is also the time to recommend to the salon manager or owner that the salon should investigate the possibility of introducing it to expand business opportunities.

Do some research yourself on the cost of equipment and training, profit margins and expected returns, and then do a short presentation to the staff. You will learn a lot and so will they – as well as being impressed with your initiative.

You could offer to give a short presentation to colleagues on new products or services

Test your knowledge

1   Give two ways you would ensure that as a new therapist in your salon you are able to identify additional services and products.

2   List five ways in which you can find learning opportunities at work.

3   Name four factors which influence clients to use your products or services.

4   Why is it important to match the product to the client's needs?

5   Name four treatments which you could promote when doing a facial and manicure.

6   List three points to remember for clear communication when introducing products and services.

7   Why is it important to be as accurate as you can when giving information on products?

8   Describe two appropriate times within your treatment when you could answer questions from the client.

9   Why is it important that the client fully understands how to use a product, and how can you check this?

10 When may you have to refer the client to another salon? Which one would you recommend, and how would you know which one to suggest?

Promote additional products or services to clients
What your assessor is looking for

Unit G6

This unit is all about making the client aware of the choices of products and services and, in turn, increasing your salon's turnover and profit. The assessor will expect you to show off your knowledge and have a good command of product information as well as an understanding of how to maximise the salon's treatments with home care recommendations.

Sources of evidence could be the following.

- On your client record card, make a note of any products purchased, any recommendations you make for the future, and other services that would be suitable for your client's needs.
- During your consultation, or during the course of a treatment (where suitable), let the assessor hear you recommending suitable products and treatments. The client does not necessarily have to have them; rather it is your verbal recommendations that form the evidence as well as the correct knowledge that you are imparting.
- Design a questionnaire to show client knowledge of treatments. This will indicate how little or how much the client knows about her options. You could then highlight staff weaknesses in knowledge of products or services and recommend a training day. For example, of the 17 ladies having a manicure this week, only five of them realised they could have a warm oil treatment to help dry cuticles.
- Design a poster to promote a particular product or service, perhaps with a seasonal theme – a free nail polish application with every Christmas make over, or a pedicure polish carried out with every spring waxing treatment. Make the poster as informative as you can to attract new business.
- Design an aftercare and homecare leaflet for a treatment, suggesting suitable products for home use that will carry on the good work of the salon treatment.
- Organise a training seminar for other staff or students where you promote a particular treatment or product that you feel confident in, which perhaps is not selling as well as it could. Make it very 'hands on', get others involved in using the product and demonstrate how to promote it.
- Copy and enclose in your portfolio the order form or delivery note that you may have had to complete if a product was out of stock or it was a special order.
- Include any evidence of outside selling seminars or lectures you have attended while in employment. Enclose any training certificates from commercial training you may have received that enhances your knowledge of products or services offered to your clients.

Develop and maintain your effectiveness at work

Unit G8

Introduction

This unit is all about you and your professional growth, which will, in turn, lead to your personal growth too. As your skills develop so will your confidence. This gives you courage to tackle new training and experiences, which provide certain self-assurance. Before you get to that stage you have to go through a professional growing period during which you start as a student and end as an employee.

As part of the transition from student to potential employee, you have to step outside your own sphere to realise that you are joining a business and that it is vital to contribute to the effectiveness of that business if you want to stay employed.

In this unit you will cover the following outcomes:

G8.1 Improve your personal performance at work
G8.2 Work effectively as part of a team.

As you develop skills in dealing with people, your confidence will grow

Improve your personal performance at work

G8.1

In this outcome you will learn about

- how to become employable
- carrying out your job role to salon and National Occupational Standards
- performing your task – salon job roles and procedures
- creating opportunities to learn
- agreeing your job role and being comfortable with it
- knowing your limits and when to ask colleagues for help

- contracts of employment
- your rights as an employee, and salon grievance and appeals procedures
- being commercially aware, and salon targets
- improving your performance and identifying training needs
- identifying your own strengths and weaknesses – the appraisal system
- trends in the business.

How to become employable

To learn how to become a good employee and develop a business focus, we will look at the differences between your life at the moment, i.e. as a student, and the working life of a therapist in a busy salon.

Student – your life at college	Employee – your life at work
In the safe college environment you are the main focus of attention: quite rightly, college is all about you working towards your portfolio collection, you developing your skills through practice and you receiving lots of positive feedback	In the world of work, you are not working with your best friends (in fact, you cannot choose your work colleagues and there is no guarantee that you will like all of them), and there is a shift away from you personally towards what is expected *of* you.

Student – your life at college	**Employee – your life at work**
from your tutor. You also become used to working with your friends, you know your lecturers or trainers very well, and there is little business pressure as you are concentrating on gaining your qualification, rather than building up a company.	Instead of working towards a qualification, you are working to increase a client base and helping to grow the profit of a salon. This is an ongoing process – no one in business can afford to stand still. A business quickly dies if it is not nurtured and developed by enthusiastic, motivated staff giving a professional service, which separates your salon from its competitors. No, it is not your business - yet - but by being the very best employee you can, you can gain invaluable experience for when you do own your own salon or go into a mobile business. You can then become a good employer to others. So, you can see there is a real shift away from your personal needs to those of the business you are joining. However, becoming a good employee does involve your growth: of skills, confidence and ability. Certain tools are needed to nurture and cultivate this growth. A good manager will guide you and help you develop your new skills as long as you play your part too.

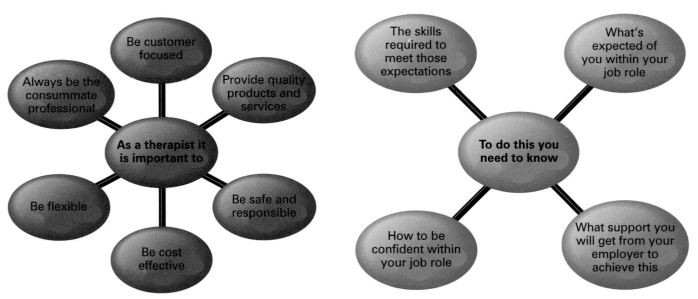

Qualities that are expected in a therapist, and how to gain them

Carrying out your job role to salon and National Occupational Standards

When you first start work in a salon, it is very important that you have a full understanding of what exactly is expected of you; only then can you carry out your duties well, and to the best of your abilities.

What are the National Occupational Standards (NOS)?

The National Occupational Standards are the beauty therapy standards that all students taking a level 2 qualification work to. They cover all the ranges within each unit. This gives you a good practical grounding in each area of work, in turn making you very employable. In fact, employers have a great deal of influence over what

Reality Check!

It is a fact of life that no one gets to choose who they work with unless they own the salon! It isn't like a college/training environment where you are very close to your best friends and tend to stick in little groups. You may enter an established salon that has a variety of employees with different backgrounds, skill areas and ages. Working with others is a hard lesson to learn, and is part of growing up.

topics are included within the standards. They consult with the Hairdressing and Beauty Industry Authority (HABIA) and all training establishments nationally teach to those same standards, giving equality and uniformity of learning.

Carrying out practical skills using the correct procedures is not only professional, it is also essential for health and safety. Deciding to take short cuts or ignoring the safe methods will invalidate insurance cover and leave the therapist open to negligence charges.

So, the training is the same wherever you are in the country, and the employers have told the trainers what they expect from a new employee. Because your training has been so thorough, you have the confidence to apply for jobs.

Salon standards

Your salon standards of behaviour and work philosophy will be the same as the NOS and you will always be expected to carry out your treatments to the highest standard. However, as you develop a commercial understanding of products, the manufacturer's recommendations for certain products may differ from the NOS, or the method in which you were trained. Be flexible and follow manufacturers' instructions when using their products – providing you have received a certificate of training from the company, your professional association or federation insurance will still cover you. (Refer to the **Professional basics** section, page 40.)

For example, Creative Nails offer very good manicure/pedicure training using their products. It will differ from your basic manicure training at college, as you are following the company's recommended procedures. Do not be frightened of learning new techniques – there is more than one way to do things. As long as the company fully trains you to its standards and provides a certificate of competence to allow you to use its techniques, you are covered by your professional indemnity insurance. In most commercial training there is a practical skills test and a short written paper to prove you have understood the theory of the techniques: even on a short one-day course, expect both tests.

A warning here: Do not think that if you have seen another therapist using the product, it is acceptable for you to attempt a treatment in the same way. You will not be covered by your professional indemnity insurance if you are not commercially fully qualified. This could be expensive should damage occur and the client decides to sue you or the salon. It is not worth the risk.

Performing your task – salon job roles and procedures

A good salon, and certainly the larger health farms or chains of salons, will provide a job specification as part of your contract. You then sign the contract, which not only lays down the working terms and conditions, such as annual holidays, but also gives a framework of duties that you are expected to carry out.

Smaller salons may do this orally at your interview. However, there is a danger that you won't take it all in at once – a written list of duties is much easier to refer to.

Speak to your salon manager and gain clarification on what you are expected to do on a daily basis. If you don't do something because you are not aware it is part of your job, at best you will be perceived as lazy or not a team player, at worst you could endanger clients, especially if your job role involves sterilisation and hygiene procedures.

When you first start in a salon, it is usual to be in a junior position – you may have the correct qualification, but you do not yet have the same experience as a more senior therapist. It is likely that you will spend at least some part of the day assisting with treatments and 'shadowing' a more senior person. You will also be given the more menial tasks in the salon, or certainly take part in the rota for toilet cleaning, setting up for treatments and general tidying up.

Whatever your task, if you tackle it with enthusiasm and energy it will be done well, and your endeavours will be noticed by your manager.

Creating opportunities to learn

(Refer also to G6 'Promote additional products or services to clients', page 78, for more tips on how to take opportunities to learn your expected tasks.)

Organisation

Most successful salons, that take the most money and are the busiest, are the ones that are most organised. The salon runs like a well-oiled machine, with everyone knowing what they have to do, tackling the jobs with enthusiasm and care, and working together as a team to make the working day run as smoothly as possible. Therefore the most organised managers are often the most productive. A salon with a rota of jobs with names beside them, and ticks when they are completed, is giving clear instructions to the staff about expectations and essential jobs, without which the salon would cease to function.

Imagine the salon running out of towels because a junior did not turn the laundry around, or running out of couch roll, products or tissues because the manager did not make the order last week.

You can find many opportunities to learn your expected tasks

If you understand the importance of your specific jobs, you very soon feel that you are performing a vital function within the wheels of your industry. For example, you may be asked to count stock because a stock check is needed for stock levels. If you run out of a good selling line simply because you couldn't be bothered to do the paperwork, you are costing the salon money in lost revenue.

Agreeing your job role and being comfortable with it

Do make sure you know what you are going to be doing, where the equipment is to carry out your tasks, and how your responsibilities relate to the team. If your job role is not explained properly, or you do not really understand it, your only option is to ask! Do not keep quiet – it could lead to real misunderstandings. Do not make the mistake of nodding and agreeing to what is being said, and then going home thinking 'I didn't understand a word of that!'

Do not sign an agreement to your job role and duties if you are unsure of the implications.

> **Remember**
>
> - I look – I see
> - I listen – I hear
> - I do – I understand

In the salon

If it is your job to switch on all the wax heaters, first thing in the morning, in readiness for a full page of waxing clients, should you check the levels of wax in the pots first? If you do not, there are several things that could happen:

The waxing therapist will have to add more wax, which takes time to melt, so the client is kept waiting – provided she can wait, of course.

All subsequent clients are kept waiting and appointments get put back because the wax takes half an hour to melt. The appointment system falls to pieces and clients, quite rightly, are not happy being kept waiting.

There is not enough product for the client booked in for a full leg wax. She cannot have her treatment so business may be lost – she storms out of the salon, and will give the salon negative publicity.

The wax pot burns dry and smokes and is ruined, or worse still, catches fire.

So is it your fault?

If your instruction was to turn on the heaters, but you were not advised to check product levels and it did not occur to you to do so, who is at fault? Neither the implications of your actions nor your duties were fully explained by the manager – but then you are a qualified waxing therapist, so should you have used your common sense? The manager assumed you would know you had to check the product levels, but you didn't check them because you weren't told to – and you didn't want to appear too pushy. You may have assumed it was someone else's job to check the levels last thing at night.

It is easy to make mistakes.

Remember

If you do not know something, do not guess – ask!

How to be comfortable within your job role

Knowledge is very comforting and prevents worry. Make sure you know what is asked of you, if given an area of responsibility. A clear understanding of issues and requirements makes for an unruffled operation and prevents confusion.

Be competent. Do the job as well as you have been trained to. Do not attempt to bluff through a job that could put a client or colleague at risk. This comes back to knowledge – do not attempt a job you have not been taught to do.

Skills and knowledge can be kept up to date through regular training, reading trade journals, attending the organised beauty trade shows or exhibitions and through the media. Be enthusiastic to learn new skills and regard it as a challenge rather than a chore. The more skills therapists have to offer, the more employable they are, as well as being a valuable asset to any salon.

Flexibility is a skill worth cultivating. Try to accommodate the client who arrives without an appointment with help from colleagues. Do not make her feel it is just too inconvenient or that she is stupid to even ask. Reschedule the appointment if you cannot help at that particular time.

Attending beauty trade shows or exhibitions will keep you up to date

If a client is late for her appointment or there is an overbooking, then do the same. Rescheduling of appointments can work both ways – clients may have to be juggled into other time slots due to staff sickness. If this is done in an open, genuinely apologetic manner, most clients will be just as flexible.

If a client changes her treatment booking, again be flexible. If time permits, and the client's needs can be accommodated, then do so. The receptionist may need to be made aware of the change so she doesn't double book the time slot, but flexibility is the way to keep encouraging new business.

Knowing your limits and when to ask colleagues for help

It is just as important to know what you cannot do, as it is to know what you can do! To maintain a hierarchy within the salon, there has to be a person in charge – a general to your foot soldier – who takes responsibility for the larger problems in the salon. Dealing with complaints, banking the takings and ordering stock may be some of the duties you are not expected to take part in. There is a good reason for this – you may not have the knowledge or people skills to handle a serious complaint, or not enough stock knowledge to predict what the salon is going to need in the next month.

Some things are best left to those who have the experience and get paid for taking on that extra duty. Always refer to those in a higher authority than yourself and involve management in decisions or judgements that you are not experienced in. For example, giving away complimentary treatments may only be done by the manager. If no one was co-ordinating the giving of gift vouchers, the business could suffer a severe financial loss.

Accept that you are not able to perform certain tasks or duties, and be aware of the limits of your own responsibilities – the only exception to this is health and safety, which is everyone's responsibility.

Reality Check!	
Each of us must take responsibility for our actions, and we are liable for any damages that occur if we do not. Insurance cover will be void if it is proven that legislation or salon rules have been broken, so you must be aware of the limits of your own role.	

Contracts of employment

All responsible employers have a contract of employment, which has a section on discipline, the possible consequences of breaking your contract of employment and the route to a better performance at work. Most salons expect a certain amount of commercial professional development, and their contracts of employment allow time away from salon duties for additional training. The salon will often agree to help fund the training, provided the therapist agrees to stay in the salon employment for a fixed period of time – say a year. It is a good way of gaining commercial training without the personal expense.

It is always good to know the basis of your employment. There is usually a scale of disciplinary action, which can vary from a verbal warning for, say, continual lateness, to instant dismissal if caught stealing or physically assaulting a client. Rather like in a college, a good salon has to have discipline and rules and regulations to function.

Minor indiscretions are usually discussed and may result in a good telling-off, and provided it does not happen again, there are no major consequences. A poor standard of work, or a regular occurrence such as absenteeism, may result in pay being stopped or bonus incentives being withdrawn.

Your rights as an employee, and salon grievance and appeals procedures

Major problems need to be sorted out using the salon grievance and appeals procedure. It is important you are aware of how to use it, should the need arise. Equal opportunities laws are designed to give everyone the same rights, whether they are defending or justifying their actions, or appealing against unfair or biased judgements. This is much the same as when you are a candidate taking assessments. If, as a candidate, you do not agree with the decision your assessor has made, there is a format for appeal, just as there is in employment.

The bigger cases of employees suing their employer are reported in the national press, as judgement against employers for unfair dismissal or other charges often results in large amounts of money being awarded, and is seen as newsworthy.

Employee rights

Employment law is very specific in many areas. Regardless of whether you are employed full or part time, or are on a fixed-term contract, you have the right:

- to a written statement of employment
- to pay and itemised pay statements
- to payment on medical suspension (when you are unable to work through illness)
- to reasonable time off for antenatal care
- to statutory maternity leave and statutory maternity pay
- to return to work after a full period of maternity leave
- to parental/paternity leave
- to paid adoption leave
- to four weeks paid holiday, and daily and weekly rest breaks
- to request flexible working hours
- to time off for public duties
- to time off for trade union duties and activities
- to statutory redundancy payment after two years continuous employment
- to time off to look for work or arrange training during a redundancy notice period
- to time off for family emergencies
- to statutory notice of termination of the contract of employment
- to complain of unfair dismissal
- not to suffer unlawful deductions from pay
- not to be dismissed for asserting a statutory right
- not to be unfairly discriminated against on the grounds of sex, race or disability (legislation concerning 'ageism' will come into force in October 2006)
- not to be dismissed for trade union involvement or taking action on health and safety grounds
- to be treated fairly and in accordance with proper procedures.

Qualifying periods of employment are needed as follows:

- minimum period of notice – one month
- not to be unfairly dismissed – one year (there is no qualifying period where a breach of contract or discrimination occurs)
- written statement of reasons for dismissal – one year
- redundancy payments – two years
- statutory maternity pay – 26 weeks (at the 15th week before the expected date of birth).

Check it out

Does your salon have an equal opportunities policy? Most small businesses do not have a written one. However, all the salon's written policies and procedures should have equal opportunities running through them. Review these and see if there is any discrimination that you feel should be eliminated. Advice on discrimination is available from both the Equal Opportunities Commission and the Commission for Racial Equality. Look at their websites.

These are the basic legal guidelines for employment that are designed to protect you as an employee. However, employment law is complex and subject to change, so always seek professional advice before deciding on action if you are considering a court case.

Being commercially aware, and salon targets

In the **Professional basics** section, 'Treatment planning and preparation' mentions the old saying:

Time = money

This applies to treatment times as well as your preparation time.

Most therapists are perfectionists in their approach to any treatment: a leg wax has to be the best the client has ever had, the make-up application a work of art. This is highly commendable – except that if it takes several hours to achieve, the treatment time is not commercially viable.

Commercially viable treatment times are part of the criteria of student assessment. You have to try to reach a happy medium between an excellent treatment and a time factor that is realistic in the world of work. However, nothing quite prepares you for the hurly burly of the real thing!

Not only does it cost the salon money if you take too long (you could have squeezed another treatment into the extra half hour that you ran over time) but you are also infringing upon the client's rights as a consumer.

A salon's price list reflects standard treatment times, and you must keep within these

The Supply of Goods and Services Act 1982 (please refer to the **Professional basics** section, page 38) states that the person providing a service (such as a beauty therapist) must:

- charge a reasonable price
- give the service within a reasonable time
- give the service with reasonable care and skill.

The aspect we are concerned with here is the time it takes to carry out a treatment, so this means no two-hour manicures.

Salon targets

Most price lists contain a description of the treatment, the product used and the length of time each treatment will take. This is the guide for the customer, who can then allow enough time to relax and enjoy the treatment. It is reasonable, within the law and the commercial viability of the salon, to expect that the service will actually be carried out in that stated time.

Of course, there is a little give and take – the client is running late, she falls asleep during her facial and needs waking up time, or your appointments are overrunning slightly. However, if the client is in her lunch hour and has to dash back to work, having had a rushed treatment which she really didn't enjoy, you may have lost your customer altogether. It is also well within her rights to complain.

Experience will speed up your technique – the more you use your practical skills, the more automatic they become. It is easy to spot students who have a Saturday job in a salon, because they are quicker at treatments, have good customer awareness and good communication skills! Remember that practice makes perfect: more senior therapists are able to carry out the treatment whilst chatting to the client, clearing up as they go and producing excellent results. It will come to you, the more experience you gain.

There are many benefits to staying within your treatment times

Productivity targets and timescales

We all react well to incentives and praise – for most domestic animals (and small children!) training is based around rewarding good behaviour and ignoring, or punishing, bad behaviour.

We want, and should have, goals to work towards. We then feel we have achieved something knowing that all our efforts will be recognised, and we benefit from all that hard work. This applies in all types of work.

Beauty therapy is no different. A keen therapist will want to increase her client base and product turnover, if she knows that not only will her work be rewarded with praise, but there is an extra incentive to do so.

Targets should be realistic and achievable if they are to work. They should be mutually agreed between you and your manager, with a set target over a defined period of time. This could be a month, every two months or every quarter of the year, depending upon how you both feel it works best. Short-term goals are often the favourite: they feel more achievable and reinforce the work ethic when reached.

This target setting will be both personal, for your own growth and development, and commercial for the salon – sales targets, number of treatments per day and so on.

Rather than view this as a negative aspect of work, most therapists look forward to the challenge, knowing that they can only benefit by trying their hardest to achieve their target. A large salon incentive can be anything from free products or a free treatment to a weekend break, shopping vouchers or even a trip abroad.

If you read the trade magazines, you will find some fabulous prizes given by commercial companies, rewarding a therapist who has become therapist of the year or salesperson of the year.

It is important that you try to achieve your targets: it not only keeps you employed, but it makes you very commercial and gives you invaluable experience should you decide to run your own salon or develop a mobile business. Only doing two treatments a day on a mobile beauty round is soon going to put you out of business.

Improving your performance and identifying training needs

As you gain experience in a salon your performance improves. You should also specifically target your improvement and this is a bit like setting a training programme for an athlete before the Olympic Games. If the athlete doesn't push the boundaries a little more every time, the performance will stay static so will not be good enough to beat the competition.

Self-analysis and self-development are essential for your growth and maturity as a therapist within a salon environment. This is often referred to as professional development. Some companies provide a commercial professional development folder – rather like a record of achievement at school! All the training certificates and qualifications can be kept in the folder, and it helps you spot where your gaps in training may be.

Self-analysis is essential for your development as a therapist

Identifying your own strengths and weaknesses – the appraisal system

If a therapist keeps making the same mistakes again and again, and clients complain or stop coming into the salon altogether, this is a strong indication that something is wrong.

Often, with experience, it is easier to be reflective and spot our own mistakes and then change the action, or reaction, to break the cycle of behaviour. Sometimes it is not so easy to be inward-looking, and this is where a good manager will help by giving regular work-related reviews. This is called an appraisal.

Many large companies provide both self-assessment sheets for the employee to fill in throughout a set period, and a joint review sheet to be completed with the manager, to help improve performance.

Remember

Training and assessment should be viewed in a positive light – they provide opportunities to learn and progress in personal growth and the maintenance of good working relationships.

It is important to react in an optimistic way to any feedback or review.

Nobody likes criticism, but it is important to listen carefully to what is said.

An appraisal or team review should happen on a regular basis, perhaps once a month or every three months. The appraisal should:

- be at a mutually agreeable time, not an inconvenience to either party
- be constructive and open, not conducted in fear or terror of job loss
- be objective and as non-personal as possible
- be a review for both parties, not just a performance judgement
- be constructive and positive
- leave the employee feeling enthused and not depressed.

A self-assessment form can contain whatever the employer or manager feels is relevant to the job role. Here is an example of a common format:

Salon: *Blissed Out*   Date: *July 2004*

Position held: *Beauty therapist*

Therapist: *Wendy Smith*

Please add comments on how you feel you are progressing in each area listed. Thank you.

Appearance *Good. I do try to look professional every day.*

Absences *Could be better, as I have had a week off with flu this month. I haven't had any more time off.*

Time keeping *Could be better. I have been late 5 times this month.*

Job performance *Good. I feel my regular clients always ask for me, and I have worked hard this month.*

Sales *Good, as above. My sales are from my regulars.*

Strengths *I am confident with my treatments and I especially enjoy facial electrical treatments.*

Weaknesses *Time keeping. I have missed my bus quite often in the mornings.*

Any areas of change *I have been in the wet area putting clients in the sauna this month, as Jane seems to have the flu bug that I had and is still off sick.*

Staff development request *I would like to go on an eyelash perming training day if possible, as we have been asked for the treatment by our regular clients.*

Action plan for next review *To improve on time keeping and do my course.*

Reality Check!

A self-assessment appraisal is not just about achievement within the job role and the number of sales that have been completed – that is really only a part of being a therapist (even though an important aspect of remaining profitable). It is also about short-term plans and development of the individual and it opens up many areas for discussion of future plans between a manager and an employee.

It should highlight how well the individual is coping within her job role and whether the salon is asking too much of an employee. It also provides an opportunity for the therapist to offer her opinions on improvement. It should be viewed very much as a two-way discussion, not a telling-off for a bad performance at work.

Check it out

Copy out the self-assessment form (or ask your tutor for one) and use it to analyse your own performance.

Linked into the appraisal system is the setting of targets for the action plan to improve performance at work.

The SMART rule

Follow this simple SMART rule. Targets should be:

S = Specific

Have particular aims in mind rather than too grand an idea. Set a goal specific to you, e.g. I want to complete two assessments each week.

M = Measurable

Make sure they are aims you are able to measure with a start and a finish. Assessments can be measured against the NVQ performance criteria and ranges. You must know where you are now, and where you want to be. For example, product sales might be on average £50 per day now, and a 10% increase would take that up to £55 per day.

A = Achievable

Do not put an aim that cannot be realised. A short-term target may be to complete an NVQ unit by a set date.

R = Realistic

Doing ten treatments per hour is not realistic – be sensible with your aims. For example, how long will it take you to cover all the performance criteria and ranges in one unit?

T = Timed

For the target to be achieved there should be a time scale for you to aim towards. For example, by next month I will improve my timekeeping by 50%; by Christmas I am going to have my portfolio for G8 ready to be signed off by my assessor.

In the salon

Kirsty and Angel have both been at their salon for the same amount of time, and are both due a review of their job role and performance by their manager on the same day. Angel is a hard worker, reliable, punctual and enthusiastic at work, and thinks of her review as a chance to sit down with her boss and have a chat about what training she can do next. Angel feels it is really nice to have some quality, personal time with her manager, and that her job is going well, but there are some courses she would like to ask about.

Kirsty is not as reliable as Angel. Time keeping and punctuality are a bit of a problem. She is a little bit lazy sometimes and likes a good gossip. Kirsty is not looking forward to her appraisal: she feels threatened and knows she is going to be told off. She feels the manager doesn't like her much.

Who needs the appraisal the most? Why do you think that? How can both employees get the most from their appraisal? If you were the manager, how would you handle the review?

Discuss it in your group, ask your lecturer to help and work out an action plan for the two therapists. Keep it in your portfolio as supporting evidence.

A joint review

The self-assessment form provides you with the opportunity to identify your own strengths and weaknesses and to set your own personal targets.

A joint review with a relevant person, i.e. a manager, assessor or tutor, can then identify whether your personal targets are realistic and achievable using the SMART formula. These targets can be either short term or long term.

Short-term goals are easier to measure and judge. They can bring a very positive glow to the therapist who achieves them and that will encourage her to go on and improve further. A short-term goal for our therapist Wendy, from the self-assessment form on page 101, is to complete an eyelash-perming course and gain her certificate, and so offer her clients another service. This is rewarding and achievable.

Long-term goals are not so easy to measure and may be harder to keep in view. They require much more dedication to achieve. A long-term goal for Wendy may be to gain two years' salon experience and then apply for a job as a therapist on an ocean liner. This is still achievable but will take two years.

Short-term goals are like the carrot dangling on the stick – they provide incentive and reward. Lots of short-term goals can also help achieve a long-term goal, which is also very satisfying, and can help you get where you want to go!

Wendy could apply any of the following to help her get to work on time.

- Buy an alarm clock and set it at an earlier time.
- Ask if any other member of staff could share a ride with her, perhaps sharing petrol costs.
- Put an advert in the local shop for someone from her village who works in town and would be able to offer her a car share on a permanent basis.
- Learn to drive and become independent.
- Change the appointment-booking system at the salon so that Wendy starts at 9.30 am when she can realistically get to work, and then either finishes half an hour later or has only a short break for lunch.
- Try cycling to work and get fit at the same time.

Any number of these possible solutions would help Wendy achieve her goal.

Now fill out your own self-assessment plan and see if you can offer your own solutions to your problems. Think clearly and try to view yourself objectively.

Wendy can look at a number of ways to achieve her goals.

Trends in the business

As well as doing treatments well, you must keep abreast of trends and innovations within the industry.

Clients and customers are very aware of the latest treatments; press coverage of every aspect of beauty treatments is extensive, from Botox injections (a poison derivative that paralyses muscles to avoid wrinkles) to the latest in face creams.

Beauty editors are sent hundreds of samples and given treatments to promote the latest fashion within beauty, so that a favourable report gives free publicity in newspapers and magazines. Advertisements in fashion magazines also keep clients aware of the latest releases, so expect your customers to ask for them in your salon.

You should ask your salon how it keeps up with the latest trends – going to trade shows in the major cities is an excellent way of seeing demonstrations of new equipment and products by commercial companies. Be warned, though – the commercial sector is always after new salons to join its sales list, and you could end up changing products or your supplier just for the sake of change.

If your salon has a line of products that is popular and sells well, rather than changing brand, ask the sales representative to call. In a staff meeting she or he could go through the latest emerging trend and give samples or a demonstration.

Joining in national competitions is also a good way of meeting like-minded professionals and sharing good practice. You may be in opposite corners for a make-up competition, but watching someone like Beverly Corbella, voted Hairdresser of the Year, give a demonstration or win a competition will inspire those who can only stand back and watch in admiration! This can only help to raise the standard of skill levels in the industry, and to motivate and enthuse all who take part.

Work effectively as part of a team   G8.2

In this outcome you will learn about

- working with others
- communication and working together

- teamwork skills – what makes a good team
- dealing with conflict.

Working with others

(The **Professional basics** section on good communication skills, pages 10–12, needs to be read in conjunction with this element, as do pages 14–16 on treatment planning and preparation.)

To work well with others we must first analyse ourselves. This is a breakdown of how we see one another, and what we are judged upon:

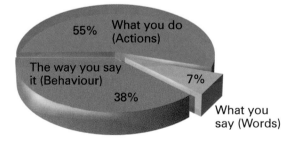

The old saying 'Actions speak louder than words' is true!

Communication and working together

When you work in a salon you may have a manager who supervises what you do, or you may have junior staff who *you* guide through the working day.

Good communication means being able to get on with all your co-workers.

When working under supervision you should:

* accept that someone is in charge
* take instructions and act upon them
* communicate effectively
* take responsibility for your job role and do it to the very best of your ability.

Working together:

* means supporting each other, not being in conflict with one another
* gives the salon a good atmosphere which the client senses
* provides a reliable service
* gives effective results
* includes the ability to listen.

Beauty Therapist wanted for busy salon:

Are you:

* Qualified to NVQ level 2 standard?
* Able to work as a team?
* Motivated and dedicated?
* Willing to train in higher qualifications?

Then we need you!
Phone 012345 56789

Employers value the ability to work as part of a team

Communication is a two-way process and the ability to be an effective listener means:

* knowing when to stop talking and listen to what is being communicated
* listening with interest and understanding
* providing encouragement and confirming you have taken in the conversation:
* nodding or agreeing with the point raised

Professional staff hold the key to an effective, friendly and efficient salon. These are the skills with which they do it:

✓ good communication
✓ knowledge of client's requirements
✓ competence
✓ initiative
✓ responsibility
✓ identification of own strengths and weaknesses
✓ flexibility
✓ teamwork.

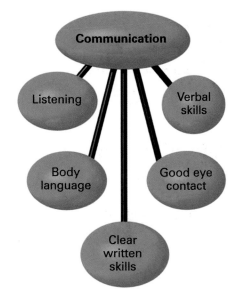

Communication is a two-way process

Good communication between colleagues will build rapport, and that will be reflected in the smooth running of the business.

Initiative means taking the first step or action of a task without being prompted to do so. If a job needs doing, do it without being asked. This will prove to your employer that you can be relied upon to work effectively without having to be prompted all the time.

Be **responsible** for all your actions. Also take responsibility for mistakes and take appropriate action to minimise damage – do not try to cover up mistakes as this will only make things worse.

Identification of your strengths and weaknesses allows for professional growth and the development of skills. This should not be seen as a personal attack, but as an opportunity for constructive guidance and evaluation of performance. A supervisor, manager and colleagues can carry this out in staff review sessions.

Teamwork is essential for any group of people working together.

Teamwork skills – what makes a good team

To be part of a team takes patience, a willingness to help each other and respect for the others in the team. Respect cannot be bought; it has to be earned through hard work and commitment.

While a little competitiveness may be healthy in the salon (e.g. the person achieving the most retail sales in a month wins a prize), a person determined to undermine her colleagues at every opportunity could not be considered a team player. The consequences may be a build-up of bad feelings between staff, resentment and ill-will – all of which are very bad for business.

As a vital part of the team you need to know:

- who is who within the salon
- who is responsible for what
- who you should go to if you need information or support.

Various skills are required to make a good team member

A good team

A good team needs:

- an appropriate leader who is fair but decisive
- enthusiastic, committed team members
- good listening skills and willingness to exchange ideas
- clear objectives and sense of direction
- a good balance of planning and action
- good communication
- clear roles (you know what you are supposed to do)
- flexibility and tolerance
- the right number of people
- the right mix of skills
- a safe environment to try things, make mistakes and learn from them
- a sense of humour!

Team problems

Team spirit can be lost when:

- group members feel that one is favoured more than others
- one member of the group works on her own and won't join in with the team
- there is a breakdown in communications

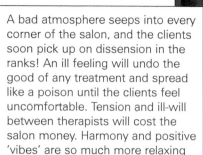

Remember

A bad atmosphere seeps into every corner of the salon, and the clients soon pick up on dissension in the ranks! An ill feeling will undo the good of any treatment and spread like a poison until the clients feel uncomfortable. Tension and ill-will between therapists will cost the salon money. Harmony and positive 'vibes' are so much more relaxing for all involved.

Remember

Being a team player involves offering lots of support, getting assistance when you need it and never letting the other team members down. Could you consider yourself a team player?

Team members need to respect and help each other

- group members are unwilling to be flexible and tolerant of others' mistakes
- there is too much work for too few people
- job roles become blurred and people encroach upon areas they should leave to others.

Dealing with conflict

If you have a problem or are experiencing working relationship difficulties, what do you do?

First, tackle the problem like a grown up. Try to avoid the childish habit of sulking, and using bad body language and a surly tone to show your displeasure at someone. Try to keep a sense of proportion. Also avoid the school playground attitude of 'be in my gang or else!' Gossiping, spreading rumours or moaning is not adult. It achieves nothing; nor is it helpful to your cause.

Second, think carefully, and do nothing while you are still angry. It may be that on reflection you realise you are in the wrong. An apology is then appropriate, and while humble pie is often indigestible, it will defuse the situation. Part of growing up is learning by your mistakes and moving forward, not repeating the mistakes. If you have acted thoughtlessly or caused upset without realising it, you need to make amends, and will be a bigger person for recognising that fact.

Negotiation and mediation

One-to-one negotiation

Often a frank, private word between the two warring parties is all that is needed to clear the air. Ask the person you are in conflict with to discuss the problem, stay calm and apologise if necessary. This will avoid prolonging the dispute. A feud that drags on for weeks is so much more difficult to resolve than one that blows over in a day or two.

Mediation

If you really feel you cannot work with the person you are in disagreement with, or feel uncomfortable or intimidated, then you must report your concerns to your manager. The manager will probably call you both in and hold a meeting where you can both air your views in a private but controlled environment. This again gives you the chance to put your case forward in a calm manner and present the facts as you see them.

The manager may wish to talk to you both individually first and then call you in together. You may find when you hear the other side of the story that you can quickly work out a solution – you may even end up laughing about the situation.

Working closely with your manager and colleagues will give you confidence

However, if the problem is of a more serious nature and you require further action, you must approach your manager in confidence and expect total privacy whilst you discuss your conflict. If the matter requires outside intervention, then you must be prepared to substantiate your allegations – if, for example, another member of staff assaulted you, or a staff member was stealing from the salon.

Cases of serious misconduct will, and should, be taken very seriously, and the matter should be taken to a higher authority– but these cases are few and far between. Most conflicts tend to be minor, with concerns over shirking responsibilities or not doing a job properly, or having lots of time off work, which puts others under pressure.

Check it out

Do some research into job roles and responsibility in your own salon environment. Who is responsible for stock, who for booking appointments and who for replenishing towels and blankets?

Produce a flow chart to remind you of each person's job title, what the job role involves and whom they are directly responsible to.

Remember

Learning to work as a team and in an effective manner will not only make you a great therapist and a pleasure to work with, it will also give you confidence in all areas of your life and is invaluable.

In the salon

Saskia and Gemma had worked together for about three months. Saskia is a very messy worker. After a treatment she left the waxing area in a mess and didn't clean up the pot. Gemma was really dismayed to find the mess as she took her client into the waxing cubicle. Gemma was so angry that she spent the entire treatment moaning to her client about it and was still fuming at lunchtime. When she met Saskia in the staff room over lunch, she couldn't bear to look at her or talk politely to her. She left in a huff. All week Gemma has not spoken to Saskia and is so fed up she is thinking of talking to the manager. Saskia is baffled by the stony silence that seems to follow her about and doesn't know what she has done.

How could this situation be handled better?

Test your knowledge

1   What makes a therapist employable? List three things the salon owner/manager expects.

2   Why is it important to understand your job role in the salon? What must you do if you do not understand instructions given to you?

3   What may happen if you exceed the limits of your authority in the salon?

4   Which Act states that the therapist must charge a reasonable price, and give the service within a reasonable time and with reasonable care and skill?

5   Why is it important to learn your salon timings, and be commercially acceptable with your treatment timings?

6   What is a productivity target?

7   Why is it important that targets should be realistic and achievable?

8   Name three things which would help improve your own performance in the salon.

9   List five heading for analysis on a self-assessment form.

10   What does SMART stand for?

Develop and maintain your effectiveness at work
What your assessor is looking for

Unit G8

You cannot use any simulation within this unit, but the evidence can be gained quite easily. Remember to keep all paper evidence of any actions, showing you have actively taken part in developmental activities at work.

Your assessor will observe your contributions to effective teamwork on at least one occasion which will be recorded.

To cover your ranges you must:

- participate in opportunities to learn from colleagues and other relevant people
- actively partake in training and development activities
- actively partake in salon activities
- set targets for productivity and personal development
- offer assistance on a one-to-one basis
- offer assistance in a group.

Evidence could be gathered in the following ways.

- Observe a senior student carrying out a treatment on the salon price list that you are not yet able to do, write a report on it and then discuss it with your class, passing on the information you have learned. An assessor could observe your class discussion (very useful for key skill evidence, communication level 2).
- Attend a training day given by a commercial company and pass the trade exam at the end of the day – eyelash perming, new facial products or Jessica nail training is ideal. Keep the exam paper and your certificate of competence as evidence.
- Take part in a one-to-one review in your tutorial period with either your tutor or subject lecturer. Mutually agree the target achievement date for your assessment progression, for example 'by October I will have finished all my practical waxing assessments'. Both sign and date the target date and when achieved, sign again. Include your evidence book with the assessment signed off.
- Include your treatment page from the salon, highlighting your column and indicating how many treatments you gave and how much money you took in a day. Write out a target on the page for the following weeks that includes an increase of 10% for both treatments given and money taken.
- Ask your salon lecturer to start a 'salesperson of the week' award. Have a table in the appointment book of who took the most sales in both treatments and products. A small prize could be offered to the winner, either a free eyelash tint, or a nail varnish. The table would show evidence of you trying to achieve and better your previous target.
- Volunteer to become salon manager for your practical class and help your fellow therapists set up and tidy up their treatment areas. Deal with problems as they arise. Keep a salon logbook of all activities within that salon session and your contribution.

Keeping the reception area clean and tidy

During the course of the day a reception area can become untidy just like a living room at home: the magazines and papers soon get messy, a few coffee cups may be scattered around on the table, the odd coat is thrown over a chair, and the carpet is in need of a run over with the vacuum cleaner!

A *clean and tidy reception area is inviting to clients*

Think of the reception as part of your living area with your clients as your guests, except that new ones are appearing more often than at home. At work, as at home, the living area takes regular upkeep to ensure it always looks clean and orderly.

Potential untidiness may be created by:

- clients' coats not put away in a cupboard
- clients' umbrellas in a heap
- magazines and papers not kept in a rack or in a neat pile
- dirty coffee cups or water tumblers left on the table
- tables with dirty marks or stains
- delivery boxes or product trays causing obstructions
- a messy floor area covered with crumbs or dust
- record cards left out on the reception desk.

The key to being tidy is having the correct storage and being able to put things in their correct place. A salon should invest in a coat cupboard, an umbrella stand, a magazine rack, a table that is easy to clean and low-maintenance flooring. Suitable colours, which do not show the dirt, also help – all white, for example, would soon look grubby and would not be easy to keep clean.

Be careful though: there is a compromise to be found between being so house-proud that you hover over the client, waiting impatiently for the coffee to be drunk so that the cup can be washed up, and not tidying up until the end of the day when the mess has accumulated into a big job.

Tidying up should be carried out with minimum disruption to clients and at moments when the reception is at its quietest. This might be when there is a natural lull in client traffic flow, as they have gone into their treatment rooms. Do not attempt to vacuum around the clients when the reception is busy, and save the bigger jobs, such as floor cleaning, for morning preparation or evening tidying.

Morning preparation for the day ahead should include:

- switching on the lighting, both overhead and in the display cabinets
- putting out the day's newspapers
- getting the coffee pot ready, filling the kettle and filling up sugar and milk containers
- checking the appointments for the day and being ready to receive those clients
- putting the float money in the till
- emptying the dishwasher and putting cups away ready for the day
- collecting and sorting the post.

Ongoing duties throughout the day should include:

- keeping magazines tidy by putting them back in their rack
- removing used cups and glasses and washing them up or putting them in the dishwasher
- putting away record cards returned by the therapists
- topping up the kettle, filling the tea caddy, etc.
- wiping up spills on the table as they happen
- dusting around when quiet.

Evening tidying will include:

- leaving the reception ready for the next morning
- putting on the dishwasher
- vacuuming the floor or other suitable cleaning for your type of flooring
- polishing all surfaces
- removing out-dated papers or magazines
- emptying the tea and coffee pots to avoid an unpleasant smell overnight or over the weekend
- filling any gaps in the display cabinets
- clearing the reception desk of all the day's paperwork
- tallying up the till and emptying the takings
- switching off all lighting.

Keeping reception stationery in stock

Stationery is vital to the smooth running of reception. The following will be necessary to fulfil all the day's tasks:

- a message pad for all communication
- treatment dockets recording the day's activities
- retail dockets for sales of products
- price lists
- product price lists
- till cashing up sheets
- stock check sheets
- menus of refreshments.

Running out of stationery reduces staff to using scraps of paper, or not writing the information down at all and therefore forgetting vital information. Lack of the correct paperwork will affect all staff. Sales commission may be lost as the treatment and sales cannot be recorded properly. This will affect staff wages, and will not make the receptionist popular.

In this section you will look at good practice in handling the wide range of clients and their enquiries – a vital requirement of a successful business.

In this outcome you will learn about

- handling enquiries
- confirming appointments
- recording messages.

Handling enquiries

The approach to clients, customers and visitors can be summed up in a simple word: **PLEASE.**

Posture

Listen

Expression

Appearance and attitude

Speech

Eagerness to help others

Posture should be good, both to give a good impression (slouching gives the impression of boredom or not caring) and to protect the spine.

Listen with your whole body, not just your ears. Look as if you are listening. Eye contact encourages the talker to continue and facing the visitor shows you are giving her your full attention. You are saying to your visitor **'you are important to me and the salon and I give you my full attention'.**

Expression should be welcoming, open and positive. You are not there to challenge the visitor or make her feel threatened. Smile and look as if you are pleased to see her.

Appearance and attitude should reflect total professionalism and mirror the high standard of the salon.

Speech should be clear, not patronising in any way, and free of any technical terms a client may not understand.

Eagerness to help others is a charming quality and very flattering to the client. Use it wisely to give attention without appearing insincere.

The visitor should be dealt with as soon as possible and the right action taken or the appropriate staff member informed. Eye contact and a pleasant greeting are important.

Introduce yourself to the visitor as you ask about the nature of the visit, e.g. 'Hello, welcome to Blissed Out salon. My name is Sinead. How can I help you this morning?'

Do not:

- ignore the client
- huff and puff as though serving that client is the last thing you want to do
- patronise the client by talking down to her.

Handle enquiries in a friendly manner

Reality Check!

Making clients angry is a sure way of losing them

Check it out

After your first couple of days as duty receptionist at your training establishment, pause for thought. How good were you at putting people at their ease? Did you remember the PLEASE approach? What would you change about your behaviour?

The receptionist

For the receptionist to be professional and capable, she needs to know everything her job role demands. As with all life skills, knowledge leads to confidence.

A receptionist may be employed for her managerial and office skills and may not be a beauty therapist. However, to be able to book in a client and talk knowledgeably about treatments, she must be fully aware of everything contained within her salon price list.

There should be a clear understanding of:

- each treatment on the price list
- what it involves
- how long it takes
- how much it costs
- what the benefits and effects are
- the aftercare and homecare needed
- what products can be sold in conjunction with the treatment.

This will allow the receptionist to talk with confidence about each treatment, to book appointments correctly, to schedule the working day into logical sequence and to advise clients appropriately.

Identifying the enquiry

The receptionist should be asking herself these questions about her visitor.

- Why has the client come?
- Where has the client come from?
- Has she come for her appointment?
- Is the client here for a price list?
- What action do I take to help the client?

Eye contact and an approachable expression will encourage the visitor to give the required information so that a decision can be made as to the proper course of action.

You might say:

'Please take a seat; the manager won't keep you a moment.'

'Would you like a drink or magazine while you wait?'

'I will inform your therapist you have arrived for your appointment, Mrs Smith.'

Customers with special needs

People with disabilities may require some help negotiating doorways and getting into the treatment area. Always offer to help, but do not assume they cannot manage – and never patronise or talk down to the client.

The hard of hearing are usually good lip readers, so the receptionist should face the client and speak clearly so the client can see the words forming. Depending upon the severity of the disability, a pad could be provided to jot down a message. A price list could be a good visual aid to help clarify what the client wants.

People who do not speak English well may have difficulties communicating with you. Again, speak clearly, use visual materials to help clarify and seek help if available.

Older clients may have problems with mobility or hearing. However, never assume this to be the case – never judge! Be on hand to offer assistance. If the client is very frail then explain that some treatment adaptation might be needed.

> **Remember**
>
> It is important that the receptionist knows the limitation of her authority and when to refer to the manager or salon owner.

> **Remember**
>
> Anyone can walk through the salon door, so it's best to be prepared!

Wheel chair access   Deaf person

Customers with special needs may require extra assistance

Confirming appointments

Appointment details always need to be confirmed. Names, times and services can sound similar, and confirming the details involves double checking - which may save confusion later on.

You will need to make sure that you confirm all the details with the client: ' So, Mrs Patel, just to confirm your appointment for Wednesday, the 10th, at 4 pm for a facial with Shauna – can I give you an appointment card with that on?' Look to the client and she will usually agree with you, 'Yes, that's correct, and yes, you had better put it on a card for me, thank you.'

If the client has just arrived for her appointment, acknowledge her presence and inform the therapist her client has arrived. If there is a slight delay, then keep the client informed, take her coat, make her a drink and give her a magazine.

If the client's treatment is personal, then you should not repeat it too loudly. Just confirm her arrival.

Recording messages

Enquiries cannot always be dealt with by the receptionist, and if the relevant person is not available you will need to take a message. During the course of your reception duties you will be asked to take messages for other staff members, the manager, or even a client having a treatment.

This valuable service also provides evidence for your portfolio. Make sure you get your message signed and dated by the person it should go to (and include the assessor number where appropriate) and it can go into your evidence portfolio.

It is very important to write down the whole message exactly as you heard it even if you think it sounds odd, or it is difficult to understand.

You will need to include:

- date and time of the call
- how important the message is – if necessary write 'urgent' on it
- a brief description of the nature of the message
- whether the caller needs a reply – a return telephone number is then essential.

It is important to listen carefully and to ask the caller to repeat any part of the message you did not understand or hear properly. Always repeat the whole message back to the caller to make sure you have all the details correctly on the pad – especially the return number.

Confidential information

It is essential to be sensitive to all confidential information. This includes information held on the record card, medical details and personal information.

A client's address, telephone number, health status/problems, medication and other personal details are all classed as confidential. You are allowed to give these details to authorised people only, such as your salon owner, manager or fellow workers. No persons outside the salon must have access to your clients' personal details.

MESSAGE	
FOR	*Deepak*
FROM	*Mrs Alessi*
TEL. NO.	*0208 321 145*
TELEPHONED ✔	PLEASE RING ✔
CALLED TO SEE YOU ☐	WILL CALL AGAIN ☐
WANTS TO SEE YOU ☐	URGENT ☐

MESSAGE: *Needs to speak to you asap - you can call her on the tel. no. above up to 5.30pm*

DATE: *10.05.04*   TIME: *9.03am*

RECEIVED BY: *Amber*

A message pad can be useful for recording messages

Reality Check!

If a client's health status or other sensitive or personal information is not kept private you are breaking the rules of confidentiality. You need to be aware of, and abide by, the Data Protection Act. (Refer to the Professional basics section, page 39, for further information.)

Electronic messages

Many large companies have internal systems for using electronic mail (email). Provided each person has access to a computer, and the system is set up centrally, anyone can receive a message on his or her computer. An address book is set up, you type in your message and send it, and it goes into the person's inbox to be opened.

Computer technology has the advantage of saving paper and allowing several people to be given the same information at once without having to write several messages. However, the drawback is that you cannot guarantee that the person you emailed will be able to open the email that day, or that he or she is even in the office to do so.

Many salons use a system of a personal pigeonhole with the name above or below it. Messages can be left in the pigeonhole and can be collected throughout the day. A pin board for messages also works well – confidential messages can be sealed in an envelope and addressed as personal so that no one opens them by mistake.

Computer technology can also be used for booking appointments and taking payments. In addition, software programmes can be installed to keep stock records and client record cards, and to print off price lists and gift vouchers. (Refer to the **Professional basics** section, 'Data Protection Act 1998', page 39.)

Regular computer training is essential so that all staff know how to access and use the information stored in a computer.

Accurate information

Try to make sure that information you give about products or services is as accurate as possible. If you make something up just to keep the client happy, your advice may be unsafe and you will lose the confidence of the client. (Refer also to Unit G6 'Promote additional products or services to clients', page 78.)

Computers can be used for booking appointments

Remember

Urgent messages, appointment cancellations and accident or emergency messages should be given in person.

Remember

Professionalism should be the theme running throughout your training, and integrity is a major part of professionalism. Integrity means being honest, acting with honour, and being reliable and truthful in all that you do.

Make appointments for salon services   G4.3

In this outcome you will learn about

- filling in the appointments page
- missed appointments
- dealing with telephone enquiries.

It is usual for the appointments for each therapist to be recorded in a large book with either a column or a page for each . This allows the therapist to see at a glance the treatments booked in for the day and to make the appropriate preparation.

The golden rule is to have a system and make full use of it.

Filling in the appointments page

Pages should be set out for several weeks in advance so that clients booking ahead or wanting special days (pre-wedding make-up, etc.) can book in confidence. It is useful when planning a course of treatments for a client – say twice a week for six weeks. This also allows the therapist to do some advanced planning should she need time off.

When booking the appointment the receptionist needs the following details:

- name
- telephone contact number
- treatment.

She also needs to know how long to book the appointment for. Time must be allowed for:

- greeting the client and the consultation
- client undressing
- client preparation during the treatment
- client getting dressed, and being given homecare and aftercare advice.

The appointments page may look like the one opposite.

Remember that if the salon has a system of coding it should be used – it will make life easier. For example: C = cancellation, L = late arrival, A = client has arrived and so on.

Some salons do not have columns for each therapist; instead they allot a workstation number or couch position and then fit the staff around the treatments that need to be completed. The advantage of this system is that the workload can easily be distributed between staff and the manager can allot the jobs as fairly as possible. The disadvantage is that regular customers do not always get the same therapist.

When booking an appointment it is important to do the following.

- Fill out the details in pencil. This allows alterations or cancellations without making the page illegible.
- Have an easy code to identify any potential problems (see above).
- Make sure that everyone can easily understand start and finish times.
- Make sure that all names and numbers are clear and legible.
- Allow the hard-working therapist a break for lunch.
- Do not be pressured by a persistent client into giving a lunchtime appointment to a therapist who has had no other break during the day. Good practice is to stagger the lunch breaks, so that there is always a therapist covering a busy lunchtime session.
- Do give an appointment card to the client with all the details recorded on it so she has a record of when she has to come in. This cuts down the possibility of a missed appointment.

Date	Time	Treatment booked	Therapist
14.2.04	11:00am	Warm oil facial + manicure	Saskia

An appointment card

Reality Check!

If time is not allowed for all aspects the first treatment of the day will overrun, making the next appointment late. This can continue all day and the knock-on effect may be that the last client is kept waiting far too long. The therapist is put under pressure, the client may feel rushed and the benefits of the treatment will be lost.

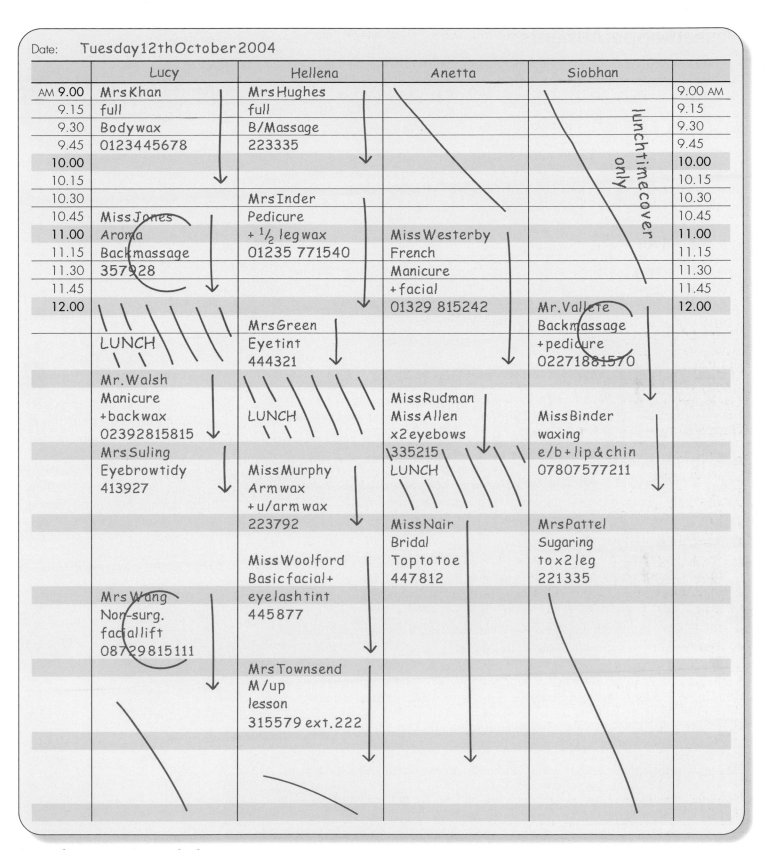

Date: Tuesday 12th October 2004

	Lucy	Hellena	Anetta	Siobhan	
AM 9.00	Mrs Khan	Mrs Hughes			9.00 AM
9.15	full	full			9.15
9.30	Bodywax	B/Massage			9.30
9.45	0123445678	223335			9.45
10.00					10.00
10.15				lunchtime cover only	10.15
10.30		Mrs Inder			10.30
10.45	Miss Jones	Pedicure			10.45
11.00	Aroma	+ ½ leg wax	Miss Westerby		11.00
11.15	Back massage	01235 771540	French		11.15
11.30	357928		Manicure		11.30
11.45			+ facial		11.45
12.00			01329 815242	Mr. Vallete	12.00

LUNCH / Mrs Green Eye tint 444321 / Backmassage + pedicure 02271881570

Mr. Walsh Manicure + back wax 02392815815 / LUNCH / Miss Rudman Miss Allen x2 eyebows 335215 / Miss Binder waxing e/b + lip & chin 07807577211

Mrs Suling Eyebrow tidy 413927 / Miss Murphy Arm wax + u/arm wax 223792 / LUNCH

Miss Nair Bridal Top to toe 447812 / Mrs Pattel Sugaring to x2 leg 221335

Miss Woolford Basic facial + eyelash tint 445877

Mrs Wang Non-surg. facial lift 08729815111

Mrs Townsend M/up lesson 315579 ext.222

A page from an appointment book

Missed appointments

Have a clear salon policy on missed appointments. Some salons make a small cancellation charge if the appointment is missed – rather like the dentist or physiotherapist. This is usually in the region of £30. There is usually no cancellation fee if the appointment is cancelled with 24 hours notice. Both staff and clients need to be clear on this policy and it could be displayed in the reception area.

Be flexible and be prepared to fit in the client who arrives without an appointment. The receptionist should always check first and then fit the client into a suitable slot. She should then inform the therapist who may not be aware that another client is waiting.

In the salon

Mrs Smith turns up for her appointment for an eyelash and brow tint, in readiness for her holiday tomorrow. She has never had a patch test and has not been informed that she needs one. How is she going to react, and what can Aisha, the therapist, do? Whose fault is it?

Dealing with telephone enquiries

The telephone is now second nature to us all and mobile phones are commonplace. Not everyone can use one effectively, however. The telephone can be a very useful business tool and should be used wisely.

How to use the phone

There are key steps to a good telephone manner. These ensure that the person on the end of the phone is treated courteously, efficiently and accurately.

- Always have a pen and paper handy to take messages.
- Answer the phone promptly, even if you are busy.
- If you do feel harassed, pause, take a deep breath in before lifting the receiver and put a smile in your voice. (It is very easy to sound abrupt on the telephone.)
- Identify the salon quickly, after making sure you are connected properly and the caller can hear you.
- Be cheery – no matter how pressurised you may feel, it should not show in the tone of your voice. No one wants to be greeted by a miserable sounding receptionist.
- Redirect the call quickly when putting it through to another extension. If the call cannot be put through, ask the caller if she or he wishes to leave a message.

Don't sigh into the phone. This gives the impression that the caller is really a nuisance, and you are doing her or him a huge favour by answering.

Do answer with a smile in your voice – just as if you can see the person's face.

Don't be curt, rude or irritated when you first pick up the phone. You never know who is on the other end, and no one deserves rudeness.

Do write a message down so that anyone can read it, and make sure it is complete.

Don't make up an answer if you don't know something or where someone is. Honesty really is the best policy. If you make something up you will only get caught out and lose credibility.

Don't slam down the phone, cut someone off or talk about the caller in a rude manner. She or he will probably hear and be most offended.

Do remember that all calls are from existing or prospective clients.

Don't use the telephone for private calls. Itemised phone bills now show who made a call, for how long and to whom. No employer would mind the odd local call or emergency message, but do not abuse an employer's goodwill.

Do ask to use the phone if it is a quick personal call.

Don't forget that calls may come out of office hours or when everyone is genuinely busy. An answer machine is a simple solution, and most people are comfortable leaving a message. Revenue may be lost if no-one follows up the message, however.

> ### Check it out
>
> Make a list of all the enquiries you answered throughout a working day. How many were telephone enquiries? How many were in person? Keep a note of these by writing down a brief account of the nature of the enquiry, the client's name, the date and time, and include this as evidence in your portfolio of evidence.

Handle payments from clients

G4.4

> ### In this outcome you will learn about
>
> - methods of payment
> - invalid payments
> - discounts and special offers
> - how the till works
> - dealing with damaged goods
> - money matters – a float
> - security procedures.

How the financial side of any business is approached is as vital as the treatment side. The client should be treated as courteously at the end of her treatment as at the beginning. Politeness is of prime importance when she is paying for her treatment.

Methods of payment

Several methods of payment are available. How the client pays is very much her choice and the receptionist must be prepared and able to cope with any payment method.

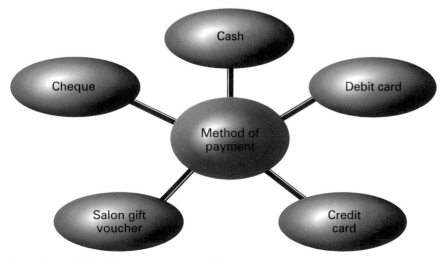

Several methods of payment are possible

All payment methods are equally acceptable and should be handled with care.

Fulfil salon reception duties
What your assessor is looking for
– possible sources of evidence

Unit G4

The evidence gained for this unit is quite straightforward. The best way of covering all the ranges is to spend a set time at the reception desk at your place of training. Ideally, a rota of students with no experience can be drawn up and matched with experienced students, who will pass on the skills needed to greet clients, make appointments and tend to all reception duties. An assessor can then observe your activities, and very quickly a portfolio of ranges starts to develop.

Even though a new student will have little experience of booking appointments and handling payments, a day spent observing others and being guided through the process is the only way to learn these new skills.

An assessor will expect you to be professionally presented, polite and courteous, with open body language and good interpersonal skills. Those qualities are far more important than getting the till operation correct at the first attempt. Think of it like taking a driving test – stalling the engine is not the end of the world as long as the correct procedures are followed. Seeking clarification from a more senior staff member, or asking for help if you think the problem is outside your own authority, will not mean you are considered incompetent – rather it shows you are mature enough to seek help and you have an understanding of your own personal limitations (which is actually a range you need to cover).

- Keep a reception diary of events, problems sorted, and how you dealt with situations such as an angry customer or a disabled client. Get it signed by the senior reception staff or your assessor at the end of the day.
- Be as helpful as you can and volunteer for any extra duties – they may cover a range you are unable to cover in the normal course of the day. For example, escorting a client on a conducted tour of the facilities may be classed as handling a confused client if she is unsure of prices, what the treatment consists of, or even how to find her way to the toilet!
- If you help on the reception desk in your place of work, then an employer's letter can be invaluable as evidence. It may not be in a beauty salon, but could be anywhere where you deal with members of the public, take payments and use a till, book clients in for hair appointments or doctor's appointments, or deal with telephone enquiries. The employer's letter should clearly outline your duties, be dated and signed and be as full as possible.

you and the
SKIN

Throughout history, nations have invaded one another. This has influenced the gene pool and therefore the skin types of people on the different continents. Immigration has also had an effect. Immigrants who settle in foreign countries and marry the people of their adopted country produce children of mixed race. If you were to look at your own family history, you may find your ancestors came from another country and your genetic inheritance comes from many different countries.

The environment in which you live and also your lifestyle contribute to the health of your skin.

Influences on the health of your skin

Skin colouring

On pages 173–177 you will find information on the structure of the skin. The skin owes its colouring to the red haemoglobin found within the blood vessels, yellow carotenoids within subcutaneous fat and the dark brown pigment melanin. Various degrees of pigmentation are present in different ethnic groups. The differences are in the amount of melanin produced and are not dependent upon the number of melanocytes present (see below).

Certain areas of skin are very rich in pigment, such as the genital area and the nipples, while practically no pigment is present in the palms of the hands and the soles of the feet (often referred to as 'glabrous' skin, this lacks hair follicles and sebaceous glands, and has a thicker epidermis).

The pigment is stored as fine granules within the cells of the germinative layer, although some granules may also be deposited between the cells. In white races the granules occur only in the deepest cell layers and mainly in the cylinder-shaped cells of the basal row. In non-white races pigment is found throughout the entire layer and even in the granular layer (stratum granulosum).

All melanin is made in special cells called melanocytes and then distributed to the epithelial cells. The melanocytes are scattered in the basal layers of the epidermis and mature as the embryo is developing in the womb. They are influenced by the units of inheritance gene code which determines race and colouring.

Some people are born without the ability to produce melanin within their skins and with no hair pigment – a congenital condition called albinism. People with this condition have pure white hair, pale skin and pink eyes. A congenital condition describes a condition that is recognised at birth or that is believed to have been present since birth. Congenital malformations include all disorders present at birth, whether they are inherited or caused by an environmental factor.

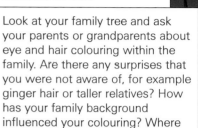

Check it out

Look at your family tree and ask your parents or grandparents about eye and hair colouring within the family. Are there any surprises that you were not aware of, for example ginger hair or taller relatives? How has your family background influenced your colouring? Where does your colouring come from?

Remember

Pigmentation is the production of colour in the body, caused by the deposit of a pigment called melanin, which protects the skin from ultraviolet radiation.

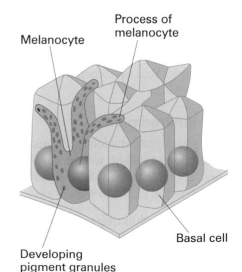

Melanocytes in skin

Oval face shape

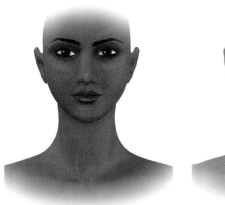

This face shape and bone structure is considered to be the ideal face shape. The chin tapers slenderly from a slightly wider forehead. The aim of make-up is to accentuate the natural shape.

Round fac[e]

The face is broad with round cont the top of t be provide from the h be worn cl The aim o slim the ap

Heart face shape

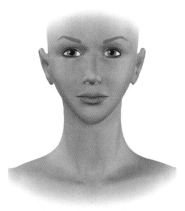

This shape usually has a wide forehead with the face tapering to a long jawline, rather like an inverted triangle. The aim of the make-up is to reduce the width across the forehead, emphasising the jawline.

Diamond

The foreh structure i cheekbon tapering t The make minimise cheekbon should be below the the cheek

The skins of people fr Malaysia, again have a type skin which is not without the see-throug

This skin has more sw at a manageable level skin has little problem and line free, strong ar into middle age. There pigmentation if care is and pigmentation can

Black skin

My name is Mary.

My skin is black, as Nigeria in Africa.

It is good skin, with foundation as I have my skin – lots of fou

I use a lot of moistu – which can be a pro

My only skin proble as I was slightly large but I am quite consc I have inherited my great even in her fift

Black skins are the res an added protection a more evenly distribute Caucasian skin.

Black skin is also more giving support to the s

Sebaceous glands are l making it less prone to slower in a black skin, shed more quickly tha

Skin cancer is not as c the harmful UV rays o white counterpart, and infection: warts are rar black skin are quite se: abrasive products, or s used to treat an 'oily' s light against the black

Skin colouring can be divided into five basic categories. These are generalised only for purposes of identification of some general tendencies:

- white skin
- mixed
- Asian
- black
- Chinese.

White skin

My name is Kirsty.

As you can see from my picture I am a typical white skin type. Being very fair, I do not tan easily. When I went to Barbados on holiday, I had to be very careful not to burn my skin.

I find I am quite sensitive to some products and I tend to stick with the products I know won't irritate me – I get a strong itchy feeling and redness over my cheeks if I use anything too highly perfumed.

Being fair does have some advantages. Lots of people pay their hairdresser to put highlights in their hair, but mine are natural, with no regrowth showing through!

White skin is the most delicate of all the skin types: it has blue and pink tones from the blood capillaries, which can be seen through the pale epidermis, and its melanin content is not as high as in non-white skins. It tends to be fine in texture and thinner than non-white skin, and is prone to early signs of ageing and wrinkles, and may bruise easily. It can be more prone to broken capillaries, especially if the skin is very pale.

The skin of blond or red-haired people tends to have a fine hair growth, and as the hair colour is light or fair, it is not noticeable. Light skins do not tan easily and are at risk of skin damage, especially if there are large amounts of freckles present. Fair skins burn quickly and are less tolerant of ultraviolet so care should be taken in hotter climates.

Of course, not all white skin is very pale and delicate. Some skin tones are darker if the parents have brown or black hair, in which case the skin may tan more easily and be less prone to being easily damaged. Some white skins, noticeably the Irish and Scottish, have striking dark hair colouring with paler skin tone.

Mixed race skin

A client with mixed race skin will need a very thorough consultation, to ensure that the skin analysis is correct, as those with this skin type are not typical of any particular type. For example, a client with a black father and white mother may have a combination of the skin colour, producing a darker tone to the skin, without necessarily having the sheen or tendency to develop keloid tissue which a black skin has. The skin will be more of a product of the environment. The correct product use will also dictate how clear the skin is, and whether the acid mantle is intact and doing its job correctly.

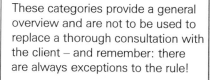

Remember

These categories provide a general overview and are not to be used to replace a thorough consultation with the client – and remember: there are always exceptions to the rule!

Treat each client as an individual, not just a category of skin colour, as different factors come into play with each client: different lifestyles, dietary intake and use of products will determine how the skin behaves and reacts.

Here is an example
during the consulta

A student with a Ch
with blocked pores
this really a dry ski

The problem is usua
epidermis is being d
too strong and causi
taking place in the s

The horny layer is n
dry patches, and the
area. Good exfoliati
then correct water-b
oily skin.

Chinese-type skin

My name is Masic

I do have an oily s
skincare products
vegetables and stir
condition. In Japa
problems with ob
countries. I am su
condition. My mo
well as she has!

This skin tone origin
typical skin colouring
has good tolerance o
hyper-pigmentation
skin if carrying out e
skin group may deve

Asian skin

My name is Poona
village in the Punj

All of my family h
grandmother is no
thick head of dark
healthy. I am not
Mum is prone to
face and neck.

As the epidermis is thicker, black skins ea
tissue. This is seen as an over-thickening
is more noticeable against a darker backg

During consultation ask questions about
guide you by her own experiences about

There is one other skin type you may con
for your NVQ, is still a recognisable skin

Mediterranean skin

My name is Hannah and I come from
my parents are originally from Greece.

I have a typical Mediterranean skin – d
don't have to worry too much about bu
really easily – we all do in my family. T
side about my skin type – the only prol
to get some blackheads around my nos
so I am very careful to cleanse my skin
prevent comedones.

These darker, more olive-toned skins are
Mediterranean: people in all the countri
such as Spain, Italy, southern France, Po
skins, which tan easily. Mexico and Sou
Portuguese immigrants who have similar
the equator.

This skin type tends to be oilier, due to
to keep the skin lubricated in the heat. T
much, and is slow to form wrinkles. As t
hair is more noticeable and often grows

This skin is robust and less prone to dan
burning.

Face shapes and contours

It is not only the skin colour that charac
skull and the bones form the contours o
different races.

The position of the bones of the skull gi
the attachment for all the muscles. The
cheeks are, how far apart the eyes are a
the face, along with the frontal bone, m
shaped. Apart from weight loss or gain,
alter your face shape unless you have co

Viruses

The common cold	Cold sores (Herpes simplex)	Warts

The common cold

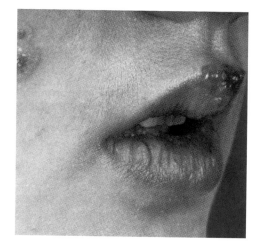

Cold sores

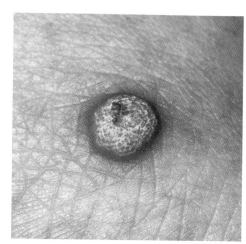

Warts

Freely recognised. Streaming eyes and nose, coughing and sneezing, easily spread.

Found on the lips, cheeks and nose. Blisters form, the skin is broken and painful; the blisters are especially likely to spread when open and weepy and then crusts form.

Small compact raised growths of skin – can be light or brown in colour, present on the face and neck.

Bacterial infections

Impetigo	Boils	Conjunctivitis	Stye

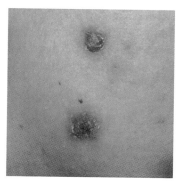

Impetigo

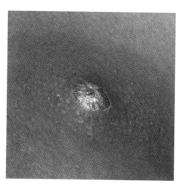

Boils

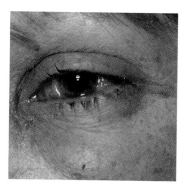

Conjunctivitis

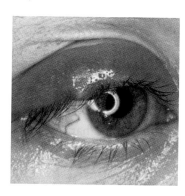

Stye

Highly infectious, this starts as small red spots, which then break open and form blisters. Most common around the corner of the mouth and if picked, will spread. (Some strains are particularly resistant to antibiotics.) Can be spread through use of dirty equipment.

This infection forms at the base of a hair follicle. Bacteria can spread through an open scratch in the skin. The area is raised, red, and painful. Pus may be present.

This is a nasty eye condition. The eyelids are red and sore, with itching. Mainly caused by bacteria present, it can be irritated by a virus or an allergy.

This is a small boil at the base of the eyelash follicle. It is raised, sore and red; there may be considerable swelling in the area.

Fungal infections

Ringworm (tinea corporis)

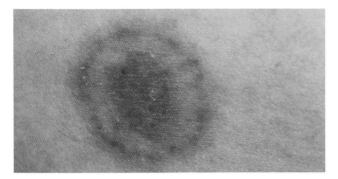

Ringworm

Red pimples appear and then form a circle, with clear skin in the middle. It is highly contagious and scales and pustules follow. It can be spread onto the face from any other area of the body. Can be passed onto humans by contact with domestic animals.

Blepharitis

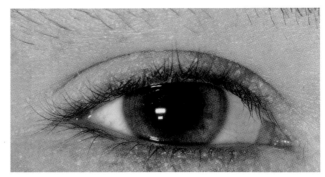

Blepharitis

An infection of the lid causing inflammation, the eye will look red and sore. Depending on the severity of the condition, it may be better to avoid eye make-up application altogether, and focus attention on the mouth, with a pretty lipstick shade.

All of the conditions mentioned would be a contra-indication to make-up application to the face. The beauty therapist carries a heavy responsibility for protecting everyone from contamination via these micro-organisms.

Conditions restricting the effectiveness of make-up

The following conditions are contra-indications that will not necessarily stop the treatment from taking place, but they may mean that make-up application has to be restricted and / or adapted. Most of these conditions are common sense, and professional judgement can be used. If the problem is not directly on the face or neck, where make-up application takes place, then just avoid the area.

Each one will depend upon the individual case, the client granting permission, and then giving **written permission** on the record card.

Cuts / abrasions / broken skin

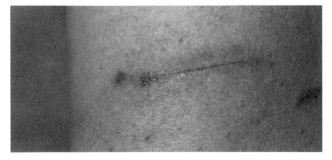

Cut

If recent, a scab will be forming, the skin may be tender and swollen in the area, and bruising may be seen. If cuts and abrasions are recent, then avoid the area altogether. If the area has healed over, and is not too recent, get the client's agreement that gentle application can take place, with careful consideration to hygiene.

Bruises or swelling

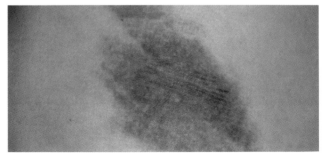

Bruise

Easily recognised as a swelling, with discoloration in varying shades. Avoid altogether if recent or painful to the touch. If healing has taken place, a gentle application of make-up will help to blend in the colour differences to the client's normal shade. Always ask for client's agreement.

Pigmentation disorders

These disorders are caused by irregularities in the skin's melanin production. They are not infectious and are not a contra-indication to facial or make-up treatments. Pigmentation disorders do affect the client's appearance, however, and may make the client feel embarrassed and self conscious; as a therapist, you therefore need to treat them sensitively. The use of camouflage cosmetics may help more effectively with the matching of the pigmentation than ordinary foundations and concealers.

Melanoderma

This is a general term used to describe patchy pigmentation. This is usually an increase in melanin caused by applying cosmetics or perfume which contain light-sensitive ingredients – the skin becomes extra sensitive to UV light (e.g. bergamot oil used in the perfume industry). Some drugs have a similar effect. This can also follow inflammation and is sometimes the cause of brown patches following sunburn.

Vitiligo	Chloasma	Freckles (Ephilidies)	Lentigo

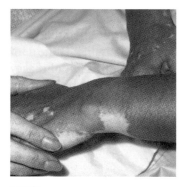 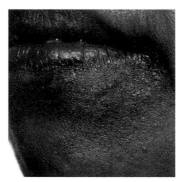  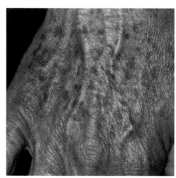

Vitiligo

This is also called hypopigmentation. It is a condition in which small patches of skin have lost their pigmentation, and appear a lighter colour than the rest of the skin. These lighter areas burn easily in the sun and need to be protected. It is not raised or painful to the touch. If the discoloration is in large patches a specialist camouflage make-up should be applied to conceal and match the skin tone. This may mean referral to a specialist. If the patch is small, clever choice of foundation and careful application is acceptable. Any pigmentation disorder may require the use of specialised make-up products to ensure even coverage, and the correct colour match of the skin.

Chloasma

This is also called hyperpigmentation. It consists of irregular patches of brown pigment caused by the over-production of melanocytes. This often appears on the face during pregnancy and is sometimes linked to the contraceptive pill. The discoloration usually disappears when the hormone balance is restored.

Freckles

These are tiny, flat irregular patches of pigment on fair-skinned people, particularly blonde / redheads. They are due to the uneven distribution of melanin, and this becomes more noticeable on exposure to strong sunlight. The freckles often increase in size and join together. The skin between the freckles contains little or no melanin so burns easily. As a therapist you should recommend a good sunscreen to the client.

Lentigo

Larger and more distinctive than a freckle, and may be slightly raised. This pigmentation does not increase in number or darken on exposure to UV light.

Haemangioma

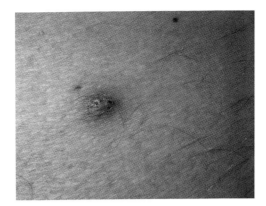

Haemangioma

This consists of various conditions caused by the permanent dilation of superficial blood vessels. Stimulating treatments will therefore be a contra-indication to treatment, but camouflage cosmetics can be used.

Dilated capillaries

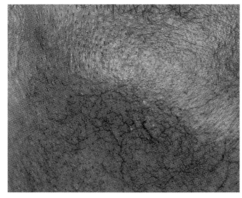

Dilated capillaries

This is the result of loss of elasticity in the walls of the blood capillaries – the cheeks and the nose are often most affected. Exposure to weather, harsh handling and lack of protection, along with spicy hot foods and alcohol, can also be contributing factors. Clients with dry/sensitive skin types are most likely to be affected.

Split capillaries

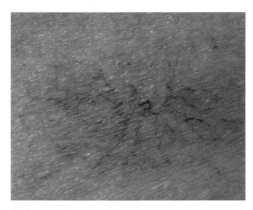

Split capillaries

Weakening and rupturing of capillary walls – clients should avoid stimulating treatments. This condition can be treated by diathermy.

Naevus

This is the term used to describe a variety of birthmarks and developmental abnormalities. It is the most common disorder involving melanocytes.

Strawberry naevus

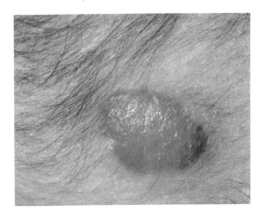

Strawberry naevus

This is a raised and distorted area, often on the face, bright pink / red. It appears a few days or weeks after birth and usually clears up completely by the age of eight.

Spider naevus

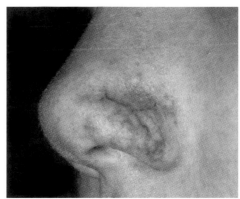

Spider naevus

A central dilated vessel with leg-like projections of capillaries. The face and cheeks tend to be most affected and this often occurs during pregnancy due to the increase in oestrogen levels.

Port wine stain

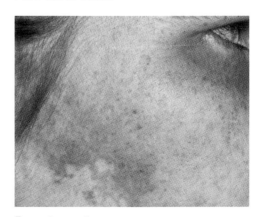

Port wine stain

This is a bright purple, irregular shaped flat birthmark that can vary in size. These birthmarks are thought to be due to damage by pressure during foetal development. These birthmarks grow with the body and can be quite disfiguring to the client. As a therapist you should always treat such marks sensitively with good cosmetic camouflage make-up.

Bones of the head, face, neck and shoulder girdle

This section will teach you about the position of the bones of the head, face, neck and shoulders.

The arrangement of bones that are joined together is **known** as a skeleton. The skeleton gives the body shape, it provides attachment for muscles and protects delicate organs. For good facial work the therapist needs to identify the bones of the head, neck, face and shoulders.

Bones that form the skull

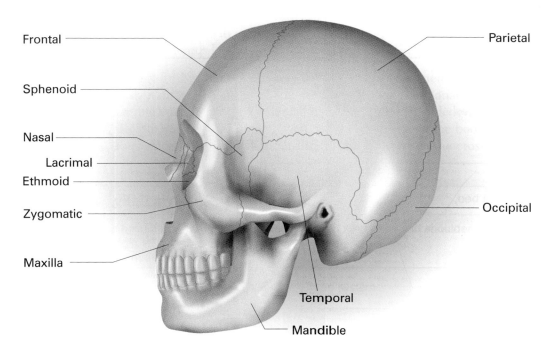

Bones of the skull

	Bone	Position
1	Occipital bone (×1)	At the back of the skull
2	Parietal (×2)	Positioned at the back of the head and forms the roof of the skull
3	Frontal (×1)	Forms the front of the skull, forehead, and upper eye sockets
4	Temporal (×2)	At the side, around the ears
5	Sphenoid (×1)	At the base of the skull, wing shaped, forms the temple
6	Ethmoid (×1)	Positioned between the frontal and sphenoid bones and forms roof of the nasal cavities
7	Lacrimal (×2)	One in each eye orbit
		These bones are fused together to form the shape of the skull, and their joins are known as sutures.

The skull is attached to the body via the vertebral column. The vertebral column enables the head to turn and tilt. The weight of the head is supported by the neck, the shoulder girdle bones and muscles.

The bones of the face

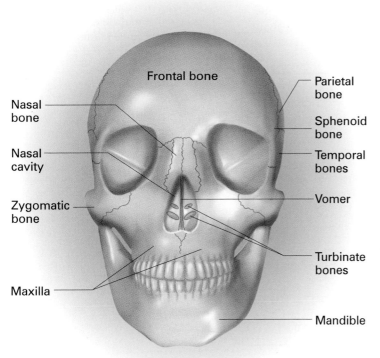

Bones of the face

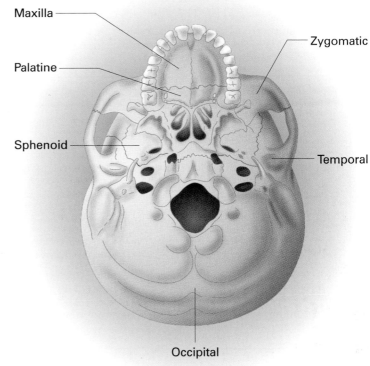

Bone of the face from above

Bone	Position
1 Zygomatic bones (×2)	These form the cheek bones
2 Maxilla (×2)	These form the upper jaw, most of the side wall of the nose and the front part of the soft palate
3 Mandible (×1)	This is the lower jaw and is the only moving bone in the face, allowing movement of the mouth for chewing and talking
4 Nasal (×2)	These form the bridge of the nose
5 Turbinate (×2)	The bones inside the nose
6 Vomer (×1)	This forms part of the nasal septum
7 Palatine (×2)	These form part of the side walls of the nose and the hard palate

The openings in the base of the skull provide spaces for the entrance and exit of many blood vessels, nerves and other structures. Projections and slightly elevated portions of the bones provide for the attachment of muscles. Some portions contain delicate structures, such as the part of the temporal bone that encloses the middle and internal sections of the ear. The air sinuses provide lightness and serve as vibrating chambers for the voice.

Bones of the shoulder girdle, upper vertebra, upper arm and chest

The bones of the shoulder girdle allow the arms to move freely. The clavicle is more commonly known as the collar bone, and you can feel it in the area where the collar of a shirt or blouse would sit. The scapula is commonly referred to as the shoulder blade. The scapula is only secured to the skeleton by muscle, so it is fairly free to move about.

Check it out

Draw your arms back, and look in the mirror. Can you see your scapula? It may be easier to identify this on a partner.

Bones of the shoulder girdle

Bones	Girdle
1 Clavicle (x2)	Across the front of the chest, going from each shoulder to the breast bone
2 Scapula (x2)	At the back of the shoulder girdle, sitting on top of the rib cage
3 Sternum (x1)	This is often called the breast bone; it forms part of the rib cage
4 Cervical vertebra (x7)	The vertabrae which form the neck; the first two are called the Atlas and Axis, and support and allow free movement of the head
5 Humerus (x2)	These bones form the top of each arm; they move in a groove in the clavicle by a joint called a ball and socket

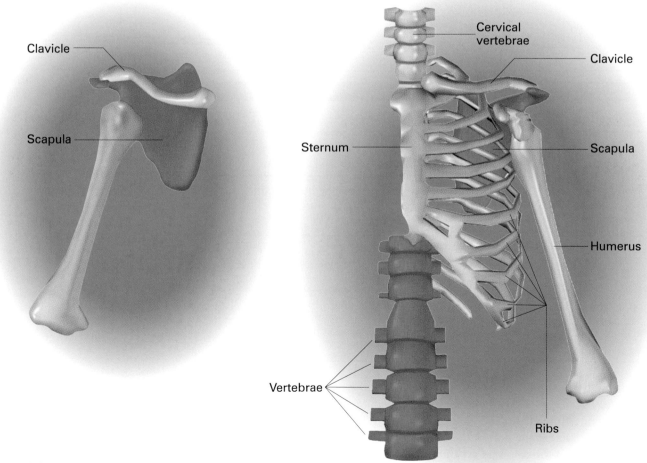

The bones of the shoulder

Bones of the arm and leg

Bones of the forearm and hand

The forearm is made up of two bones: the **radius** and the **ulna**. The ulna is the larger of the two bones.

The radius and ulna form a hinge with the humerus (the bone of the upper arm). This hinge joint enables the arm to flex and extend. The rotation of the hand is made by the radius being able to cross over the ulna. A ligament connects the two bones.

The wrist is made up of eight individual bones in two rows. Collectively these bones are known as **carpals**, although they each have individual names.

The palm of the hand is made up of five bones called **metacarpals**, and the fingers are made of three bones called **phalanges**. The thumb contains only two phalanges bones.

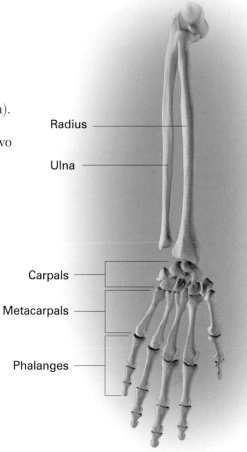

Radius

Ulna

Carpals

Metacarpals

Phalanges

Bones of the forearm and hand

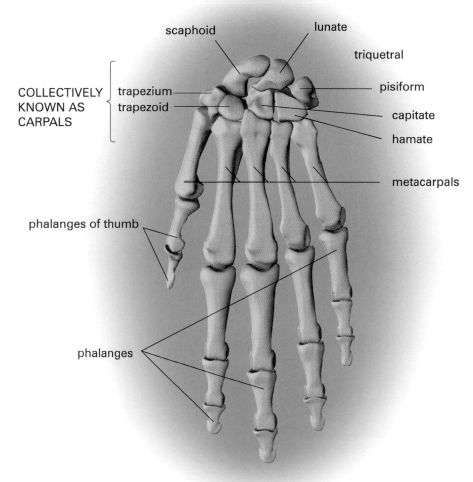

scaphoid

lunate

triquetral

pisiform

COLLECTIVELY
KNOWN AS
CARPALS

trapezium

trapezoid

capitate

hamate

metacarpals

phalanges of thumb

phalanges

The bones of the hand and wrist

Check it out

Have the palm of your right hand facing you. Now rotate your palm so it turns away from you. This rotation movement is known as **pronation**. Now rotate your hand so your palm faces you again. This is called **supination**.

Remember

A simple way to remember which forearm bone is which: ulna contains the letter 'l' and this bone goes to your little finger.

Bones of the lower leg and foot

The bones that make up the lower leg are the **tibia** and **fibula.** The tibia is often called the shinbone. This bone is the stoutest in the body and transmits body weight directly to the ankle joint. The fibula forms part of the ankle joint.

The foot is constructed in a similar way to the hand. Seven bones, all with individual names, make up the **tarsals** (like the wrist). Five **metatarsals** together support the major arches of the foot.

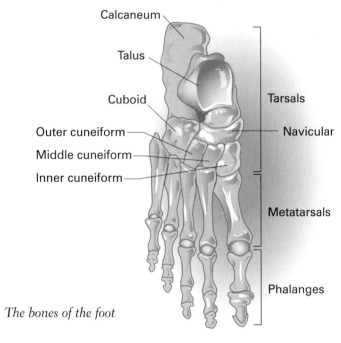

The bones of the foot

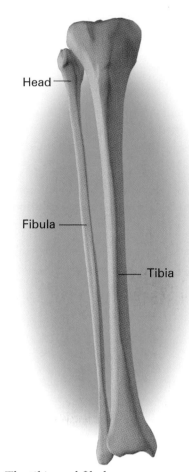

The tibia and fibula

The foot has four arches: two **transverse** (across the foot) and two **longitudinal** (from heel to toe). The function of these arches is to:

- provide support for the body
- act as shock absorbers
- aid posture.

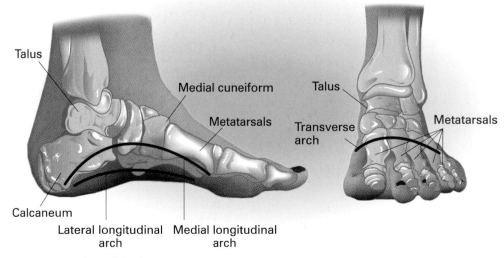

The major arches of the foot

Like the fingers, the toes are made of **phalanges.** The big toes have two phalanges each and the other toes have three.

Structure of the skin

See the section 'You and the skin', pages 134–163. Skin is a remarkable organ that is able to adapt and perform various functions. It can mould to different shapes, stretch and harden, but can also respond to delicate touch, feel pain, pressure, hot and cold, so it is regarded as an effective communicator.

Skin makes up about 12% of an adult's body weight and consists of three layers: the epidermis, dermis and the subcutaneous layers. You can think of these layers like clothing.

The epidermis is the outer skin, like a breathable waterproof jacket – this is the skin we *see*. Our skin, or dermis, is under this and could be thought of as a blouse or shirt with lots of pockets containing many different items. Underneath this is a cushioned soft layer for protection, like a soft thermal vest. This bottom layer contains fat which helps to insulate and keep in warmth. The layers vary in thickness over different areas of the body. The thickest layers are over friction and gripping areas and the thinnest are over the eyelids, which must be light and flexible.

You can help yourself to remember the functions of the skin by the word **Shapes.**

S = Sensation
There are five types of nerve ending within the skin to help identify pain, touch, heat, cold and light pressure.

H = Heat regulation
The skin helps regulate the body's temperature by sweating to cool the body down when it overheats and shivering when it is cold. Shivering closes the pores. The tiny hairs that cover the body stand on end to trap warm air next to the skin and therefore prevent heat loss, when cold.

A = Absorption
Absorption of ultraviolet rays, from the sun, help with formation of vitamin D, which the body needs for the formation of strong bones and good eyesight. Some creams, essential oils, and some medication can also be absorbed through the skin.

P = Protection
Too much ultraviolet light may harm the skin, so the skin protects itself by producing a pigment, seen as a tan, called *melanin*. Bacteria and germs are prevented from entering the skin by a protective barrier called *the acid mantle*. This barrier also helps protect against moisture loss.

E = Excretion
Waste products and toxins are eliminated from the body through the *sweat glands*.

S = Secretion
Sebum and *sweat* are secreted onto the skin's surface. The sebum keeps the skin lubricated and soft, and the sweat combines with the sebum to form *the acid mantle*.

Layers of the skin
The skin is made up of three layers:

1   Epidermis
2   Dermis
3   Subcutaneous layer.

Test your knowledge

1   Name the five layers of the epidermis.

2   What is the function of the erector pili muscle?

3   What does desquamation mean?

4   What is another name for the collar bone?

5   Is the scapula fixed or can it move freely?

6   Name the bones that make up the skull.

7   What is the name of the cheek bone?

8   What is the protein that nails are composed of?

9   Name the half moon shape at the base of the finger nail.

10   Hairs have a gland that lubricates them. What is this called?

11   How many voluntary muscles does a person have?

12   Where are the pectoral muscles and what are their functions?

13   List four functions of the blood.

14   Name the three vessels that carry blood around the body.

15   What colour is lymphatic fluid?

16   What vein joins lymph and blood together again?

17   Name the two bones that make up the forearm.

18   How many arches does the foot have? What are they called?

19   Which is the stoutest bone in the body?

20   What is another name for the calf muscle?

21   Which type of blood vessel carries oxygenated blood from the heart to the extremities?

practical
SKILLS

  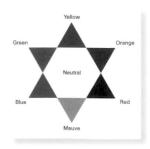

Improve and maintain facial skin condition

Unit BT4

Introduction

A facial is a lovely treatment to offer any client: it is both extremely relaxing and very beneficial. In fact, for a professional beauty therapist, a facial can be as relaxing to give as it is to receive. The client is cocooned on the couch, wrapped warmly and securely, with the luxury of knowing that expert hands are cleansing, massaging and improving the skin's condition. Many clients fall asleep during a facial, as the relaxation is so deep.

A facial makes a perfect present, and vouchers for the treatment can be purchased in most salons. For many women a facial is the height of luxury; for a beauty therapist it rates very highly on the scale of favourite treatments to give.

This unit is all about improving and maintaining facial skin condition using a variety of treatments.

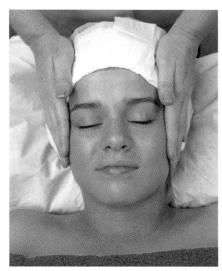

A facial is both relaxing and beneficial

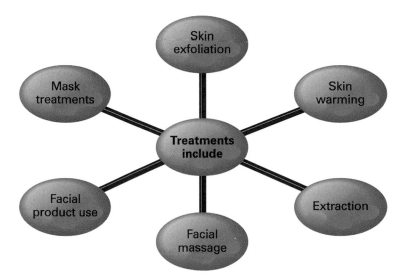

All of these treatments will be carried out on a variety of skin types, age groups and conditions. It is also important to remember that you need to maintain your health and safety, along with rigorous good hygiene practices throughout.

In this unit you will cover the following outcomes:

BT4.1 Consult with the client
BT4.2 Prepare for the treatment
BT4.3 Plan the treatment
BT4.4 Improve and maintain skin condition
BT4.5 Complete the treatment.

Consult with the client

BT4.1

A full consultation is vital before the treatment can begin. (Refer to **Professional basics**, pages 19–21, for detailed information on how to conduct a consultation. Anatomy and physiology relating to the head and neck are covered in **Related anatomy and physiology**, page 166.)

A facial is a treatment that helps the therapist in a number of ways, as shown in the diagram.

A facial has many benefits

In this outcome you will learn about	
• consultation techniques	• client modesty
• the client treatment plan	• contra-indications
• agreeing services and outcomes	• recording clients' skin care.

When examining the face and neck it is important to consider these points:

- Check the skin prior to the treatment for any contra-indications that would prevent treatment, or any adaptation that may be necessary.
- Identify the client's skin type correctly. This is essential, both to enable the therapist to give the right treatment, and to recommend the most suitable products.
- Look for any minor skin problems that can be given specific treatment for improvement.
- Take into account the client's age, lifestyle, nutrition and general health. These will be reflected in the colour and texture of the skin, muscle tone in the face, elasticity, the number of wrinkles present and skin discoloration. Record the client's colouring and pigmentation, as well as any other facial features; this will help with a make-up application and when recommending other treatments, such as eyebrow shaping.

Consultation techniques

There are three techniques to a facial examination:

- questioning
- visual
- manual examination.

Questioning the client before her facial will establish the factors that contribute to the skin's condition. Gentle questioning will help identify the client's normal skin-care routine and products used as well as the client's expectation of the treatment – clients do need to be realistic. It is important that the client understands that a skin condition may take several treatments to clear. A realistic treatment plan, with both time-scale and cost, should be discussed prior to the treatment taking place.

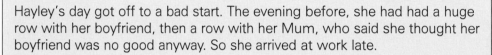

> ### In the salon
>
> Hayley's day got off to a bad start. The evening before, she had had a huge row with her boyfriend, then a row with her Mum, who said she thought her boyfriend was no good anyway. So she arrived at work late.
>
> Her first client was new to the salon and needed a full facial consultation. Hayley really wasn't in the mood for this. Still, it's her job, so she had to get on with it.
>
> All was going well until Hayley removed the client's make-up to have a look at the skin under the magnifying lamp. As she started the rhythmic cleansing movements, she began to feel really sorry for herself and the tears started to well up. Hayley was thinking: 'It's not fair – no one listens to me. Mum going on at me is just not fair. What if it is all over between me and Jimmy?'
>
> The tears were flowing now, and actually falling onto the client's face. Hayley gave her a tissue before rushing out of her work cubicle, as she really needed a good cry in the toilets. The client was left alone in the cubicle to dry her face.
>
> What should Hayley have been thinking about? Where should her focus have been? How is the client feeling? What would you do if you were the client? What would you do if you were Hayley's manager?

Visual examination should be done under a strong light with a magnifying glass. The skin should be clean and free of make-up. Any areas of sensitivity, problem areas such as comedones (blackheads) or an oily T- zone can be recorded on a facial record card.

Manual examination should be gentle, and will give some indication about elasticity of the skin, its warmth and texture. A gentle pinch of the skin in the main facial areas should allow the skin to spring back into its original shape. Poor elasticity of the fibres will mean that the skin takes longer to recover from the pinch test and this could be due to age. The warmth of the skin will indicate how good the circulation is to the face, and the texture will be felt as smooth, coarse or rough. Lumps under the skin may need further investigation.

> **Remember**
>
> Consultations of any kind should be carried out in a polite and friendly manner. Remember good eye contact, open body language and thorough questioning – and show interest in her replies!

> **Remember**
>
> Facials do instantly make the skin look cleaner and fresher and feel softer, but a skin problem, such as mild acne, will definitely take more than one treatment for a good result to be seen.

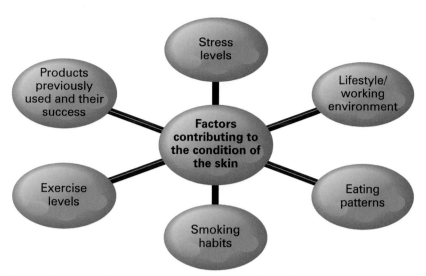

Many factors are important to the condition of the skin

Preparation of the client for examination

Initial discussion with the client will be done whilst the client is still clothed and sitting with you. The discussion will cover contra-indications, his or her expectations of the treatment and your treatment plan. Obviously a full treatment plan cannot be given until you have closely examined the skin, but you may not get that far if the client has an infectious condition and the treatment cannot go any further. It is much better to terminate the treatment with the client at that point, rather than place him or her on the couch and remove the make-up if appropriate, only to find that the treatment cannot go ahead as a contra-indication is present.

The client treatment plan

Refer to **Professional basics**, pages 19–21 and 29. Revisiting these pages will remind you of assessment techniques and questioning techniques, along with treatment, services and product advice and, most importantly, client expectations.

If the client is suitable for treatment with no contra-indications, you can go ahead and prepare the client for the beginning of the facial and the full skin analysis.

The treatment plan should be agreed with the client and recorded on the personal record card, along with a suitable time frame for a course of treatments, a price and budget structure (payment planning or perhaps a discount for payment in full) and details of recommended treatments and products. Remember that if you are off sick, another therapist will not know what you have agreed with your client if you have not written it down fully on the record card.

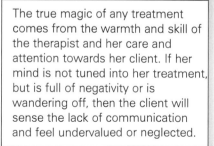

Agreeing services and outcomes

This combines very well with G6 'Promote additional products or services to clients', so revisit this unit and remind yourself how to agree services and treatment outcomes with your client. Above all, you want your client to be happy with your recommendations – your client is a valued customer, whom you want to keep for a long time, and your professionalism and integrity will ensure this.

Client modesty

The client's modesty must be preserved. In a closed cubicle ask the client to remove all outdoor and top clothes and put on a gown.

For the female client

Tights and half-slip may be kept on, but shoes should be removed. Bra straps may get oily and should be dropped off the shoulder, or the bra may be taken off altogether, depending on client preference. If the client chooses to push her straps down onto the top of her arms, there is still a danger they will get massage medium on them, as you will be going halfway down the upper arm with your movements.

For the male client

Facial massage includes the upper back and shoulders, and these therefore need to be free of clothing. The shirt or T-shirt of the male client should be removed, and his chest covered with towels and/or blankets to prevent his upper body getting cold.

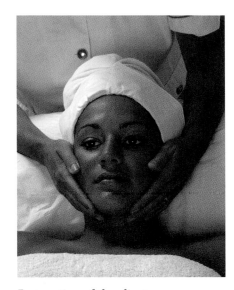

Preparation of the client

For all clients

Assist the client onto the couch and remove the gown. Depending upon the time of year, wrap the client in either a blanket with towels or just towels, so that he or she is comfortable and warm. There is nothing more distracting than clients feeling insecure or cold – they need to feel relaxed.

The client should remove all jewellery, accessories, wig, if worn, and glasses. Clients wearing contact lenses may prefer to remove them during the written consultation stage if they have suitable storage for them. Some clients prefer to keep them in, even though make-up will be removed and the eye area will be massaged. Be guided by the client's choice, as only the client will know which is most comfortable.

A headband or turban should be used to remove all hair from the face.

Before beginning the examination, remember the following.

- Wash your hands thoroughly.
- Remove any make-up women may be wearing, and cleanse, deep cleanse, tone and pat dry the skin using a tissue.
- Ideally your male client will have had a clean shave prior to the facial examination – otherwise the cotton wool may stick to the beard growth or stubble. Also the state of the skin may be camouflaged behind a day's growth of hair, and a true picture of the skin's condition may not be seen.
- The texture of the skin and the muscle tone will be felt as the cleansing movements are made.
- You need a pen and your record card so you can fill in all the client's details.
- Remember to include on the record card the client's current skin care routine and how successful it is (refer to **You and the skin,** page 144, for a sample record card).

Contra-indications

The general contra-indications to a facial treatment are:

- cuts and abrasion of the skin's surface
- scar tissue less than six months old
- recent sunburn
- any undiagnosed lumps or swellings
- severe eye infections
- any bacterial, fungal or viral infections
- conjunctivitis
- bruising to the area
- a known allergic reaction.

For a full visual reminder of contra-indications, refer to **You and the skin**.

Taking necessary action if a contra-indication is found

Treating a client with a known contra-indication has consequences. The client could experience pain and discomfort if the treatment went ahead and the condition could be made worse, or spread to other parts of the body. The therapist could be found to be negligent, both by her insurance company and by her professional body, and the expected support may not be forthcoming should the client decide to take legal action. Any client with a suspected infection should be referred to her GP. But be careful – it is not a therapist's job role to give a medical diagnosis.

If no contra-indications are present, continue the skin analysis.

Recording clients' skin care

All the findings from your consultation and skin analysis should be recorded on the client's personal chart. The style of the chart may vary from salon to salon, but the basic information recorded is the same. See page 144.

Refer to **You and the skin** (pages 143–147) to refresh your knowledge of skin types and how to recognise them.

It is important that all information is recorded – the client may not be booked in with the same therapist every treatment, and records of any allergies, reactions and favourite products will help keep the client safe and avoid duplication.

> **Remember**
>
> There is a risk that if a treatment is given when some of these conditions are present, it could put the therapist and other clients at risk from cross-infection. The condition could be made worse by treatment, or it could be prolonged.

> **Check it out**
>
> Often product suppliers produce their own analysis sheets, or your training establishment may have its own for assessment purposes. Research where your particular skin analysis sheets have come from and compare them to a local salon's analysis sheet. How do they differ? How is the information recorded?

Prepare for the treatment

BT4.2

Preparation is key to giving a relaxed and flowing treatment. All aspects of the treatment need to be carefully prepared to enable you to give the client your full attention and a super-pampering treatment.

The working environment

Preparation of the working environment must include the legal, hygiene and treatment requirements for facial work. Your personal appearance must also meet accepted standards. Being fully prepared allows you to concentrate on your client and give a relaxed treatment without the distraction of having to leave the area to get products, equipment or towels. A little preparation time should be built into each appointment slot, so that each client feels special.

Your legal and personal obligations are all covered in **Professional basics,** 'You, your client and the law' (pages 31–47).

The Health and Safety at Work Act (page 31) and G1 'Ensure your own actions reduce risks to health and safety' are also important, as the client's safety is a vital aspect of any facial treatment.

Risk assessment for facials

Facials have many potential hazards. Remember to complete a risk assessment to minimise risks prior to the client coming in for the treatment.

Here is a risk assessment table for some aspects of facials – how many more points could you add?

In this outcome you will learn about

- the working environment
- risk assessment for facials
- removing make-up
- performing a skin analysis.

Reality Check!

No client is going to feel comfortable in a dirty workplace environment. She probably won't even stay if she feels it is unhygienic.

Risk assessment for facials

Refer to **Professional basics** for a complete discussion of risk assessment.

Hazard: look for hazards that you would reasonably expect to result in significant harm under the conditions in your workplace. Use the following examples as a guide.

- **Environmental risks**, such as slipping / tripping (e.g. poorly maintained floors or stairs)

- **Fire** (e.g. from flammable material)

- **Equipment** (couch height, trolleys and stools)

- **Reactions to products** (irritation, swelling redness)

- **Allergies** (to nuts in almond-oil based products, cleansers and moisturisers, to cotton wool filaments)

- **Noise**

- **Poor lighting**

- **Low temperature**

Topic	Professional basics or Unit G1
Hygiene requirements	Pages 23–27
Treatment requirements	Pages 28–30
Personal appearance	Pages 8–10
Protective clothing	Page 34
Environmental conditions	Pages 32–36
Client's comfort and safety	Pages 42–43
Sanitising hands	Page 26

Many of the topics in BT4.2 are covered in the **Professional basics** section, or in G1
'Ensure your own actions reduce risks to health and safety'.

Removing make-up

Step-by-step facial cleanse

Ensure the client is correctly prepared for the treatment.

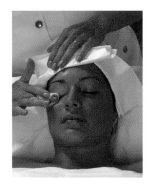 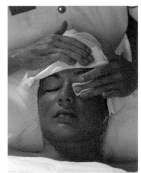 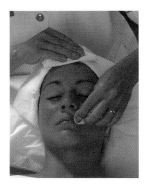 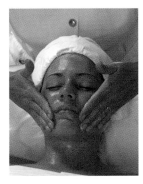 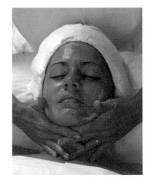

1 Using damp cotton wool apply eye make-up remover, working around the eye, over lid, underneath and over lashes. Work from inner to outer area. Remove with damp cotton wool.

2 Follow the same routine with the other eye. Be careful to support the eye area, and do not drag, or apply any pressure.

3 Apply a small amount of cleanser, using damp cotton wool and remove the lipstick, in small circular motions.

4 Apply dots of cleanser over the entire face. Working from the neck upwards, use upward movements towards the jaw line.

5 Work from the jaw line; use alternate hand movements to cover the entire cheek area.

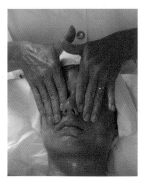 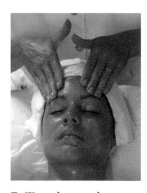 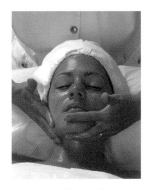 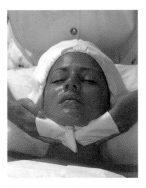 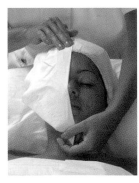

6 Using the index fingers, work into the nose, with small circular motions, without blocking the nostrils in! Use light pressure only.

7 Travel over the bridge of the nose, onto the forehead working out towards the temple areas. Using index fingers, apply a little pressure to the temples.

8 Sweep back down to the chin, working over the jaw line with alternate hand movements, to finish the cleanse routine.

9 Remove cleanser, following the same routine direction as for the application of cleanser, with tissues, damp cotton wool or sponges.

10 Blot the face with the tissue folded in a triangle. Pat gently with the hand, turn tissue over and repeat on the other side of the face.

How did you do?

You can check your facial cleansing techniques quite easily. To ensure that the eyes are grease free, go back to the eyelashes and run a dry cotton bud along the length of the lash. If the cotton bud is dirty, you will know you haven't cleaned thoroughly enough.

You can repeat the exercise for the skin by running a dry cotton bud along the cheek bones.

Don't be disappointed if you haven't got it right the first time. Your technique will improve with practice.

Performing a skin analysis

Refer to **You and the skin** for skin analysis (page 135), how to identify skin type (page 143), skin conditions (page 149) and any contra-indications (page 147).

Plan the treatment

BT4.3

In this outcome you will learn about
• recommending suitable treatments and products • suggesting a treatment plan
• selecting suitable equipment and materials • specific preparation of the client.

Recommending suitable treatments and products

Before you can recommend any suitable treatments or products you have to know them thoroughly and have experience of the treatments yourself, so you can talk about the sensations as well as the effects.

You need to have a full knowledge about both the products and the treatments before you go onto facial massage techniques. You will need to refer back to this planning section on a regular basis as you work through this section.

Facial products

A range of professional facial products for salon and home use

---

Remember

Some clients are allergic to the metallic fibres present in cotton wool, so be sure to ask before you remove with it. Tissues will do equally well, and some salons prefer sponges for removal. However, sponges are not easy to sterilise, and have to be washed in very hot soapy water to avoid cross-contamination.

Check it out

Do some research to discover the latest trends in techniques. Today's discerning skin-care and massage clients can be quite knowledgeable and expect the latest massage techniques and anti-ageing preparations. The eastern-influenced Ayurveda treatments are also very popular and skin-care companies are trying to match the trends. Find out what commercial training is available and try to offer alternative treatments, such as manual lymphatic drainage massage to the face, which is very good for draining the sinuses.

Remember

In a salon situation you will need to have all equipment to hand while talking through the client's needs. You will choose the equipment you need according to the results of your skin analysis. So, while you may think you do not need equipment information at this stage in your training (as you have yet to learn a facial cleanse routine), you will need the information to make an informed decision at the consultation stage in a proper client situation.

To improve the facial skin condition, there are many products available on the market that can be used to good effect within the facial treatment:

- cleansers
- toners
- moisturisers
- exfoliants
- masks
- massage products
- specialist skin preparations.

The cosmetic and skin-care preparation market is huge. The range of manufacturers producing good-quality products both for salon use and for retailing is ever-growing. Your salon or teaching establishment may have their own particular favourite which, from experience, they prefer.

Skin damage

Reasons for skin damage	How to recognise the signs or symptoms
Excessive exposure to the sun or artificial sunlight (sun beds)	The skin ages prematurely, causing breakdown of collagen and elastin which supports the skin; uneven pigmentation can also occur
Excessive lines and wrinkles from alcohol intake and smoking	Contamination of skin, clogged and blocked pores, irritations occur and a tendency to comedones and allergic reactions
Pollution from chemicals, traffic and thinning of the protective ozone layer	Leads to dehydration and over-activity of the sebaceous glands causing problems
Heat and steam	Over-stretches the skin, causing damage
Incorrect use of skin-care products	Inappropriate products can cause comedones to form or an over-sensitive skin

A range of manufacturers produce good-quality skin-care products

The table below shows a good skin-care routine.

Procedure	Action on the skin	Products available
Cleanse am and pm	Removes dirt, sweat, sebum and make-up from the skin's surface	Cleansing creams, lotions and milks, facial wash-off bars, gels
Tone am and pm	Tightens the skin, stimulates the circulation and eliminates any trace of remaining cleanser from the skin	Toning lotion astringent, skin tonic bracers and fresheners
Exfoliate once a week	Sloughs off the dead cells from the top layer of the epidermis to improve texture and colour whilst stimulating circulation	Cleansing grains that form a paste when mixed with water, ready-mixed granular paste, fruit acid peels
Day cream am	A protective film to keep the skin soft and supple – it restores the oils to the skin after toning, helping to keep the outer layers hydrated	Moisturiser creams or milks
Night cream pm	An absorbent, intensive, rich cream to restore the skin's well-being without leaving the skin feeling oily	Rich moisturisers in cream form
Face mask once a week	Deep cleanses, soothes and balances the skin	Clay masks, peel-off masks, thermal masks, fruit masks, biological masks
Eye make-up remover pm	A very gentle eye make-up remover, finer than a cleanser for the delicate eye area	Lotions and creams, wash-off gels
Eye balm when needed	A delicate balm for upper and lower lid area - soothing, refreshing, reduces puffiness	Moisturising lightweight creams or lotions

A good skin-care routine

Cleansing creams

Key ingredients

- An emulsion of oils, usually mineral oil.
- Waxes, usually beeswax or paraffin.
- Water and water-soluble ingredients.
- Emulsifiers.
- Fragrance.
- Preservatives.

What they do

- A mineral oil will dissolve grease and oil-based products on the skin, i.e. make-up.
- Waxes provide a creamy firm texture to the product.
- The water content cools the skin and provides slip to allow easier spreading.
- Emulsifiers prevent the ingredients separating, i.e. oil and water.
- Fragrance makes the cream more appealing.
- Preservatives provide the product with a good shelf life and prevent deterioration.

Summary of action

- A deep efficient cleansing action, removes even heavy make-up.
- Leaves skin smooth and supple.
- Ideal for dry or normal skin types; too rich for an oily skin.

Cleansing creams and moisturisers

Method of use

- Decant a small amount onto a spatula, close lid, spread from spatula onto fingertips and massage over face and neck area using upward circular movements.
- Remove with tissues or damp cotton wool.

Cleansing milks

Key ingredients

- An emulsion of oils, usually mineral oil.
- A smaller proportion of waxes than in a cleansing cream.
- A higher proportion of water and water-soluble ingredients than creams.
- Detergent.
- Emulsifiers.
- Fragrance.
- Preservatives.

Cleansing milk

What they do

- Detergent will act as a surface-active agent, which helps emulsify and create foaming action.
- For other ingredients, see above.

Summary of action

- A light cleansing lotion, which is easier to remove than a cleansing cream.
- Some cleansing milks can be worked into lather with water to wash off the skin.
- Ideal for most skin types except the very dry.
- Preferred by people who like a lighter feel to their cleanser.
- Also ideal for younger or greasier skins.

Method of use

- Either apply directly onto the skin on damp cotton wool pads stroking in an upward motion, or apply with the fingertips in small circular movements.
- Remove with tissues or damp cotton wool.

Cleansing lotions

Key ingredients

- Detergent solution in water.
- Emulsifiers.
- Fragrance.
- Preservatives.
- Anti-bacterial ingredients.

What they do

- Anti-bacterial ingredients help a greasy or problem skin.
- For other ingredients, see above.

Summary of action

- A light cleansing lotion, which can be applied on cotton wool pads.
- Ideal for most young skins, especially problem or blemished skins.

Method of use

- Apply directly onto the skin on damp cotton wool pads, stroking in an upward motion.

Cleansing bars

Facial washes and gels

Key ingredients

- A mixture of cleansing and wetting agents (often derived from palm oil).
- Water and water-soluble ingredients
- Fragrance and foaming agents.
- Preservatives.
- Conditioners and colour.

What they do

- Cleansing agents will absorb the oil particles of dirt.
- Conditioners will match and balance the natural pH of skin.
- Colour and fragrance will give appeal, for example tea-tree may be added to give an anti-bacterial, healing property to a wash that is enhanced with a colour additive.
- For other ingredients, see above.

Summary of action

- Use a small amount on a moist skin, massage lightly over face and neck, and rinse off with water.
- Foaming properties will vary depending on hardness or softness of water.
- This method of cleansing can be used with a facial soft bristle brush for added stimulation.
- This is ideal for use with a brush cleanser unit (a small motor rotates the brush) and can be applied to the chest and back. This makes a very good salon treatment for a congested skin, and is very popular with male clients who suffer with problem skin.
- Some gels can also be used as shaving foam, cleansing at the same time. Check individual manufacturers' instructions for use – there are many preparations that can be bought over the counter.

Method of use

- Apply directly onto moist skin in circular motions avoiding contact with the eyes
- Rinse off.

Facial washes and gels

Toners and skin fresheners

Key ingredients

- Alcohol, usually ethanol.
- Astringents, such as witch hazel.
- Antiseptic, such as hexachlorophene.
- Humectants, such as glycerine.
- Additives, such as cucumber, althea extract (from plants).
- Preservatives and perfume.

What they do

- The alcohol removes traces of grease on the skin and helps with the drying action.
- The water content cools the skin and dilutes the alcohol content.
- Fragrance makes the toner more attractive and hides the alcohol smell!
- Antiseptic properties help heal a congested skin.
- An astringent tightens the skin and makes pores appear smaller.
- Additives such as cucumber and plant extracts soothe and soften skin.
- Humectants attract water and help re-hydrate the skin.
- Colour and fragrance give appeal, for example cucumber may be added to give a soothing property to the toner and it may be enhanced with a colour additive – blue or green are associated with cooling and calming properties.

Toners and skin fresheners

Summary of action
- Toners cool and refresh the skin, and are available in differing strengths depending upon skin type.
- Strong toners for oily skins contain more alcohol, which dissolves grease; the astringent properties tighten the skin.
- All toners contain mostly water and humectants, which help with moisture retention.
- Fresheners are available which contain only soothing agents, such as azulene or camomile. As no alcohol is present they are not as good at removing grease from the skin, but are ideal on a sensitive skin.

Method of use
- Apply to the skin with damp cotton wool pads, stroking in a firm but gentle rhythm all over the face and neck.
- Toners can help smooth, soften and heal skin, increasing cell regeneration.
- They prepare the skin to receive a moisturiser by removing any trace of grease left by the cleanser.

Exfoliants
Key ingredients
- Abrasive powders such as finely ground olive stones, nuts, oatmeal, corn cob powder or synthetic micro-beads.

Detergent
- Water and water-soluble ingredients.
- Kaolin, or other clay-based ingredients.
- Sodium lactate.
- Added moisturisers and vitamins.

What they do
- An abrasive will act as a gentle buffer to remove the dead skin cells, felt as small grains on the skin.
- Detergent continues the cleansing process.
- Water and water-soluble ingredients help provide slip, so that the cream or paste flows over the skin easily and does not pull or drag the skin.
- Kaolin or other clays will absorb grease and dirt particles, gently cleansing and bleaching the skin slightly.
- Sodium lactate is an excellent humectant to regulate moisture content within the skin.
- Added moisturisers and vitamins impart a light, smooth feel to the exfoliant without being sticky or greasy.

Summary of action
- The definition of exfoliate is to peel, flake or scale, in this case the skin's cells.
- As the top layer of the epidermis is constantly shedding, an exfoliant helps the process along.
- Helping the skin clear the accumulation of dead cells brightens the complexion, softens the skin and makes the skin very receptive to receiving moisture.
- Exfoliants come in many commercial forms: a powder, which must be mixed with water, a ready-made paste, or in a suspension (with water) that can also be left on to form a facemask.
- These exfoliating facemasks usually have a higher proportion of clay to make the mask dry and set on the face.
- All skin types benefit from exfoliation providing care is taken when choosing a suitable type for the skin problem.

Exfoliants help to brighten the complexion and soften the skin

Method of use

- Apply a thin layer onto damp, cleansed skin in circular motions, avoiding the eyes. Work upwards with light pressure. Care must be taken over the delicate cheek area; if sticking or dragging of the skin occur, add more water without soaking the client.
- Rinse off.
- Follow manufacturers' instructions, as some exfoliants can also be left on the skin as a facemask, which is left to dry then rinsed off.
- Some facemasks double as a peel, and the mask is removed by using dry fingers in a circular motion to slough off the remaining cream before rinsing.

Fruit acid peels

Key ingredients

- Available as lotions or masks containing alpha hydroxy acids (AHA).
- AHAs are fruit acids from citrus fruits, bilberries and sugar cane.

What they do

- The fruit acids help dissolve the surface skin cells whilst stimulating the blood supply.
- They soften the skin cells and give the skin an appearance of being smoother and brighter.

Method of use

- The products come as a mask or a lotion to be applied to the skin in an upward smooth motion.
- They are ideal for a dry, mature skin.

Summary of action

- AHA treatments can cause a slight contra-action after treatment. The skin may go pink, with a tingling sensation and mild itching. This is a normal reaction and the client should be warned to expect it.

Moisturising cream

Key ingredients

- An emulsion of oils and waxes such as coconut or jojoba oil.
- Water and water-soluble ingredients.
- Fragrance.
- Preservatives.
- Emulsifier.
- Humectants such as glycerine or sorbitol.

What they do

- Creams contain approximately 60% water, which re-hydrates the skin.
- Oils and waxes condition and improve the skin's natural water barrier; some oils such as jojoba oil prevent water loss, so are ideal to add to a cream.
- Emulsifiers prevent the ingredients separating, i.e. oil and water.
- Preservatives provide the product with a good shelf life and prevent deterioration.
- Colour and fragrance will give appeal, for example coconut oil has a very distinctive smell which appeals to most people.

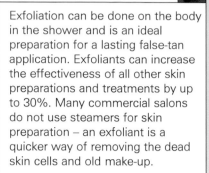

Remember

Exfoliation can be done on the body in the shower and is an ideal preparation for a lasting false-tan application. Exfoliants can increase the effectiveness of all other skin preparations and treatments by up to 30%. Many commercial salons do not use steamers for skin preparation – an exfoliant is a quicker way of removing the dead skin cells and old make-up.

Summary of action

- Moisturising creams can be used morning and evening depending upon skin type and cream used.
- Moisturising creams are recommended for dry skins that need the softening effects of the oil and waxes.
- Cream is especially good for skin in dry conditions, such as hot sun, or central heating, and in very cold weather.
- Make-up application is made easier with a moisturiser underneath it. Be careful about applying cream too near the delicate eye area, which may absorb the cream and become puffy. Only eye cream should be used in the eye area.

Method of use

- Apply a light film to create a natural protective layer and prevent dehydration of the skin.
- To avoid too much cream sitting on the skin surface, check the amount applied by pressing a clean tissue to the face one minute after application. If grease is present on the tissue, too much cream has been applied, or the cream is too rich for the skin type.

Face masks

Key ingredients

- Varies depending upon type of mask used. Refer to pages 238–243 where all the products are discussed.

What they do

- Masks are deep-cleansing and draw any impurity to the surface of the skin.
- They may be slightly astringent to help dry up an oily skin, or re-hydrating for a dry skin.
- Refer to specific mask information.

Summary of action

- Refer to specific mask information.

Method of use

- Refer to specific mask information.

COSHH considerations

- Health hazard: inhalation of fine particles can cause irritation when mixing powder.
- If inhaled move to fresh air; if coughing persists seek medical advice.
- If mixing large quantities, a face guard is advisable.
- Storage should be in a cool dry place in a closed container.
- If in contact with eyes rinse with plenty of water; if irritation continues seek medical advice.
- If ingested seek medical advice immediately.

> **Remember**
>
> There are many moisturisers on the market, with different prices and varying promises to work wonders on the skin. The brand name, the packaging and the promotional skills that go with the cream can dictate the price. Also affecting the price is the quality of oil used and whether other key selling ingredients are included, such as vitamins.

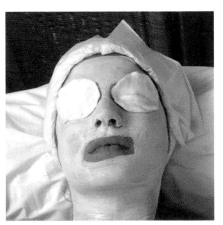

Face mask

Hand care

Hands often show the first signs of ageing (like the neck area), especially if neglected or unprotected.

Encourage the use of hand creams – again, prevention and protection are better than cure!

The client should rub in any excess moisturiser into her hands, rather than waste the product, and a hand cream should become part of a night-time routine.

Refer to the manicure section (Unit BT7, page 369) for further information.

Lip care

Lips can be sadly neglected, until cold sores and chapped lips become a problem.

When you are removing the client's eye make-up the lipstick can also be removed, and the cleansing medium and massage motion will help keep the lips moist.

Lip balms, flavoured lip-gloss and lip creams are available to help dry or sore lips. Remember the lips need protection against the sun, as they have no melanin of their own. Whilst most lipsticks contain a sunscreen, naked lips will not be protected.

Suggesting a treatment plan

Skin type	Products most suitable
Normal (depending on personal product preference)	Eye make-up remover lotion Light cleansing cream or lotion Facial wash if preferred Toner with 10–20% alcohol content Light moisturiser cream or lotion Eye lotion
Dry	Eye make-up remover oil or cream Cream cleanser Low-alcohol-content toner, or no-alcohol if sensitive too Paraffin wax mask Non-setting mask Eye cream Cream moisturiser
Greasy	Eye make-up remover lotion Cleansing lotion or cleansing milk Facial wash or foaming gel Toner with 2–50% alcohol content Cleansing grains or peel Clay-based masks Moisturiser milk Light eye gel

Skin type	Products most suitable
Combination	T-zone – follow greasy skin recommendations Dry cheek areas – follow dry skin recommendations Normal cheek areas – follow normal skin recommendations Young congested T-zone - follow congested skin recommendations with normal skin recommendations on cheeks
Sensitive	As for dry skin Specialist products are available for hypersensitive skin Check for known allergies to products Check for allergies to cotton wool
Dehydrated	As for dry skin Specialist treatments are available in most salons using advanced techniques such as a galvanic facial (NVQ Level 3 work). Be aware and read the salon price list. Another therapist may be able to help the client's skin.
Congested	Eye make-up lotion Cleansing lotion or cleansing milk Facial wash or foaming gel Toner with 25–50% alcohol content Cleansing grains or peel Clay-based masks Moisturiser milk Light eye gel

Selecting suitable equipment and materials

As well as deciding on the type of products that will meet your client's needs when planning her treatment, you should give some thought to the equipment and supporting materials you will need before beginning the facial. Refer to BT4.4, 'Pre-warming the skin' below.

Specific preparation of the client

This will be depend on the equipment used. You need to consider each piece of equipment as well as manufacturers' recommendations.

Improve and maintain skin condition   BT4.4

This outcome is all about performing the facial treatments: you have completed your skin analysis in a hygienic manner, you have prepared your products and equipment and the treatment plan is agreed with the client. The client is in a safe and comfortable position, with the skin cleansed and ready to receive your attention.

In this outcome you will learn about

- pre-warming the skin
- extraction
- skin exfoliation techniques
- massage techniques
- mask treatments.

Pre-warming the skin

Warmth applied to the face is a very good way of helping to maximise the effects of the treatment. Warmth will help relax the muscles, open the pores and soften the skin in preparation for further treatments. Extraction and nourishing the skin are extremely effective after warming.

There are several ways to warm the skin:

- hot towels
- facial steaming
- self-heating products such as thermal masks.

Hot towels

Hot towels are a very convenient method of warming the skin. They can be applied without equipment and are ideal for the mobile therapist who does not have access to a facial steaming unit.

Hot towels were always used in the old-fashioned barbershop when a close shave was offered with the haircut. A hot flannel would have the same effect, but may make a client claustrophobic.

How do I do it?

- Fold a hand towel into four and immerse in hot water leaving an edge for the hands to grip.
- Remember health and safety – if the towel is too hot to wring out with the hands, it is too hot to go on the face. It needs to be hand hot.

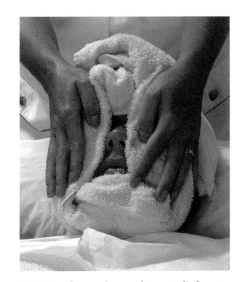

Hot towels can be used to apply heat

Petrissage

There are four different categories:

- kneading
- wringing – mostly used on body
- rolling – mostly used on body
- picking up.

Petrissage **always** follows effleurage. It is a compression movement performed using intermittent pressure with either one or both hands, using the hands in different positions. Most petrissage movements work on all or part of a muscle and it is important that, as a muscle is slowly released from application, pressure is reduced.

Petrissage movements must be applied rhythmically and not in a hurried way. Too much pressure may result in damage to the skin — adaptation to the client's needs is vital.

The benefits of petrissage are:

- Aching, hard muscles are relaxed, helping to prevent the formation of tension modules.
- Skin regeneration is stimulated.
- It has a toning effect on muscle tissue.
- It helps eliminate muscular fatigue by aiding in the removal of lactic acid.
- It helps the removal of waste products and lymphatic flow.

Remember

Always use effleurage to link petrissage movements.

Frictions

Frictions are classified within the petrissage group, but their purpose differs. Friction movements will loosen adherent skin, loosen scars, and aid in absorption of fluid around the joints. The pressure is firm and the movement is usually applied in circular directions on the face. Fingertips or thumbs are mostly used in small areas.

The benefits of frictions are:

- Adhesions and loose skin are freed.
- Scar tissue can be stretched and loosened.

Tapotement

Tapotement is a percussion movement and involves what its name implies – tapping. The tips of the fingers are used over the face to create very light tapping movements, which stimulate the skin.

It is very important that sufficient adipose tissue is present to perform the treatment. It is not used on sensitive skin to avoid possible over-reaction and skin damage.

The benefits of tapotement are:

- It increases localised blood supply.
- It increases nervous response due to stimulation.

Vibrations

Vibrations are fine trembling movements performed on or along a nerve path by the fingers. The muscles of the operator's forearm are continually contracted and relaxed to produce a fine tremble or vibration, which runs to the fingertips. It is used at the occipital region in facial massage.

The benefits of vibrations are:

- It can relieve pain
- It can relax the client due to its sedative effect.

Step-by-step facial massage routine

All movements should be carried out six times. The massage should last for 20 minutes.

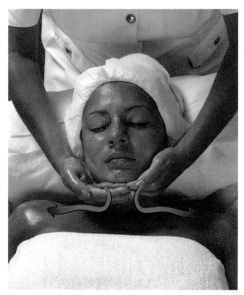

1 Apply massage medium all over the face, neck and shoulders and spread evenly. With both hands together, start at chin, and move down either side of neck towards shoulders.

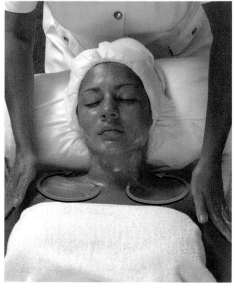

2 Apply pressure over the chest and go over the shoulders, working along the upper back towards the spine.

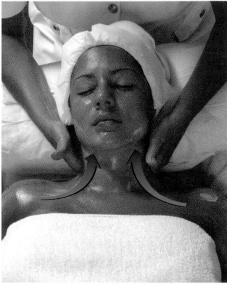

3 When your hands reach either side of the spine, work upwards and gently stretch the neck, lifting the head slightly off the couch.

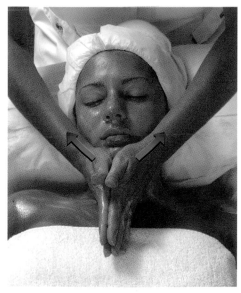

4 Face brace: with hands in an upside-down prayer position, begin under the chin, with heels of the hands resting lightly on the chin.

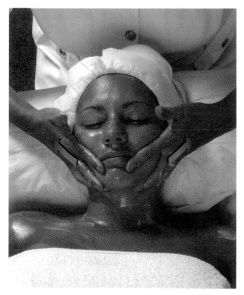

5 Work upwards, over the cheeks, lifting quite firmly The cheeks will move slightly, as the client is relaxed.

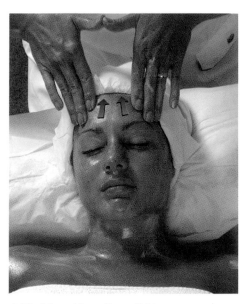

6 Finish with a firm, lifting movement on the forehead.

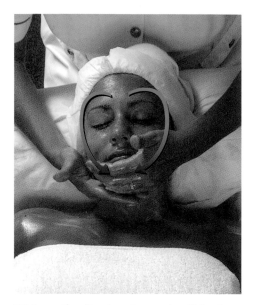

7 From the forehead, gently slide the hands back to the jaw line.

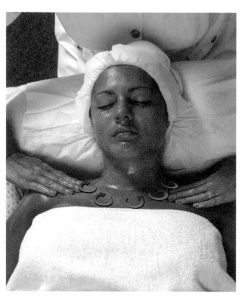

8 Perform rotaries of petrissage, starting from the chin and moving down either side of neck towards the shoulders and beyond, paying special attention to the arm and deltoid muscle.

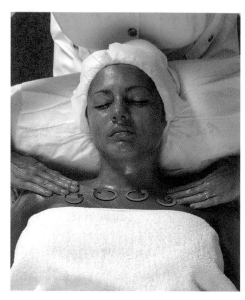

9 Use small circular motions across all of the chest area. You may only be able to use your fingertips if the client is small. No long nails for this movement!

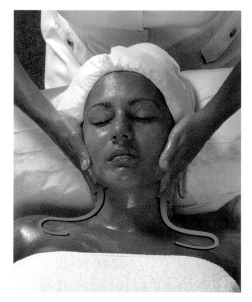

10 Continue your circular massage up the sides of the neck, ready to begin another movement.

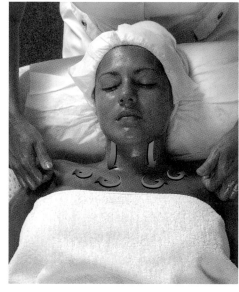

11 Turn your hands into loose fists and rotate your fingers to form knuckling. Come down from the neck and across the chest, over shoulders and back to the occipital cavity.

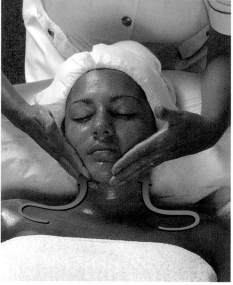

12 Finish the movement at the jaw line ready to begin alternate triangular sweeping.

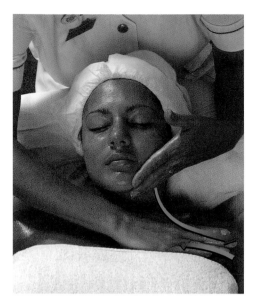

13 Support the jaw with your left hand; with the right hand, stroke down the right side, to the shoulder. Stroke across the chest to the other shoulder.

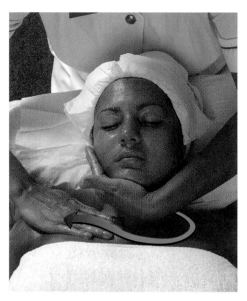

14 Take your right hand behind the shoulder.

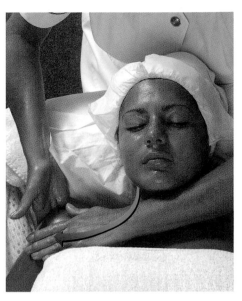

15 Stroke your left hand across the chest to meet the right hand at the right shoulder.

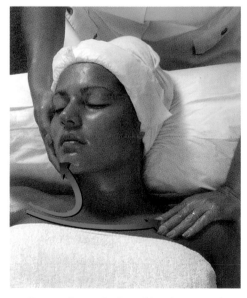

16 Bring the right hand back up to the jaw and left hand back across the chest.

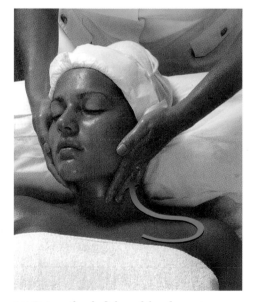

17 Bring the left hand back up to meet at the jaw.

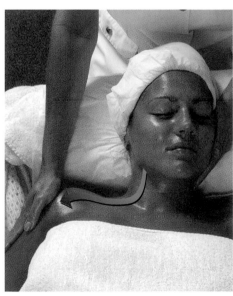

18 Bring the right hand back down at the shoulder.

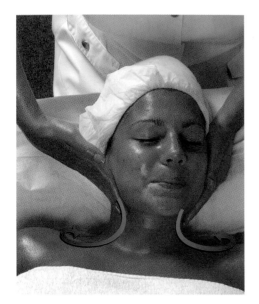

19 Perform trapezius rolling –work hands together on one side, then the other.

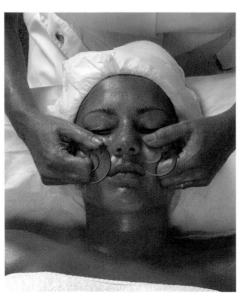

20 Cheek lift – index finger to little finger – turn and twist off.

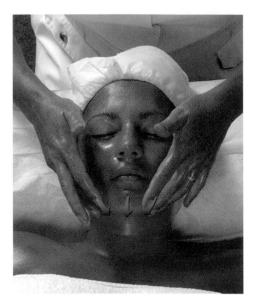

21 Tap along the jaw line.

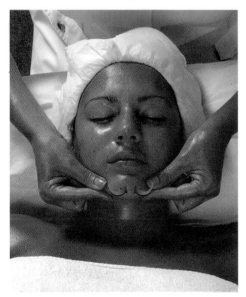

22 Perform rotaries along jaw line – thumbs abducted – centre outwards.

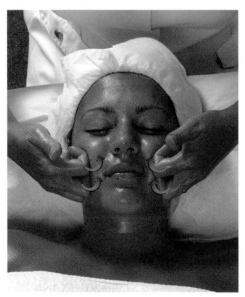

23 Knuckle over chin and cheeks.

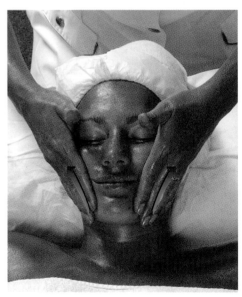

24 Facial lift – work hands along each side of the face – lift and join hands together over the forehead, then divide off.

25 Forehead brace – both hands lift up the eyebrows to the hairline.

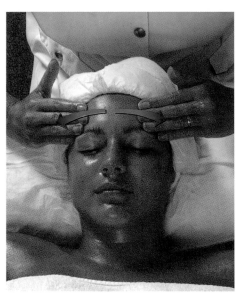

26 Turn hands sideways and gently pull the forehead from the centre, smoothing out the temples.

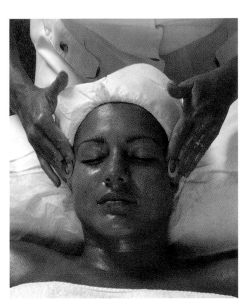

27 Finish with slight finger rotation pressure at the temples.

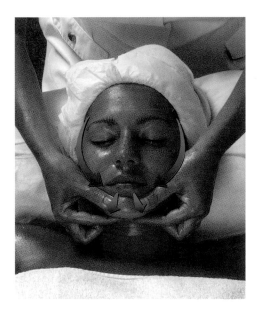

28 Slide hands down to the jaw. Pinch along the jaw line, using thumb and forefinger.

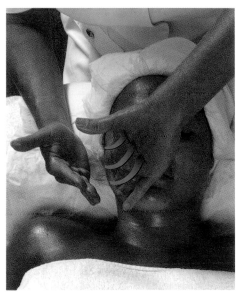

29 Using alternate hand movements, begin roll patting over cheeks and forehead.

30 Repeat this movement over both sides of the face.

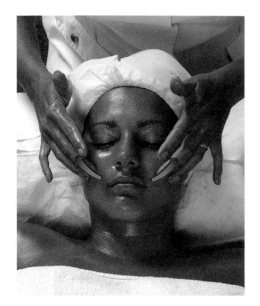

31 Tap over cheeks, using light pressure – fingertips only.

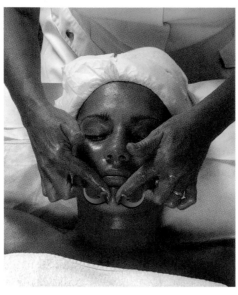

32 Apply frictions, using index fingers, around mouth and chin.

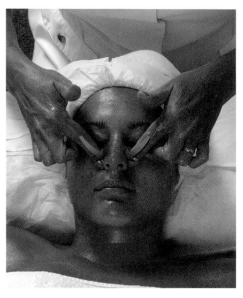

33 Apply frictions, using index fingers, around nostrils.

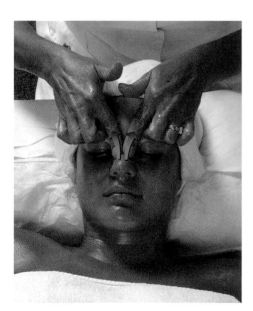

34 Work up nose with index fingers.

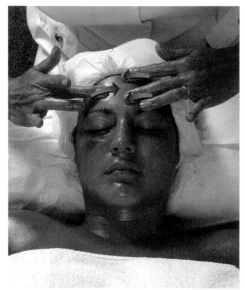

35 Zigzag with middle fingers going into a V created by the other hand over forehead.

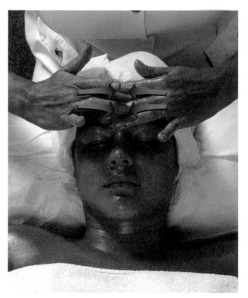

36 Working right across and down the forehead, cover all areas – this movement is especially appreciated by clients who suffer from headaches.

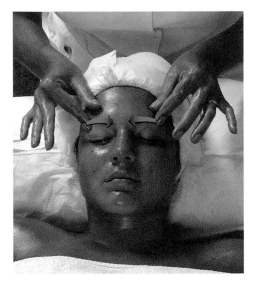

37 Do small circular pinching movements along the length of the eyebrows.

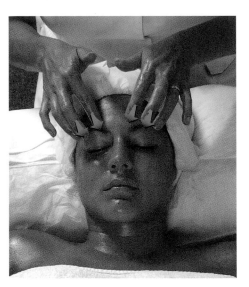

38 Piano playing across brow: circle eyes and bring all fingers across the brow. Start with little finger and finish with index finger.

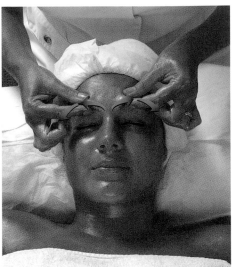

39 Pinch brows – centre to sides. Slide back and repeat.

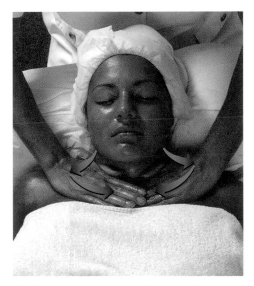

40 Come back to jaw line and begin superficial effleurage down either side of the neck.

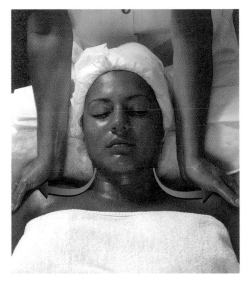

41 Perform superficial effleurage over shoulder area, gradually slowing down as you finish the massage.

Mask treatments

A large variety of face masks are available, both over the counter and in salons. Face masks can be made out of many different natural ingredients, and there is a huge choice of prepared or ready-mixed masks. They can be divided into two categories.

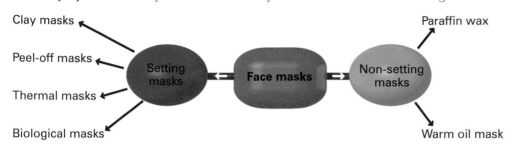

Masks can have different actions depending upon their formulation.

The choice of mask depends on accurate skin analysis and knowledge of the effects of the basic mask ingredients.

Some masks come already mixed and some need mixing – generally the pre-prepared types tend to be more expensive. The ones that need mixing require more skill and knowledge of the ingredients and portions, but the basic ingredients can be purchased in bulk and stored.

Natural ingredients can also be used as a face mask and provide great variety and fun!

Actions of a face mask

Properties of face masks

- They should be smooth and free from gritty particles and unpleasant odours. In powder form, they should be easily dispersed in water to produce a paste.
- They should be easily removed from the face after use without causing discomfort.
- They must be harmless to the skin and non-toxic.

Contra-indications to the application of face masks include:

- skin disorders and diseases
- excessively dry or sensitive skin
- loose, crepey skin
- cuts and abrasions
- recent scar tissue.

NB Clients who are claustrophobic may prefer a non-setting mask.

Materials required for a face mask treatment include:

- bowls
- spatulas
- mask brush – flat and sanitised
- damp cotton wool
- headband
- tissues
- skin tonic
- moisturser
- couch roll
- client record card
- scissors for eye pads.

Clay masks

Clays can be classed as natural ingredients because they are found in the earth. They are good at drawing out impurities and deep cleansing. Some can be quite stimulating and are good for improving the circulation; others are mild and soothing on the skin. The key is to know which ingredients are suitable for which skin type.

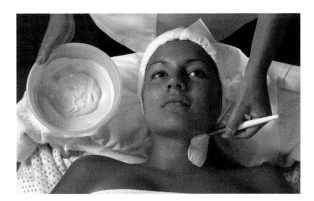

Calamine face mask application

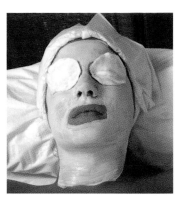

Calamine face mask

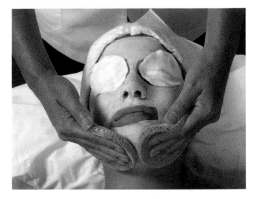

Removing a calamine face mask

Skin type	Clay powder	Benefits	Mixed with
Dry skin	Calamine (a pink powder)	Contains zinc carbonate to soothe the skin and calm down a high colour	Rose water, orange flower water (or distilled water for sensitive skin)
	Magnesium carbonate (a white powder)	Refines and softens the skin, mildly astringent	A couple of drops of vegetable oil, almond oil or glycerol can be added
Greasy skin	Fuller's earth (a grey / green powder)	Deep cleansing	Distilled water with a drop of witch hazel if required. Witch hazel is not suitable for a sensitive, greasy skin as it can be quite stimulating
	Sulphur (a pale yellow powder)	Drying action so can be used on individual blemishes	Distilled water with a drop of witch hazel if required
Normal (balanced)	Magnesium (a white powder)	Refines and softens the skin, mildly astringent	Mix with equal proportions of rose water, orange flower water or witch hazel
	Calamine (a pink powder)	Contains zinc carbonate to soothe the skin and calm down a high colour	Mix with equal proportions of rose water, orange flower water or witch hazel
	Fuller's earth (a grey / green powder)	Deep cleansing; not suitable for sensitive skin as it can be quite stimulating	Mix with equal proportions of rose water, orange flower water or witch hazel
Combination	Follow the dry/normal skin for cheek areas and greasy skin for T-zone skin, depending upon the severity of each area		

Active ingredients

A clay mask needs to be mixed with active ingredients to turn the powder into a liquid paste. The liquids are selected to complement the skin type and mask to be used – they reinforce the action of the mask.

- **Rose water** gives a mild toning effect, which increases the toning action of a mask. Made from rose petals. Recommended for dry, normal and mature skin types.
- **Orange flower water** gives a stimulating, tonic effect. This is natural plant extract from the fruit of the tree.
- **Citrus dulcis** is very fragrant. Recommended for normal, dry and mature skin types.
- **Witch hazel** has a drying, stimulating effect, so is contra-indicated on fine sensitive skins, but much better suited to greasy or combination skins. It is made from the dried leaves and bark of the hamamelis virginian tree. It has a tissue-firming action on the skin.
- **Almond oil** can be used on dehydrated or neglected younger skins or on the more mature skin. A natural oil obtained from the kernels of the seeds of whole almonds, it improves the condition of the skin.
- **Distilled water** is ordinary water that has had the chemicals, such as magnesium bicarbonate or calcium carbonate, removed from it. These can be removed by boiling the water or chemically removed by water softeners.
- **Calamine lotion** is a liquid which contains zinc carbonate to soothe and heal the skin. Iron oxide produces the pink colouring.

Skin type	Recipe	Time on face
Normal skin	1 part kaolin 1 part fuller's earth Mix with water and a few drops of witch hazel to form a smooth thin paste	8–12 minutes
Dry skin	1 part kaolin 1 part magnesium carbonate Mix with rose water or orange flower water to form a smooth thin paste	10–15 minutes
Oily skin	Fuller's earth Mix with witch hazel to form a smooth paste	5–15 minutes
Sensitive skin	1 part calamine 1 part magnesium carbonate Mix with rose water to form a smooth paste	5–10 minutes
Sulphur mask (for acne)	1/2 tsp Epsom salts 1 tsp oatmeal 1 tsp magnesium carbonate 1 tsp precipitated sulphur Mix with hot water to form a paste	Apply over gauze, leave for 15 minutes, keeping warm with infrared lamps
Stimulating mask (for open pores, capillaries and contracting the tissues)	6 parts magnesium carbonate 2 parts fuller's earth Mix with rose water or almond oil according to the moisture content of the skin	5–15 minutes
Astringent mask	6 parts magnesium carbonate 1 part calamine Pinch of alum Mix with witch hazel	Apply over gauze. Apply one coat until almost dry, then apply second coat 10 minutes

Suggested recipes for setting masks

Peel-off masks

Peel-off masks are gel or latex based. (Paraffin wax masks also come into a peel-off category, although they are classed as non-setting.) Because perspiration cannot escape from the skin's surface, moisture is forced back into the epidermis. Some peel-off masks also create heat, so could come under the thermal category. **Gel masks** are purchased as a ready-made suspension containing starches, gums or gelatine, to allow the correct consistency. Synthetic non-biological resins are commonly used as well. The mask is applied over the skin. When it makes contact it immediately begins to dry. It can be peeled off over the face as a whole facial mould when sufficient technique has been mastered. The gel mask can be used on most skin types, depending on the ingredients used, so check with individual manufacturers' instructions.

A **latex mask** is an emulsion of latex and water. The water evaporates leaving a rubber film to form the mask. Alternatives are synthetic PVC resins. These have a firming, tightening effect on the skin and can be used on a dry or mature skin.

Biological and natural masks

These include the following:

Fruit extracts, e.g. avocado mashed to a smooth paste.
- Action: helps stabilise the skin's pH and acid mantle.

Herbal and vegetable, e.g. cucumber sliced and placed over the skin.
- Action: calming or astringent effect

Biological, e.g. natural yoghurt applied in bought state.
- Action: refines the skin's texture, helps rid skin of waste, counteracts possible infection.
- Egg – with almond oil for dry skin or lemon for oily skin.
- Honey – has a softening effect on dehydrated or mature skin.

Warm oil masks

Risk assessment for warm oil equipment
Refer to **Professional basics** for a complete discussion of risk assessment.
Hazard: only look for hazards that you could reasonably expect to result in significant harm under the conditions in your workplace. Use the following examples as a guide: <ul><li>**Fire** (e.g. from electrical flex or lead)</li><li>**Burning of equipment** (through light bulb burning out)</li><li>**Burns to skin** (lamp too close to skin, left on too long, treatment not timed)</li><li>**Ejection of bulb** (hot bulb falling onto skin, not screwed in properly, lamp should not be directly over skin)</li><li>**Electricity** (e.g. poor wiring)</li><li>**Manual handling** (outer casing is hot and will burn, if towel is not used for protection)</li><li>**Falling machinery** (if supporting arm is not screwed in properly)</li><li>**Contamination** (from brushes and equipment not sufficiently sterilised)</li><li>**Cross-infection** (if possible contra-indications are ignored)</li></ul>

Remember

A gel mask does adhere to the facial hair and can be painful during removal, rather like a plaster coming off! If the client has a lot of facial hair, offer an alternative mask.

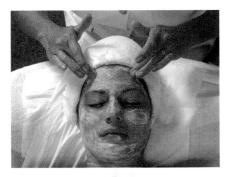

A peel-off face mask

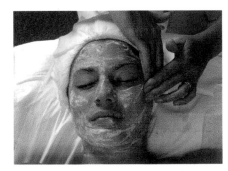

The mask dries very fast

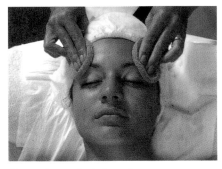

Removing a facial peel

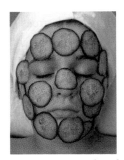

Natural cucumber face mask

- Avoid the temptation to apply make-up for 12 hours, where possible.
- Evening cleansing is not necessary, but if the client prefers, a light cleanse, tone and moisture should be recommended.
- Suitable and compatible homecare products should be recommended. These will complement the work of the therapist in the salon.
- Explain to clients that whilst it is unlikely that contra-actions will develop after a facial, they should avoid any overstimulation and further heat treatments. If a reaction is going to occur, it will usually be a reaction to a cream used whilst the facial is going on, not afterwards.
- Highly perfumed products should be avoided.
- No depilation (hair removal) should take place after a facial.
- If any rash, irritation or itching occurs suggest putting a cool flannel to the area. Remove the offending product from the skin with damp cotton wool, and apply a light calamine lotion to soothe the skin.

Long-term and homecare advice

- Regular use of homecare products will help the skin.
- Regular facials will help to regulate a problem skin; timings and intervals are a personal decision between the therapist and client and may depend on cost.
- Future treatments may be discussed with a view to specialist help for specific problems, such as facial steaming for comedone extraction, or regular paraffin wax mask application for a dry skin condition.
- Targeting a problem and then giving intensive treatments to help that condition is very rewarding. The client is pleased and the therapist has job satisfaction.
- A treatment plan should make allowances for timing intervals, the cost involved and how convenient it is for the client to get to the salon.
- Give the client a price list and all relevant information for present and future treatments with you.
- Giving your client accurate information about additional products and services
- Refer to G6 'Promote additional products or services to clients', page 78.

A client leaving the salon in a relaxed and satisfied state is very rewarding, but your work is not yet over. There are important details to complete, which are as much a part of your job role as everything else that you do.

Completing client records accurately

Refer back to **Professional basics** (pages 17–18) for client record keeping. It is important, both for the client and yourself, that you fill out the skin analysis sheet and any other details accurately. This will avoid any health and safety problems and keep the client safe, therefore safeguarding your own professional reputation. Do not return the record card to be filed incomplete, thinking you can do it later – you will not remember and vital information may not be recorded.

Take time to fill out all parts of the card:

- Were there any reactions during the treatment that will affect the future treatment plan?
- Did the client express any preferences or dislikes for massage movements, products or mask?
- Would you leave something out next time?
- Did the client feel claustraphobic with eye pads on?
- Were products purchased?

Be constructive when filling out the card: remain positive and helpful in what you write and avoid making any negative comments or personal observations about the client. After all, clients are entitled to see their own records under the Data Protection Act. Also avoid leaving the card lying around for anyone to read. Once you have completed the write-up, give it to the person who is responsible for filing.

Leaving the work area and equipment ready for further treatments

The client has left the salon, and you are basking in job satisfaction. Now it is time to go back to your workstation and clear up. Look around you. How much mess have you made? Could you have been tidier as you went along? Unless the client is the last one of the day, you will not have the luxury of time to clean and tidy the area. If your next client is due straight away, you could be in trouble if you have to spend a long time tidying and preparing for your next treatment.

Good habits to stay tidy

- Organise the layout of the trolley in an ordered fashion – have all the labels of products facing you so you can easily see which is needed. Arrange the products in order of use, and replace them back in their slot when you have finished with them. They will always then be at hand, and you will always look tidy and controlled. Have a space for everything and everything in its place. Have a system where all necessary tools are in a jar or pot (even a plastic beaker is easy to clean), the tissues and cotton wool in their own plastic bowl or tub.
- Tidy as you go along – put used tissues and cotton wool into a small pedal bin (lined with a bin liner) as you finish with them, rather than leaving them on the trolley.
- If you can, wash up mask brushes and bowls whilst the mask is setting on the client's face. This may not be possible if you do not have a sink near the workstation, as you should not leave the client unattended.
- Minimise waste by using only the amount of product required. This is not only cost effective, but it also means there is very little product left over to clear up.
- Always put lids back on to pots if decanting products. This avoids the possibility of a spillage, which is time consuming to clear up. It also stops alcohol-based products from evaporating.
- Mop up spills as they occur and do not allow them to endanger others.

If you follow these hints you will not need a major tidying session at the end of your treatment. Becoming tidy is a skill that comes with experience.

> **Remember**
>
> Your workstation may be shared by other therapists. Most salons have a waxing area, a facial area and a body treatment section, so if your next client is in the waxing room, you have to leave your facial station clean for another therapist to use. Would you like to inherit a messy work area from another therapist?

Shape the eyebrows to meet client requirements

BT5.4/11.4

In this outcome you will learn about

- procedure for eyebrow shaping
- aftercare
- trouble-shooting eyebrow problems.

Procedure for eyebrow shaping

1   Remove all traces of make-up and clean the area with an appropriate cleanser. Wipe with sanitising solution and prepare the area.

2   Inspect the treatment area to assess the amount of work required. Measure shape and consult the client. A magnifying lamp can be used to give maximum visibility.

3   Brush the brows into shape before you begin.

4   Open pores – it is often suggested that before you begin shaping, you should place warm, damp cotton wool pads over the area. This relaxes hair follicles and softens the eyebrow tissue, making hair removal easier.

5   To remove hairs, gently stretch the skin between your fingers and pluck out the hairs in the direction in which they grow. Begin by removing the stray hairs between the eyes. Hairs below the natural brow shape can then be tackled. The few odd hairs that grow unevenly above the brow may also be removed, provided they do not form part of the main eyebrow growth.
    If there are any tough, spiky or white hairs these can sometimes be removed without spoiling the overall shape.

6   Consult the client as you work, ensure she has a hand mirror and consults with you as you proceed.

7   Place the removed hairs on a tissue placed at the side of the client, or held wrapped around your fingers.

8   Periodically soothe the client's brow with antiseptic, as this helps to remove any stray hairs.

9   When all the shaping is complete, place a dampened cotton wool soaked in witch-hazel over the area to soothe, cool and remove excess erythema.

10 Give aftercare advice and book the client's next appointment.

If blood or tissue fluid is accidentally drawn during the treatment, the following steps should be taken.

1   Apply pressure to the area with clean cotton wool soaked in sanitising solution.

2   Do not panic, keep calm, and explain to the client so she is aware of the problem.

3   Apply soothing solution to the area.

4   Dispose of waste carefully in accordance with health and safety regulations and local by-laws.

Placing hot cotton wool pads on the brow opens the pores (Step 4)

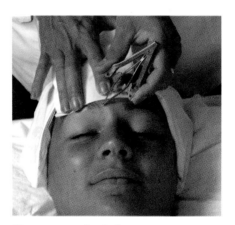

Using spring-loaded automatic tweezers makes plucking very quick and virtually painless (Step 5)

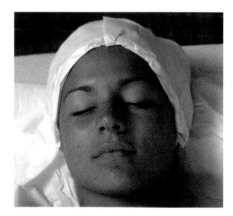

The finished look should be clean and tidy and opens up the whole face.

An eyebrow re-shape may take up to half an hour and an eyebrow tidy up to 15 minutes. In all cases it would depend on the density of the hairs, shape required, hair growth and the client requirements. Clients who visit the salon regularly often have an eyebrow tidy as an integral part of their treatment plan. On average an eyebrow tidy would be carried out every 4–6 weeks.

Aftercare

Clients should be given the following aftercare advice when they have had an eyebrow shape or tidy.

- Cooling mild antiseptic products, e.g. witch hazel, should be applied.
- No make-up should be applied to the area for 12 hours, as the follicles are open and infection may occur.
- Stray re-growth hairs can be removed at intervals to prolong the effect.

Contra-actions

These usually take the form of erythema to the area, but in some cases blood spots occur and sometimes swelling. You should try to reduce the swelling before the client leaves the salon, by applying a soothing antiseptic. In extreme cases, a cold compress or ice should be applied. All contra-actions should be recorded on the client record card.

Trouble-shooting eyebrow problems

Bare sparse brows

Fill in with pencil, using short strokes in the direction of the hair growth, and blend with a brow brush. Ensure that the pencil is sharpened as you move from one eye to the other, to prevent cross-infection

Stray hairs

Remove any stray hairs with tweezers.

Thin brows

Instead of a pencil, try a shade of powder that matches the brow colour. Apply with a stiff brush, following the natural line, and ensure that you blend in well to prevent the line looking harsh. This will create the illusion of doubling the thickness.

Unruly or thick brows

Long unruly hairs should be trimmed. Hold the brows straight with a brow comb and trim to the required length. To help the hairs to lie flat, either use a little hair gel or a small amount of hairspray on a comb. Never spray directly onto the face.

Remember

A nervous client may require eye pads or be advised to keep eyes shut. Heavy brows should be gradually reduced over two or three visits to minimise discomfort and allow the client to become accustomed to her new image.

Eyebrow shaping

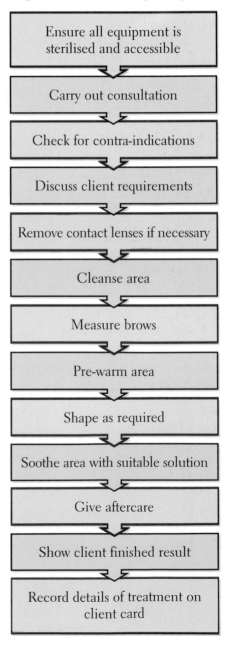

Ensure all equipment is sterilised and accessible

Carry out consultation

Check for contra-indications

Discuss client requirements

Remove contact lenses if necessary

Cleanse area

Measure brows

Pre-warm area

Shape as required

Soothe area with suitable solution

Give aftercare

Show client finished result

Record details of treatment on client card

Tint eyebrows and lashes to meet client requirements

BT5.5

In this outcome you will learn about

- eyebrow and eyelash tinting
- how colour works
- choosing a tint
- preparing the client for tinting lashes and brows

- applying the lash tint
- applying the eyebrow tint
- assessing the results
- aftercare.

Eyelash and eyebrow tinting

The benefits of tinting

- Eyebrows help to emphasise facial expression and eyelashes frame the eyes.
- Tinting may be carried out on clients with light-coloured brows and lashes to define their appearance.
- Brows and lashes can be tinted to complement hair colour.
- Tinting can mean that coloured mascara need not be applied, which is good for those who are allergic to it, or in the summer months when mascara is likely to smudge if it is very hot.
- Tinting is also ideal for clients who wear glasses or contact lenses.

Patch testing

A patch test should be carried out prior to tinting, perming and the application of false lashes (refer to BT11.5, page 273) with the product that you plan to use.

Many professional associations now recommend that this test be carried out 24–48 hours prior to each treatment, even on a client who has the treatment on a regular basis at the salon. The client may have become sensitive to the product, or the salon may have changed products and therefore the ingredients may be slightly different from the ones used previously.

All tests should be recorded on the client record card with the date the test was carried out and the results of the test. An allergic reaction would show as a red, itchy, sore area. Treat with a cold compress and soothing cream. This reaction would mean that the client is unsuitable for the treatment.

If the test is not carried out and a problem does occur, it is possible you could invalidate your insurance policy. A test only takes a few minutes and can easily be performed by the receptionist.

Method

- Cleanse the area of the skin to be tested (behind the ear or the crook of the arm).
- Mix the same make and colour of tint to be used with manufacturer's recommended quantity of 10% volume peroxide.
- Apply the tint to the area selected with a brush, about the size of a ten pence coin.
- Allow to dry.
- Ensure the client is aware that the tint should be left on the skin for 24 hours. If no reaction occurs then wash off.
- If a reaction occurs, the tint should be removed immediately with water and a

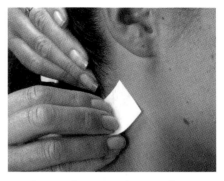

Patch test: cleansing the area first

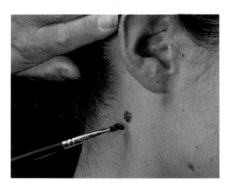

Patch test: applying the product

Remember

Always note the date and the results of patch tests on client record cards.

---

soothing lotion applied to the area.

- A reaction will be recognised by an itching, red-hot inflamed area. This should be treated with a soothing substance.

Precautions for lash and brow tinting

- Discuss the client's requirements with her.
- Ensure all equipment is clean and sterilised.
- Ensure that all eye make-up is removed with a non-oily product.
- Check for contra-indications.
- Remove contact lenses.
- Apply barrier cream to the skin around the eyes only and not to the hair to be tinted, as the tint will not act. The barrier cream is used to prevent the tint spreading beyond the area being treated.
- Ensure the client keeps eyes closed at all times when the tint is on the eyes. As a therapist you are responsible for giving your client full instructions. This is vital, especially when treating nervous clients.
- Do not leave the client while the tint is processing.
- Complete details of the tint on the record card.
- Ensure that the eyebrows are tinted prior to shaping, to avoid tint seeping into the follicles, resulting in a reaction.

How colour works

- The selected dye and hydrogen peroxide are mixed together to produce a chemical reaction. When first applied to the hair, they enter the middle of the hair as small particles, but, because of the chemical reaction, they swell. This swelling prevents the colour from coming out when washed and so becomes permanent. This process is known as oxidation. The colour of the hair changes and this will remain until the hair grows or falls out.
- Never mix the ingredients until you are ready to use them. Oxidisation starts to occur and the tint starts to work as soon as it is mixed, so the product will not be able to enter the hair properly, resulting in poor colour.
- Replace caps on the tint and hydrogen peroxide, as they will oxidise and again the result will be unsuccessful.
- When using two colours of tint, mix them together and then add peroxide.

Choosing a tint

The skin around the eye is very thin and sensitive, therefore dyes designed for lash and brow tinting have been specially formulated to avoid any eye or tissue reactions. Any other type of dye or any hydrogen peroxide solution stronger than 10% dilution should not be used in this area. It is dangerous and may even cause blindness.

The products used for eyelash and brow tinting are usually available as creams or gels in basic colours of black, blue, brown and grey. These colours are mixed to form variations in tone, i.e. blue / black provides a darker colour.

The choice is a matter of personal preference and depends on:

- the client's overall skin type and hair colouring
- the type of eye-make-up usually worn
- the age of the client.

As clients grow more mature, they lose a lot of natural colour from hair and eyes. Brown

Remember

The details on the client record card should include:

- date of patch test
- products used
- development time of the treatment
- areas treated
- contra-actions
- aftercare.

or grey tints are preferable to black for producing a softer, more natural effect. This is an example of when you need to be aware of the fact that the client's expectations may not be realistic. The client may expect a very dark finish or longer eyelashes. It is therefore your responsibility to explain to the client that certain expectations cannot or should not be achieved, due to suitability. It is important to provide the client with sufficient professional advice and emphasise that lash and brow treatments are designed to enhance the natural features.

This applies to shaping and eyelash perming too. Expectations are realistic when they can be achieved with success and when the treatment is suitable for the client. The effect of tinting depends on the natural colour of the hair, e.g. blond hair colour develops rapidly, usually in 5 minutes. Red hair is more resistant and development will take longer, perhaps 10 minutes. White hair will take slightly longer to process, due to the lack of the pigment melanin. Make sure the colour you choose gives a realistic natural effect.

Preparing the client for tinting lashes and brows

- Help the client into a comfortable, semi-reclined position and protect hair and clothing.
- Clean and tone the area to ensure that all grease and make-up is removed from lashes and brows. If grease is left on the skin, a barrier will be created and the tint will not take properly.
- Protect the skin above the eyes with a barrier cream. Take care not to get any barrier product on the lashes or brows that require tinting.

Barrier cream

Tinting equipment

Tinting

You will need:

- tinting equipment
- protective headband and towel
- couch roll to protect the work area
- small non-metallic bowl for mixing tint (a metal one would react with the hydrogen peroxide)
- lined container for waste
- sterile spatula
- sterile applicator or tipped orange stick
- clean water in the event of eye irrigation becoming necessary
- hand mirror

- client record card
- materials
- damp cotton wool and tissues
- eye shields made from cotton wool or paper shields
- selection of coloured tints
- hydrogen peroxide (usual 10% volume, but always check manufacturer's instructions)
- eye make-up remover (non-oily)
- cleanser
- toner
- barrier cream.

This prevents the tint from staining the skin and spoiling the effect of the treatment. It will also prevent the tint from penetrating the hair if it touches it.

Use a tipped orange stick or cotton bud to apply the barrier cream to the skin above the eyes.

When applying the cream below the eyes, either:

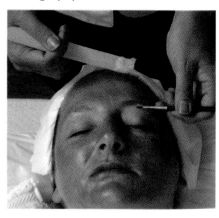

Decant barrier cream onto a spatula and paint onto the skin surrounding the eyebrow to prevent accidental staining

- stroke it directly onto the skin and position the eye shields on top, close to the base of the lashes,

or,

- coat the underneath surface of the shields with barrier cream and slide them into position.

Applying the lash tint

Precautions should be taken to ensure that neither the tint nor the applicator penetrates the eye. There should not be any problems provided:

- the eye is well supported by gently holding the area
- the tint is carefully applied
- the lashes are not overloaded with tint
- the client's eyes are kept still.

Step-by-step eyelash tinting

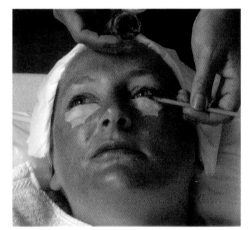

1 *After placing shields under the eyes, begin to apply tint to lower lashes, made up to manufacturer's instructions*

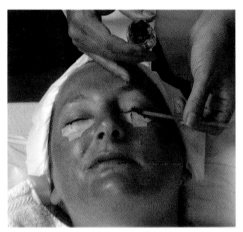

2 *Ask the client to close her eyes, and apply tint to the top lashes. Cover the eyes*

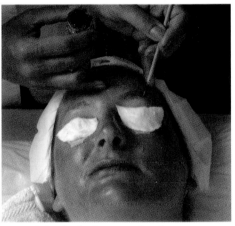

3 *While the lash tint is developing, you can tint the eyebrows if required*

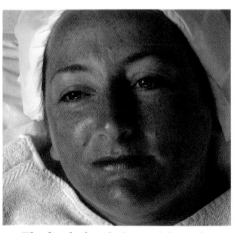

4 *When processing time has elapsed, remove all traces of the tint*

5 *The finished eyelash tint defines the lashes and enhances the eyes*

Remember

Make sure you do not ask the client to look up into an overhead light because this will over-sensitise the eyes and make them water!

Check it out

Check out the COSHH regulations referring to the products that you use for tinting.

1   Once the client has been correctly positioned and the make-up removed, mix the correct colour of tint according to the manufacturer's instructions. A guide is a 5mm length of tint with 2 – 3 drops of hydrogen peroxide, mixed in a tinting bowl with a disposable brush or orange stick to a smooth paste.

2   Remember, before applying the tint a barrier cream should be applied to prevent staining.

3   Ask the client to look upwards and cover the lower lashes with tint (if the client has watery eyes the lower lashes can be covered with the upper lashes when the eyes are closed, but the result is often not so effective). (See photo 1 on the previous page.)

4   Ask the client to close the eyes and apply the tint to the upper lashes. (See photo 2.)

5   Gently lift the skin to the eyebrows, so the tint can be applied right down to the base of the lashes and include shorter hairs which grow near the inside corner of the eyes.

6   If the client complains of discomfort or the eyes begin to water, remove the tint immediately using damp cotton wool pads, and irrigate the eye.

7   Note the time and allow for the tint to work according to the manufacturer's instructions. The colour should be checked at intervals and the tint reapplied if necessary. As a guide allow 5–10 minutes, depending on the colour characteristics of the client.

Removal of eyelash tint

1   Place a pad of damp cotton wool on each eye. Hold the eye shield and pad of cotton wool together at the base and swiftly remove, enclosing any excess tint.

2   Remove any remaining tint with slightly damp cotton wool, using a gentle downward motion, and remove excess with a cotton bud. (See photo 4.)

3   When both eyes have been cleaned, ask the client to carefully open the eyes.

4   Support the eye and work quickly on the lower lashes with damp cotton wool and a cotton bud.

5   Stand in front of the client to check that all the tint has been removed.

6   Finally, wipe the area over with damp cotton wool to remove traces of the barrier cream.

7   Offer a hand mirror to view the final results.

8   Inform the client of possible contra-actions and aftercare. If irritation occurs, apply a damp cotton wool compress to the area.

9   Enter details onto the client's record card. This should include the colour selected and the processing time for the tint, and any contra-actions and other information relevant to the treatment.

The process of eyelash tinting should take about 20 minutes.

Applying the eyebrow tint

Step-by-step eyebrow tint

This can be performed after lash tinting, prior to shaping. Many salons and therapists perform this treatment while the lash tint is processing, to ensure they are cost-effective with their time. If shaping is carried out first, the tint will seep into the open pores causing irritation.

Tinting

Ensure all the equipment is hygienic and close to hand.

Carry out a consultation (ensure a patch test has been carried out). Check for contra-indications.

Remove contact lenses, if required.

If shaping is to be carried out always tint first and shape after.

Cleanse area with non-oily product.

Apply barrier cream and pre-formed shapes if tinting lashes.

Mix tint and apply (never pre-mix the tint). Note processing time on client record card.

Remove tint after the required processing time.

Show client results. Give aftercare advice.

Record details on client record card.

1   Prepare the skin and brows the same way as for treating the lashes. Apply barrier cream around the eyebrows taking care to avoid the hairs.

2   Apply the tint against the hair growth using an orange stick or a fine brush, working gradually from the outer and underneath hairs towards the centre. See photo 3 on page 263.

3   After one minute, remove a little tint from the inner corners of the eyebrow and check how the colour is developing. Apply more tint and repeat colour checks at one-minute intervals until the desired effect has been achieved. The developing time for tinting brows is much shorter than for lashes, usually between one and three minutes. Always refer to manufacturer's instructions for product guidance. Care must be taken to prevent the brows from becoming too dark as this can create an unattractive harsh effect.

4   Remove tint with clean, damp cotton wool.

5   Wipe over the area to remove all traces of barrier cream.

6   Discuss the final effect, possible contra-action and aftercare with the client.

7   Enter details of the treatment on the client record card.

The process of eyebrow tinting should take approximately 15 minutes.

How to irrigate the eye

If tint accidentally enters the eye, do not panic; the client may be feeling discomfort and a slight burning sensation. Calm the client and explain the procedure you are going to follow.

1   Tilt the client's head slightly to one side. Carefully trickle some tepid water into the corner of the eye and allow the eye to be rinsed of the foreign body.

2   Hold some tissue or a small kidney dish to collect the excess water.

3   Apply a damp cotton wool compress to cool and soothe the eye.

It is not acceptable to use an eyebath because of the risk of cross-infection.

Possible causes of eye irritation:

* very sensitive eyes
* too much or incorrect strength of hydrogen peroxide
* something in the eye
* inadvertently poking the eye.

Assessing the results

* A successful tinting treatment produces the required colour changes to the lashes and brows without staining the skin.
* Even the shortest eyelashes should be coloured from the base.
* The appearance of blond roots after the eyelash tint shows that not enough care was taken. The skin fold of the eyelid was probably not lifted away from the base of the hairs when applying tint.
* The tint will not have covered the brows successfully if:
  – there was grease or make-up on the hairs
  – old tint was used
  – the hydrogen peroxide had lost strength
  – the tint and peroxide were incorrectly mixed
  – the tint was removed too soon.

Aftercare

- As with all treatments, the client should be advised against touching or rubbing the areas immediately after the treatment.
- If redness or irritation occurs, apply a damp cotton wool compress.
- The client should be aware that the effects will last approximately 4–6 weeks as the hairs grow out. Strong sunlight will make the results fade *faster*.

Perm eyelashes to meet client requirements   BT5.6

In this outcome you will learn about

- how perming works
- client consultation
- preparation of the client
- applying a perm
- problems with perming.

This treatment is a semi-permanent way of curling the upper lashes and the result will last from 4–6 weeks; as the old hairs are lost and replaced with new hairs the curl diminishes. The use of perming solutions, although chemically based, is far less damaging than regular use of eyelash curlers.

Eyelash perming is recommended:

- to emphasise the eyelashes, making the eye look larger and to give more definition
- for clients who wear contact lenses or glasses
- for mature clients with sagging eyelids
- for clients who do not wish to wear mascara
- for holidays or for sports women
- for clients living or working in hot environments
- for clients who have short straight lashes
- for special occasions.

There is a variety of eyelash perming products available and most companies offer training sessions. It is always important to follow the manufacturer's instructions when using any product, but special care should be taken when working with chemicals around the sensitive eye area. Refer to COSHH regulations.

How perming works

If we look at hair under a microscope its internal structure resembles a coil spring, held in place by scaffolding links called disulphide bonds. The perming process breaks down these scaffolding links and with the use of neutralising agents rebuilds the links allowing the hair to take on the desired shape.

The three stages to perming are:

- **Softening** – perm lotion opens and swells the cuticle of the hair so the product can enter the cortex.

Eyelash perming

Ensure all materials are to hand and hygienic.

⬇

Consultation and patch test have been carried out.

⬇

Check for contra-indications.

⬇

Discuss client requirements (they may require lash tinting as well).

⬇

Cleanse the area with a non-oily product.

⬇

Select the rod size you require (remember the smaller the rod the tighter the curl).

⬇

Apply wave gel. Process according to manufacturer's instructions.

⬇

Apply film wrap or towel according to manufacturer's instructions.

⬇

Neutralise according to manufacturer's instructions.

⬇

Show client the finished result.

⬇

Give aftercare.

- **Moulding** – the perm lotion deposits hydrogen into the cortex of the hair. The hydrogen breaks down the scaffolding disulphide bonds and the hair is able to mould itself to the shape of the perm rod.
- **Fixing** – a neutralising product is applied to the hair which removes the hydrogen from the cortex by adding oxygen (known as oxidation). This process re-forms the hairs' scaffolding disulphide bonds in the new position which permanently fixes the curl.

The softening stage

Perm lotion opens and swells cuticle scales

The moulding stage

Before perming, disulphide bonds intact

The hydrogen attaches itself to the disulphide bonds and breaks them into single sulphur bonds

Perm lotion is added and releases hydrogen

The fixing stage

Neutraliser is added and oxygen is released. Oxygen joins with the hydrogen to make H_2O (water)

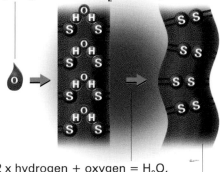

2 x hydrogen + oxygen = H_2O, which is rinsed from the hair

Sulphur bonds re-form to make disulphide bonds in a newly curled formation, which permanently fixes curl

The perming process

It is important when perming lashes that manufacturers' instructions are strictly followed and only products designed for perming lashes are used for this treatment. Products used to perm hair have a very high pH and could be extremely dangerous if used on the eye area. Products for lashes are usually a gel formation so that the product does not run into the eye or onto the delicate surrounding skin.

Even though these products are often referred to as cold wave gels, some manufacturers advise the use of a clear wrap or even a towel to be placed over the lashes during processing to ensure the heat is kept constant over the lashes (a draught could affect the result). This can also help keep the lashes fixed to the rod.

Client consultation

It is important with all treatments to carry out a thorough consultation and to establish what a client requires from the treatment. The same contra-indication checks apply to perming as for other eye treatments. It is vital that no skin infections or open wounds are present, as a chemical is being applied to the skin. Ensure that no reaction has occurred to the products patch-tested. A reaction would show itself as itching, redness and swelling. Treat with a suitable product.

Preparation of the client

- Ensure the client is in a semi-reclined position.
- Remove jewellery.
- Remove contact lenses, if required.
- Secure hair away from the face.

Definition of terms

Disulphide bonds: two sulphur bonds joined together.

Remember

The products to be tested are adhesive perm solution and neutraliser and they should be tested, as with tinting and lash application, in the crook of the client's elbow or behind the client's ear.

- Protect the client's clothing.
- Ensure all products and basic trolley equipment are close to hand. Use non-oily eye make-up remover, to remove any make-up.
- Have a bowl of water ready to irrigate the eye if required.

Applying a perm

Step-by-step eyelash perming

A full consultation follows a patch test, which should have been done 24 hours previously. Thoroughly cleanse the eye and lashes, removing all traces of make-up.

Blot the eyes to ensure they are grease-free and dry. A non-oily remover should be used so as to avoid any grease forming a barrier (a witch-hazel-based remover is often used).

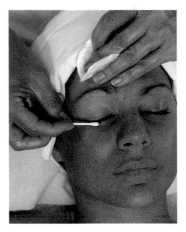

Use a cotton bud to thoroughly check the lashes are clean and dry.

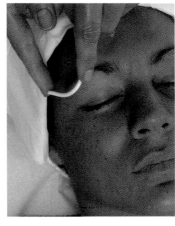

Choose a suitable-sized rod, depending on the lashes and the curl required.

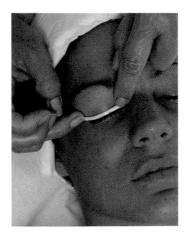

Apply a small amount of adhesive to the main body of the rod. Check that no lashes are caught underneath. Bend and shape the rod to sit tightly in the eye shape.

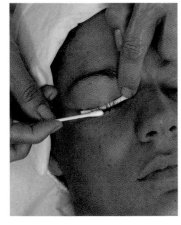

Curl lashes over the rod with no bends or kinks. Use a cotton tip to apply solution to the lashes. Follow manufacturer's instructions for development and neutralising times. Use clear wrap or towel if recommended.

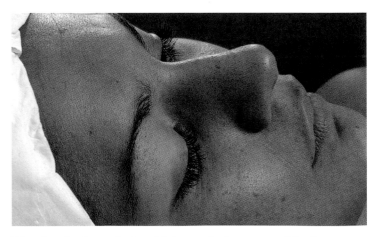

The finished result should be curly but natural looking, with not too tight a curl. Tinting can be carried out during this procedure, but check instructions before attempting it.

Problems with perming

Problem	Possible cause	Solution
Too curled	Rod too small	Re-perm larger rod, half time
No result	Too large a rod	Re-perm
	Insufficient processing	
	Incorrect neutralising	
	Oil barrier on lashes	
Uneven curl	Incorrect positioning of rod	Re-position rod
	Uneven application of lotion/gel	
	Not curling all the lashes over the rod	
Buckled or hooked ends	Failure to wrap hair correctly around the rod	Trim off ends

Product safety data

Eye make-up remover

Description

- The product is prepared from mild cleaning agents in a cosmetic base.

Ingredients

- All ingredients are commonly used in cosmetic products and meet accepted standards of purity.

Hazards

- This product is considered to be non-hazardous under normal conditions of use.

Flammability

- Non-inflammable.

First aid procedures

- Ingestion: drink milk or water.
- Eye contact: Wash well with water; if irritation persists, seek medical advice.

Spillage

- Clean using absorbent material, followed by washing with detergent and water to avoid slippery floors.

Handling and storage

- No special precautions considered necessary.

Eyelash tint

Description

- Oil / water-emulsion (cream).

Ingredients

- Water/ cetearyl alcohol/ PEG-sorbitan lanolate/ sodium cetearyl sulfate/ diaminotoluene/ aminophenols / dyest. CI 77499 and / or 77007 / no preservatives.

Medicated foundations

This type of foundation is a liquid containing antiseptic ingredients, making it suitable for greasy, blemished skins. It can be used over mild acne, but care should be taken with hygiene. It is worth remembering that severe acne is a contra-indication to a make-up application.

Mousse foundations

This type of foundation is suitable for combination to normal skin. Most are made with mineral oils, although some are made with herbal extracts. This type of foundation can be slightly more expensive to buy. If you do apply this foundation to oily skin be aware that it can be streaky if not carefully applied.

Skin type	Recognition	Suitable foundation
Normal	Small pores, fine texture Soft, supple, flexible, healthy	Cream / powder
Dry, dehydrated	Matt, uneven texture Lacks suppleness Lines and wrinkles Dilated capillaries common on nose and cheeks	Cream
Oily	Shiny, thick, blackheads Papules and pustules Open pores	Medicated liquid foundation Non-oily block / cake
Combination	Any combination of skin type – the most common is oily T-zone with dry cheeks	All-in-one fluid and powder combination
Sensitive / dry	Combination of dry areas with sensitivity Tight red appearance, broken capillaries	Hypo-allergenic products
Sensitive / allergy-prone	Reacts to products Skin flushes easily, which may appear in patches Dilated capillaries	Hypo-allergenic products

Cautions when applying foundation

Apply with a clean sponge or flat brush – these help when applying to awkward areas such as nose or eyes. Thin coverage can be achieved by using a natural sponge slightly damp. This type of sponge can, however, leave streaks because it is porous, so careful blending needs to take place. When a heavier coverage is required a latex sponge provides a smooth finish; a latex sponge is also less expensive.

Blend the foundation from the centre of the face to the hairline; this prevents clogging foundation in the hairline. You need to work quickly or the foundation will streak. Cover eyes and lips as this will provide a good base for eye-shadow and lipstick. When applying foundation to a more mature client who may have crepey skin around the neck and eyes, add a little moisturiser – this thins out the foundation and helps to prevent creases.

Check the application around the nose, hairline and chin to ensure smooth application and no visible lines.

Airbrush application

Many cosmetic houses and salons are now using airbrush applicators to apply foundation. The foundation is selected in the normal way to suit the client's skin colour and tones, and is then sprayed over the face. This form of application provides a flawless finish with no sponge or finger marks, and is excellent for bridal or photographic make-up.

In the salon
Mrs Jones comes into the salon with very dry skin and her foundation looks patchy. What could you recommend to help this client improve the appearance of her make-up?

Face powder

For a really professional appearance, most cream-based make-up products should be set with powder. Loose powder should be used for all professional make-up applications and the correct shade of pressed powder supplied for retail purchase by the client. A powder is applied to:

- 'fix' the foundation
- give a smooth matt finish
- reduce shine
- absorb grease
- protect the skin
- help conceal minor blemishes.

Loose powder

Loose powders come in two different textures – heavy and fine.

Heavy powders are often pigmented to complement the foundation and give a good cover; they contain a high proportion of kaolin and chalk.

Fine powders contain talc and a majority are translucent, which allows the colour of the skin or foundation to show through.

Some powders contain metallic particles for a pearlised effect, suitable for evening wear. If you decide to use a pearlised powder remember that it will accentuate lines and blemishes, so it will not be suitable for mature or blemished skins.

Loose powder should always be applied in a salon in preference to pressed powder because of hygiene. If, however, you apply pressed powder it should be decanted onto a palette before being applied, to prevent contamination.

Loose powder should be used for all professional make-up applications

Pressed powder

This is a product in a block that fits into a compact. The binding agent is usually gum or wax, which joins the particles together. Pressed powder is used for touching up the make-up during the day; however, this powder is not fine enough to produce an even finish on freshly applied foundation.

Always avoid areas with excessive hair growth as powder will collect there and draw attention to the area. Also avoid applying to dry flaking areas, because the area will dry out further and it will be accentuated.

Cautions when applying powder

- Dispense a small amount onto a palette.
- Firmly screw up a cotton wool pad and press into the powder, shake off excess in rolling movements, gently press into the foundation, covering all areas including eyes and lips.
- Remove any excess with a brush – firstly against the hair growth and then down the face to smooth the facial hairs and produce an even finish.
- Use a clean brush to remove any powder that has settled on the lashes or eyebrows.

Contouring cosmetics

These are a range of products which are similar to foundations and powders, with the addition of coloured pigments. They come in powder, liquid, cream and gel. Contour cosmetics consist of:

- blushers
- highlighters
- shaders.

Blushers

Blushers add warmth to the make-up and give the skin a healthy glow to help define the facial features. They come in a wide range of colours. Pale colours can be used to soften and highlight areas. Bright colours can accentuate, and deep tawny colours and bronzes can shade areas. Blushers also come in a variety of forms, including gels, creams and powders.

Gels

- Best on clear skins.
- Give cheeks a natural-looking healthy glow.
- Good for the summer.
- Can be applied directly over moisturiser.

Creams

- Give skins a moist dewy finish.
- Work best when applied over moisturisers and foundation.
- Good for normal or dry skin types.

Powders

- Matt or frosted finishes available.
- Applied for best results over powder with a large brush.
- Good on oily skins, but suitable for all skin types.

When choosing a blusher it should complement the foundation or natural skin tone. When applying a blusher it is best to build up the colour gradually to achieve the desired effect. It is the depth and tone of colour that needs to be selected carefully.

The use of blusher can help to alter the shape of the face. If you wish to reduce the width of the face, but give an illusion of length, keep the blusher to the side of the face, blending from just underneath the cheekbones to the temples. To create extra fullness apply the blusher to the cheeks or blend from the angle of the cheekbones to the ears. If you don't wish to change the shape of the face the blusher is usually placed on or near the cheekbones.

Highlighters

Highlighters are used to emphasise features and to create the illusion of extra length and width. The pale colours of highlighters reflect light. Use white, ivory and cream on pale skins for a subtle effect. When using a highlighter on a dark foundation it should belong to the same tone family:

- pale pink over rose shades
- pale peach over warm foundations.

Pearlised products are effective as highlighters, but avoid these on mature skins or hairy areas as they will draw attention to the areas.

Blushers add warmth and give a healthy glow; highlighters emphasise features

> **Remember**
>
> To check if the colour of a product is strong enough to show up effectively, take a small amount of colour onto your finger – if the colour on your finger has the same depth as that in the compact, the colour will be suitable.

Shaders

Shading is used to create artificial shadows or to reduce the size of areas. The colours suitable for shading contain brown pigments, which range from medium beige to dark brown. Beige is dark enough to shade when used over a pale base.

It is important to remember that the darker the foundation the deeper the shade needs to be. Warm brown colours should be avoided as a shader as they tend to look orange when applied over foundation and then act as a blusher.

Cautions when applying contouring products

- Use soft round-ended brushes that make blending easier.
- Tap any excess powder blusher onto a tissue or palette before applying, for a more subtle application. It is easier to build up colour in this way.
- When using a gel or cream apply with a damp sponge.
- Blusher application should start on the cheekbones level with the midpoint of the eye.
- Regularly check you are achieving a balanced effect.
- Keep blusher and highlighter away from the corners and the lines of the eye.
- Ensure contouring is subtle for day wear for a natural appearance.
- Use corrective techniques to try to achieve a balance in the facial features. This helps emphasise the best areas and takes attention away from problem areas.

> **Remember**
>
> - Light colours define areas.
> - Dark colours make areas recede.
>
> Foundation may also be used to change the shape of an area, minimise or make it less noticeable. To do this use a foundation two or three shades darker than the natural skin colour and blend into the ordinary foundation with either a sponge or brush.

Corrective make-up

Contouring products can be used effectively to emphasise and diminish areas to achieve the desired face shape. The oval face shape with almond-shaped eyes is often admired, although trends change with fashion and very few people truly fall into that category. When carrying out your consultation, ensure that both you and your client have realistic expectations about what you can achieve.

Oval face shape

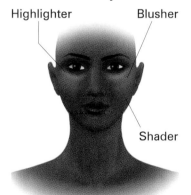

Highlighter   Blusher   Shader

The aim of any corrective make-up is to enhance bone structure and balance contours by blending blusher along the cheekbones towards the temples, applying shader below and highlighter above.

Round face shape

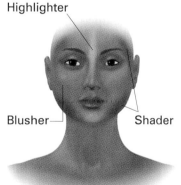

Highlighter   Blusher   Shader

The corrective work should create an illusion of length – to reduce the width from the sides of the face to the temples. To create length – subtle highlighter blended in a narrow strip down the centre of the face, blusher applied on the cheekbones up to the temples, shader over angles of the jaw and temple areas.

Square face shape

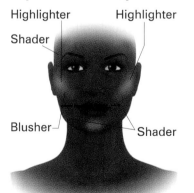

Highlighter   Highlighter   Shader   Blusher   Shader

The aim of the corrective work is to soften the jawline and reduce the width of the forehead and lower half of the face. Shader should be blended over the angles of the lower jaw and forehead. Blusher should be applied upwards from under the cheeks towards the temples or along the fullness of the cheeks.

Oblong face shape

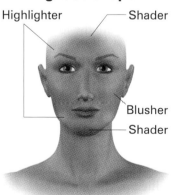

Highlighter   Shader   Blusher   Shader

The corrective make-up should reduce the length of the face, and create width and fullness. This can be achieved by applying shader to the tip of the chin and narrowest part of the forehead. Apply highlighter to the temples and lower jaw and blusher to cheeks to add fullness.

Deep-set eyes

Use light or frosted shadows on the lid if it is appropriate for the client and occasion. Apply a darker shade above the crease to recess this area. Apply a little shadow or soft eye pencil on the outer half of the bottom lid to balance the depth of the eyes.

Oriental eyes

Divide the area beneath the brow in half vertically. Use a lighter shade on the inner half and a darker shade on the outer half and blend well together. The application of a darker shadow creates a socket line. Apply a highlighter under the brow and blend together.

Almond eyes

Unless the eyes are set too close together or too far apart you don't have to worry about corrective techniques. Choose colours that complement the iris, and ensure the brows are groomed to make application of shadows easy.

Close-set eyes

Keep all medium or dark colours on the outer half of the eye. This will draw attention outward and the eyes will seem further apart. Ensure that the brows have been correctly shaped to maximise the space between the eyes.

Wide-set eyes

Extend the shadows to the inner corner of the eye and blend inwards to the bridge of the nose to minimise the space. Also ensure the brows are correctly shaped.

Cautions when applying eye-shadow

Always use clean brushes and applicators. Do not overload the applicator with shadow as excess powder could fall into the eyes or onto the face – spoiling the other make-up. It is also not cost effective to overload the applicator.

Support the skin and protect the surrounding make-up with a tissue. Remember that the skin around the eye is very delicate so don't be heavy handed and over-stretch the skin.

Ensure your client keeps her eyes closed when applying the shadow and always keep the client informed of what you are about to do.

Check the shadow is balanced on both eyes.

If applying shadow beneath the eyes ask the client to look away from the brush to prevent blinking or the eyes watering.

Eye-liner

This product is used for emphasising the shape of the eyelid and strengthening the colour of the lash line. It is good to use when strip lashes have been applied to give a more natural appearance. Liners are available in a number of colours and types. Like all make-up, eye-liner follows fashion trends and was very popular in the 1950s and 1960s.

Cake eye-liner

This is the most versatile product but the most difficult to apply. It is applied with a fine brush that is dampened before applying to the eyes.

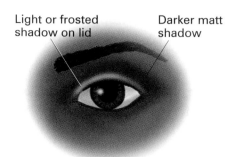

Deep-set eyes

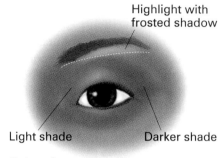

Oriental eyes

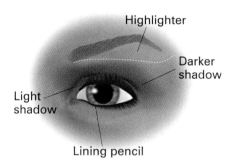

Almond eyes

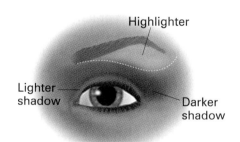

Close-set eyes

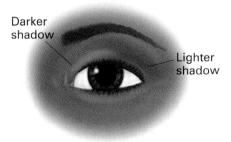

Wide-set eyes

Liquid eye-liner

This is a gum solution containing pigments, which gives a heavier effect.

Pencils

These are available in a range of colours, usually soft enough to blend with the shadows because of their wax formulation. Ensure they are sharpened between each eye to get an even application and to prevent cross infection occurring.

Kohl

This is a soft waxy black pencil which is applied to the inner rim of the lower eyelid to enhance the white of the eye. A kohl pencil is not recommended for use on a mature client.

Cautions when applying eye-liner

- Gently lift the skin from beneath the brow so the line is drawn up to the base of the lashes.
- Ensure the client keeps the eyes shut when liner is applied to the upper lid.
- Always apply liner outwards towards the corner of the eye.
- Check that the thickness and angle of the eye-liner are the same for both eyes.

Mascara

Mascaras are available in a variety of colours – including a clear mascara. Mascara is used to accentuate the eyes by darkening and thickening the lashes. Many now contain moisturisers and lash building ingredients which include filaments of nylon and rayon. These fibres temporarily lengthen the lashes. Clear mascara enhances the natural features of darkened lashes and is especially useful after the lashes have been tinted.

Cake mascara

A mixture of waxes and pigments in a soap base, this is applied with a brush. This type of mascara is gaining popularity again in salons as the brush applicator can easily be cleaned and sterilised.

Liquid mascara

Applied with a brush or wand, this type of mascara is contained in a water or alcohol and water base with extra features e.g. waterproof, thickening, and protein enriched. Read the packaging to find out what exactly the mascara contains. When applying this type of mascara to a client, disposable brushes should be used for each eye to prevent any contamination of the product.

> **Remember**
>
> When using lash-building mascara, caution should be taken with clients who have contact lenses as the fibres can cause damage to the lenses. Check that the product is suitable.

Cautions when applying mascara

- Ensure that the client is relaxed as this makes the application of mascara easier – especially to the upper lashes.
- Apply mascara downwards on upper lashes and then upwards for maximum coverage.
- Place tissue under lower lashes, before applying, to prevent mascara marking the skin.
- Instruct the client to look away from the wand when applying the mascara to the lower lashes.
- Build up the mascara in fine coats to prevent clogging. Allow to dry between applications.

Eyebrow pencils

These pencils are used to strengthen the colour of the brows and define shape. They should be applied to the brow in light feathery strokes for a natural look. The use of an eyebrow pencil is good for filling in bare areas if the brows are sparse. Use short strokes in the direction of the hair growth and blend into the natural brow shape with the aid of a brow brush.

Eyebrow pencils are produced in a limited range of colours to complement the natural brow colour. As with other pencils they should be sharpened between eyes to prevent cross contamination occurring.

Cautions when using eyebrow pencils

- Brush brows into shape.
- Check the colour tone and shade of the pencil – this should look natural and complement the rest of the make-up.
- Ensure the pencils are sharpened after doing each brow, to prevent cross-contamination, and ensure feathery strokes are used rather than one harsh line for a natural look.

a Separate brow hairs

b Smooth them into shape

> ### In the salon
>
> Mrs Patel is preparing for her daughter's wedding, and comes in for a pre-wedding make-up practice. Her eyebrows are thick and her eyes are quite small – what can you recommend?

Lip cosmetics

There is a variety of cosmetics on the market for lips, in a range of colours and forms. There are lipsticks, glosses and pencils. These are used to define the mouth, by adding colour, and to protect the lips from the environment. Lip cosmetics can, as with other forms of make-up, be used as corrective make-up to enhance shape. All lip products contain the same ingredients of oils, fats and waxes, with the addition of safe pigments for colour.

c Fill in the gaps and extend the length of the brow by using fine strokes that follow the natural hair growth

Lipsticks

These contain a high wax content that makes them hard. Some products also contain sunscreens to protect the delicate skin of the lips from ultraviolet light. Lipstick should be applied with a brush to outline the mouth and spread colour over evenly.

Lip gloss

This product can be used over lipstick or on its own for a natural look. It is usually of a gel consistency and is available in either lipstick form or as a gel.

Lip pencil

This is used for outlining the lips before applying lipstick and contains a high proportion of wax, which means it is less likely to smudge. It is useful to prevent lipstick colour from 'bleeding' into the fine lines around the mouth. It is also helpful for correcting lip shapes.

Lipstick sealer

Usually produced as a liquid, this is a colourless sealer, designed to prevent lipstick fading and to keep it in place. Applied with a brush.

Lip primer

This is used mainly for mature clients to prevent 'lipstick bleeding'.

Choosing a suitable lipstick

When selecting a lipstick it should be used to balance the colour scheme and co-ordinate with the clothing. Strong and vibrant colours draw attention to the mouth, so avoid them if you are trying to take the emphasis away from the mouth or jaw area. Strong colours look best with subtle and muted eye make-up colours.

Deep-colour lipstick or pencil should be used when outlining a corrective lip make-up. Pale, pearlised lipstick or lip gloss give lips a fuller appearance.

To reduce fullness, bronze, purplish pinks and blue-toned reds are useful.

Thin lips

Cautions when applying lip cosmetics

- Apply foundation and powder to the lips before applying lip cosmetics. This gives a good base and makes lip cosmetics last longer.
- Outline the mouth first and then fill in the colour.
- Blot the first application with a tissue as this helps to fix the colour.
- Apply a second coat for a final finish.
- Never apply lip cosmetics to any infected area or if the lips are excessively chapped or cracked.

Full or thick lips

Corrective lip make-up

Thin lips

The thickness of the lips can be increased by drawing a line slightly outside the natural lip shape.

Full or thick lips

Use dark colours to make the lips recede and create a new lip line inside the natural one by blotting out the natural line with foundation and powder.

Thin or straight upper lip

Thin or straight upper lip

Create a new bow to the upper lip by pencilling just above the natural line to add fullness.

Thin lower lip

Thin lower lip

Create a new lower lip line slightly below the natural lip to give balance to the mouth.

Asymmetric lips

These lips are unbalanced so create a lip line where required to achieve balance.

Asymmetric lips

Droopy mouth

Build up the corners of the lower lip, slightly extending upwards at the corners to meet the upper lip line.

Droopy mouth

Facial problem areas

Jawline shapes

Broad jaw

A broad jaw can be minimised by the use of a darker shader, starting from the temple area down and over either side of the angle of the mandible, bringing the centre of the face into sharper focus and so creating a more balanced width.

Step-by-step evening make-up

1 Begin with the client fully prepared, covered and with moisturised skin.

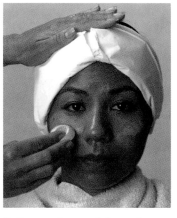

2 Concealer and foundation can be applied, with a damp sponge. For evening make-up, the shade can be a skin tone darker than for daytime.

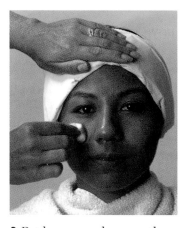

3 Pat loose powder over the foundation, remembering eyelids and lips. This will help the eye-shadow and lipstick stay on throughout the evening.

4 With a fat brush, sweep downwards to remove any excess powder, which may be clinging on to the tiny facial hairs.

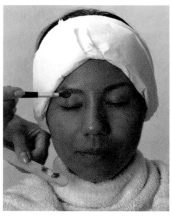

5 Decant your chosen eye-shadow colours onto a wooden spatula. For evening make-up choose sparkling or iridescent colours, to complement the eyes and / or outfit.

6 Remember to sharpen the eyeliner pencil before applying. Not all clients like an inner kohl line, so remember to ask, before attempting to apply.

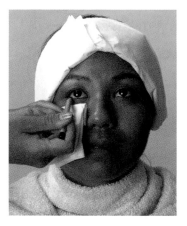

7 Always protect the make-up by using a tissue barrier to rest your hands on; this stops you from transferring any grease from your hands onto the skin.

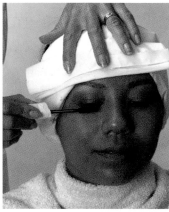

8 Apply mascara with a disposable wand, in light movements from base to tip. It helps if the client looks down. Try not to let your hand shake.

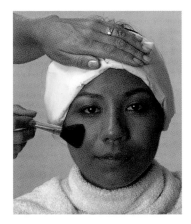

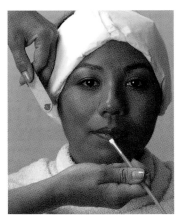

9 Evening blusher and shaders can be applied. A slightly sparkling blusher gives the cheeks a glow. Sweep from the plump part of the cheek upwards to create a high-cheeked appearance.

10 Sharpen pencil and apply lip liner along the natural lip line, unless correction is required. Using a tissue to rest upon, draw a subtle light line.

11 Decant the chosen lipstick onto a wooden spatula and apply, just inside the lip liner. A gloss can be applied over the top, if suitable and agreed with the client.

12 The finished look should complement and enhance the client's features. Make sure her clothing and hair are restored before revealing the finished result.

Step-by-step special occasion make-up

Special occasion make-up can be a little more individual than day make-up, but not quite as heavy as evening make-up. The key to making the whole look glamorous but not overdone is to co-ordinate the make-up colours with the outfit and add a touch of sparkle, with a lip gloss or shiny eye-shadow. Ask the client what she will be wearing; see the outfit, if possible, and definitely have a trial run before the event.

1 Study the client's natural skin and hair colouring, to avoid choosing make-up colours that clash. Research the type of special occasion and what the client will be wearing.

2 Decant and apply concealer / colour corrector, if required. Take into account that your client may or may not be used to wearing much make-up. Keep application and colour light, particularly when applying make-up to mature skin.

3 Apply foundation with a sponge or clean fingertips, blending from the centre of the face, outwards. Ensure foundation chosen is suitable for skin type – foundation for mature skin should be light in texture and colour.

4 With a dry piece of cotton wool, pat loose powder all over the face, remembering eyelids and lips. Translucent powder is suitable for mature skin.

5 A light stroke with a large blusher brush will remove any excess powder. Stroke the brush all over the face, in a downward motion, to avoid a powdery look to the face.

6 Eye shadow is decanted and applied lightly over the lids. If the client wears glasses, or has quite lined eyelids, make the colour and application fairly light.

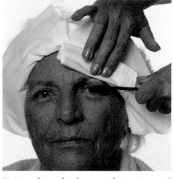

7 Apply a light application of mascara using a disposable wand. Soft shades of navy, grey or brown mascara are less harsh than black on mature skin.

8 Decant the blusher onto the wooden spatula and apply lightly to the cheeks. Soft corals, peaches or pinks usually suit mature skin.

9 Sharpen the pencil and apply a light lip liner, which prevents the lipstick bleeding into the lines around the mouth.

10 Choose a complementary lipstick and decant, then apply.

11 You gain the whole effect for special occasion make-up if you have a complete dress rehearsal – including the hat!

Children's face painting

Although not strictly a salon treatment, from time to time clients may request children's face painting for parties and birthday treats. No special skill is required – you just need some water-based face paints (child friendly for easy removal) and a flair for invention.

Complete the treatment

BT9.5

In this outcome you will learn about

- aftercare advice
- link selling and retail products
- leaving the working area tidy
- disposing of waste
- keeping records.

Aftercare advice

To enable the client to gain the most from the make-up treatment and subsequent make-up applications, the client should be given the following information.

- Correct preparation for applying make-up, including the cleansing and toning routine, and the correct application of moisturiser suitable for the client's skin type.
- Correct choice and application of cosmetics – colours, textures and types suitable for the features of the client and her skin type.
- Effective and hygienic use of products and equipment.
- How to keep make-up fresh by: applying pressed powder; applying a fine spray of water to keep the make-up from drying and cracking; applying more lipstick.
- Removal of make-up with products suitable for the client's skin type.
- In the event of an allergic reaction, remove all make-up, soothe with damp cotton wool and apply a soothing substance, e.g. calamine lotion.
- All details should be recorded on the client record card.

Link selling and retail products

Many therapists work on a commission basis for the sale of retail products, and a make-up treatment is a good opportunity to carry out such sales. These can include:

- other treatments within the salon
- regular facial treatment
- eyebrow shape
- eyelash and brow tints
- application of false lashes for special occasions
- eyelash perming
- manicure and pedicure treatments
- waxing.

Make-up products can be purchased by clients for use at home

Retail products

These can include:
- cleanser, toner and moisturiser to suit skin type
- foundation and powder
- matching lipstick and varnish
- make-up brushes and applicator
- eye cream
- throat / neck cream.

It is therefore important that you have a good knowledge of the products that you are recommending for home use and can demonstrate how to use these effectively. This will give the client confidence in you as a therapist. If products are purchased it is a good idea to record these sales, so you can assist the client on future visits if she wishes to re-purchase.

Leaving the working area tidy

It is important to leave the working area clean and tidy. Ensure that all products are put away and that brushes and sponges are cleaned ready for use – clean brushes in warm soapy water and rinse well. Allow the brushes to dry naturally if possible, so that the shape of the brush is not distorted.

Disposing of waste

Contaminated waste should be disposed of according to legislative requirements. Any other waste products can be put with the normal rubbish, but remember to abide by COSHH guidelines for safe disposal of all products used within the salon. If carrying out a make-up treatment and applying false lashes, read the manufacturers' guidelines for disposal of adhesive or solvent products.

Keeping records

Ensure that all records are kept up to date. For a make-up treatment this should include all products and shades used; any recommendations you have made; and products that have been purchased, so that you can follow up this information on subsequent visits.

Your questions answered

Why is it important to do a skin analysis prior to carrying out a make-up application?
It is important so that you can fully assess the client's skin type and select suitable products. This should be carried out on cleansed dry skin.

What action should be taken if the foundations are not the correct shade?
You can blend your own shades by mixing two or more colours together on a palette to obtain the correct shade.

Do I have to use a colour corrector, if a concealer has been used?
Colour correctors do just what they say – they neutralise the colour to make a more even shade – so they should only be applied where they are needed.

Is the lighting really that important when applying make-up?
The more natural the lighting and the closer to daylight, the better the finished results will look. Different coloured light bulbs and shades on light fittings can give a false appearance and you may find that that the application is too sparing or too heavy handed.

Why is it important to use the correct products on black/Asian skins?
Because of the different colours and pigmentation of the skin, specialist products should be used so the correct skin tones and a natural look can be achieved.

Applying make-up

Ensure all products and equipment are close to hand.

⬇

Carry out a consultation, checking for contra-indications, and a skin analysis to determine the products to use.

⬇

Apply moisturiser.

⬇

Apply concealer and colour corrector if required.

⬇

Apply foundation, checking the colour on the jaw line. Apply powder to set the foundation.

⬇

Apply shaders and highlighters to minimise or emphasise areas as discussed with the client.

⬇

Apply eye-shadow (hold a tissue under the eye to prevent flaking shadow).

⬇

Apply eye-liner or pencil (sharpen between eyes).

⬇

Apply mascara (using disposable mascara wands).

⬇

Apply lip pencil or liner. Apply lipstick.

⬇

Show client the finished result. Record details, including products used and where applied, on client record.

Test your knowledge

1   *How would you select the correct foundation colour?*

2   *What is the purpose of foundation?*

3   *What type of powder is recommended for touching up make-up?*

4   *When applying eye make-up to more mature clients, what type of product should be avoided?*

5   *What is the difference between day and evening make-up?*

6   *What should you do between each eye when using a pencil to line the eyes?*

7   *Why is the position of the client important when applying make-up?*

8   *What type of mascara is best to use on a client who wears contact lenses?*

9   *How would you contour a client with a round face shape?*

10 *What is the purpose of a highlighter?*

Provide make-up treatment
What your assessor is looking for
Unit BT9

You cannot do any simulation within this unit, but the evidence can be gained quite easily. Remember to keep all paper evidence of any actions, feedback or witness statements that you have been given to support this work.

Your assessor will observe your performance on at least **three** occasions, involving a different client covering at least **two** different client groups as listed in the range.

- Use all consultation techniques.
- Identify skin types.
- Use all the products listed in the range.
- Apply make-up for all occasions as listed in the range.
- Maintain environmental conditions (ventilation, heat, etc.).
- Prepare the client to suit the treatment.
- Deal with contra-indications that may prevent or restrict the treatment.
- Deal with contra-actions.
- Provide treatment advice.

Evidence of these can be provided for observation by your assessor but also by written work, projects, witness statements, photographic and video evidence, and APL (accredited prior learning) statements.

You must prove to your assessor that you have the necessary knowledge, understanding and skills to perform competently on all ranges within the criteria from this unit.

Remove hair using waxing techniques

Unit BT6

Introduction

This unit focuses on ways to temporarily remove unwanted hairs from the body. Also included is how to disguise hairs, or temporarily lighten darker hairs found on parts of the body.

Waxing is the removal of body hair by pulling it out of the skin by the roots, using some form of bond. A hot, warm or cold wax product is spread over the hairy area, and a cotton or paper strip is used to make the hair bond or stick to it. The strip is then removed in a quick, single movement. It should leave the area clean and hair-free. Hygiene, client care and lots of practice are necessary, which may mean this unit takes some patience to learn, but it is very rewarding for you and your client.

Waxing treatments always form a large part of any salon's business, as many women in western society dislike body hair. However, some cultures, such as eastern Europeans, do not dislike it. Waxing tends to be a steady source of income, with peaks at certain times of the year. With the first rays of sunshine, clients wish to shed their tights and show off hair-free legs, so spring is always busy. Christmas is another busy time, when more revealing party outfits are worn and bodies need tender loving care and that extra bit of maintenance.

In this unit you will cover the following outcomes:

6.1 Consult with the client
6.2 Prepare for the treatment
6.3 Plan the treatment
6.4 Remove unwanted hair
6.5 Complete the treatment.

Before you can give your client a full consultation, then plan and prepare for the treatment, you need to understand:

- hair facts
- wax facts
- other methods of hair removal.

This knowledge will allow you to make the best treatment decision for your client, based upon a sound understanding of the choices available to suit her or his needs.

Hair facts

(For the anatomy of hair structure and the hair growth cycle, refer to **Related Anatomy and Physiology**, page 189.)

Depilation (removal of unwanted hair, particularly by waxing and sugaring) is a popular salon treatment as it provides a quick and efficient way of removing unwanted hairs in both small and larger areas.

Superfluous hair is the term used where hair growth is normal, but the client feels it to be unattractive. Dark-haired clients, especially, may feel that their growth is visible, e.g. on the upper lip.

Some clients do not want the hair removed, but like it to be lightened by **bleaching**. Other clients wish to have their hair permanently removed using an electrical current – this is called **epilation**. (Epilation is a specialist treatment at NVQ Level 3. It is permanent removal of the hair and requires considerable skill and training.)

Many hair-removing creams can be bought over the counter, as well as electric shavers for women and disposable razors with adapted shaving foams. These ensure that the skin is kept soft and moisturised.

Hair removal is very much a matter of personal choice and the client should be given all the information available, so an informed decision can be made.

Two terms are used when talking about abnormal hair growth:

- hirsutism
- hypertrichosis.

Hirsutism is when the hair growth of a woman develops male characteristics; it is seen as a strong growth of a beard-like formation, the development of chest hair, and more prominent back hair. The pubic hairline can grow upwards towards the navel - all the hair growth patterns of a male. It is caused by hormone imbalances, usually a sensitivity to androgens, which are one of a group of steroid hormones secreted by the adrenal cortex (above the kidneys) and in the ovaries in small amounts.

Hypertrichosis is the abnormal growth of terminal hair in an area not normally seen in either sex, such as along the forehead.

Hair growth patterns can also depend on ethnic background. Japanese women can be virtually hairless, whilst women in India and Mediterranean countries often have a strong, dark hair growth.

The client needs to know the various methods of hair removal available, with the advantages and disadvantages of each, and to be given the therapist's professional advice for her particular problem area, with consideration of the cost and time involved.

Why is the human body hairy?

As the human body evolved it was extremely hairy all over for warmth; the body also laid down fat deposits to keep warm. Facial hair on men through the ages has been considered to be a sign of virility, strength and masculinity. Men only started shaving with razors during the twentieth century. In fact most Edwardian gentlemen had handlebar moustaches or full beards. There has been a big change in fashion towards clean-shaven faces, except of course for the 'designer stubble' trend of pop stars.

We still retain hairs for the purpose of warmth and protection. **Terminal hair** (refer to Related anatomy and physiology, page 189) grows long and is often coarse in texture:

- **Scalp hair** protects the head and helps keep in the heat.
- **Eyelashes** protect the eyes by catching particles that may fall into the eye.
- **Underarm and pubic hair** protect the delicate skin and cushion against friction caused by movement.
- **Body hair** protects against heat loss.

Factors determining hair growth

Both men and women have terminal hair, but hair growth is determined by several factors.

The number of hair follicles

A large number of follicles means lots of hair and the hair will look very thick. This tends to be genetic, which means it has been inherited from the parents. (If a man has baldness in his family, there is a strong possibility he will develop the same hair-growth pattern.)

Cultural influences

Hair-growth patterns as well as strength, texture and the amount of hair are also influenced by geography and race. There is a higher proportion of blond and fair-skinned people in countries such as Norway and Sweden. Face or body hair on these people is fair and not noticeable. However, the nearer the equator, and hence the nearer the sun, that people live, the darker their skin and hair colour is likely to become. Italians, Spaniards and Greeks usually have dark hair and skin. Their facial hair or body hair may be more noticeable. The British colouring can be a mixture of light and dark – Scottish and Irish people tend to have darker colouring. Generally it is darker-haired clients who are more concerned with superfluous hair, mostly because it is more visible.

Hair strength and texture

Again, this tends to run in families. People with a thick, strong hair growth may also have lots of follicles and a really full head of hair. Others may have lots of follicles, but the hair itself may be very fine in texture. Some people have the combination of few follicles with fine hair texture. For these people body hairs are not noticeable and they may never need the services of depilation.

Illness

This can have a strong effect on hair growth, usually making the hair lank and lifeless, and could affect hair styling.

Medication

Some drugs have a strong effect on hair growth. They might produce coarse, thick hair, which can be depilated, with a doctor's permission. Or the follicles might weaken and wither, causing the hair to fall out. Some forms of chemotherapy for the treatment of cancer cause baldness. Often this is only temporary and the hairs will re-grow.

Hormones

Hormones can also have an effect on hair growth. Women going through the menopause, when hormone levels may be erratic, may find they develop 'whiskers' of coarse hair on the face.

Emotion

A sudden shock, accident or the death of a loved one can cause hair loss, which may re-grow, or may not. This is called **alopecia** and can mean patches of hair loss or total baldness. It is unusual for alopecia to occur on a leg or an arm.

In our society some women dislike having hairy legs and body hair. Some men may also consider having hair removed from the body. For example, some professional sportsmen such as cyclists and swimmers may wish to enhance their performance by reducing body hair.

Remember

In some European and Mediterranean countries, hairy bodies are considered the norm. Strong underarm hair or other body hair is not considered unattractive in women. Be careful not to be hasty in treatment advice.

Wax facts

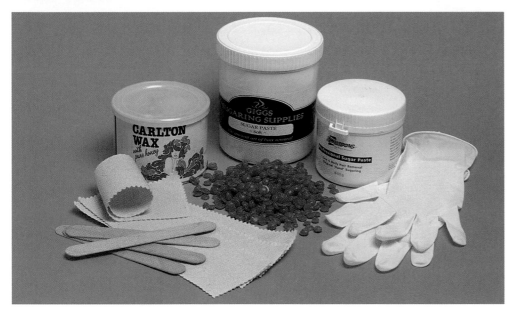

Various wax products

Advantages and disadvantages of depilation and hair lightening

Method of hair removal	Advantages	Disadvantages
Warm wax	• Quick, cost effective • Efficient over large areas • Once mastered, easy to apply	• Sticky • Can cause skin damage if reapplied over the same area • Can leave a residue, which if not fully removed can leave the client feeling sticky
Hot wax	• Good for strong hair growth • Suitable for ethnic hair types, which may have bent follicles (Refer to anatomy section)	• Skilled technique of application may take some time to master • Because of the temperature control needing to be accurate, application needs to be quick • Not suitable for some skin types • Can be messy when learning application
Strip sugaring	• As warm wax • Water-soluble	• Can be less efficient than warm wax • Tricky technique to master
Manual sugaring	• Water-soluble • Applied at body temperature, so less likely to burn the skin • Cost effective as no paper / material strips are necessary	• Difficult technique to master • More time-consuming to perform
Hair-removing creams	• No skill needed • Less pain involved • Home treatment • Minimal costs • Less bristly regrowth	• Not suitable for all skin types • Messy application • Regrowth short term • Hair only removed from just below the skin's surface

Method of hair removal	Advantages	Disadvantages
Cutting	• Quick • No skill involved • Home treatment • No pain involved	• Short term only • Blunt regrowth, as hair removed only to skin level • Risk of cutting the skin
Shaving	• Quick • No skill involved • Home treatment • No pain • Equipment cheap to purchase	• Not suitable for all skin types • Blunt regrowth • Risk of skin damage • Not hygienic • Short term only • Only removes surface part of the hair
Plucking	• Precise • Ideal for small areas i.e. on the face • Equipment cheap to purchase	• Only suitable for small areas • Risk of skin damage (bruising or pinching the skin) • Breakage of hair may occur • Can be time-consuming • Not ideal for clients who wear glasses for a DIY treatment
Threading	• Cheap • No equipment needed • Suitable for Mediterranean and Asian clients • As effective as plucking	• Skill needed to apply • Possible breakage of the hair
Impregnated cold wax strips	• Minimal skill needed • Less messy for home use • No specialist equipment needed • Quick	• Bruising or skin damage may occur as the strips stick to the skin and not to the hair • Painful to remove • Unsatisfactory results • Can be costly for large areas
Abrasives (gloves / pumice stones)	• No skill needed • No specialist equipment needed • Improves the skin texture as dead skin cells are shed (desquamation) • Cheap treatment for home use	• Hair breakage may occur • Hair is only removed at skin surface level • Could result in skin damage • Not terribly effective on strong dark hair growth
Electrical appliances (e.g. electric razors, etc.)	• No skill needed • Re-usable • Ideal for home use • Clean and quick	• Only removes surface hairs • May damage the skin • Some can be expensive • Regrowth produced is blunt and growth stubble
Bleach	• Little skill involved in application • Quick results • Suitable for facial hairs • Suitable for clients having epilation • No distortion of the follicle takes place, so no problems occur if epilation is done at a later date	• Not suitable for all skin types • Patch test required • Not suitable for large areas, e.g. the legs • Regrowth is more noticeable when it does come through • Skin irritation can occur

There are many excellent types of wax available, with various ingredients for different effects. Wax is classed according to its working temperature.

Type of wax	Working temperature
Hot hard depilatory wax	Works best at 48–68°C
Warm soft depilatory wax	Works best at 40–43°C
Cream depilatory wax	Works best at 35–43°C
Organic wax	Organic wax varies – refer to suppliers
Cold wax	Needs no heating

Type of wax and its working temperature

Ingredients

The ingredients of a wax will determine its working temperature. The ingredients will vary from manufacturer to manufacturer, but the higher the proportion of good quality **resin** in relation to **beeswax**, the more heat is required to get it to a manageable working consistency.

Resins are **organic polymers** that may be naturally occurring or synthetic. A polymer is a compound such as starch or Perspex. It forms the basis for all plastics and artificial fibres.

Natural resins occur in certain plants and trees. The fluid that oozes out from a wound in the plant or tree hardens into a solid resin to protect the injured part. The balsam, pine, gum and rubber tree all produce resins. The gum tree produces chewing gum resin.

Resins are used in the making of perfume, waxing and some cosmetics. Chemists can now make synthetic resins to prevent the over-exploitation of plants.

Large quantities of **resins** are produced as a by-product of the **petroleum oil** business, and are extracted from crude oil after it has been pumped out of the ground.

EU directive 88/379 provides information on all precautions, correct handling, storage and first aid measures.

Latest ingredient developments

Companies are incorporating rich and natural ingredients into their wax formulas to help soften and moisturise the skin. Cannabis sativa is a drug-free hemp derivative that is rich in essential fatty acids to help lock in moisture. It also has anti-inflammatory properties. For sensitive skins, tea-tree wax is very soothing with antiseptic properties. Hemp wax is also very kind to a sensitive skin, and cream waxes moisturise.

Reality Check!

These temperatures are supplied courtesy of Bellitas Ltd, beauty suppliers, known for their 'Strictly Professional' waxes. Manufacturers' instructions will vary with different products, so always refer to the recommended temperatures and heating units for maximum benefit and safety.

Types of wax

Hard depilatory wax

Waxing products

What is it?

It is a hard depilatory wax, sold in solid pellet form, which becomes molten when heated.

What is it made of?

It is a mixture of natural resins, beeswax and microcrystalline wax. Insoluble in cold water, this wax is quite soluble when hot. It has a low chemical reactivity and is stable.

What are the hazards?

Hard wax is classed as non-hazardous if used in correct professional circumstances.

What are the first aid measures?

- If used at the correct temperature and with the correct procedure for hair removal, this wax poses no hazard.
- High temperatures should be avoided, as these will cause thermal burns.
- If an overheated wax has solidified on the skin, leave it in place and consult a doctor.
- If wax enters the eyes, they should be flushed immediately with water for 15 minutes and medical attention obtained.

What are the fire-fighting measures?

- This wax is stable, but it has a flash point greater than 220° C. Make sure that the thermostat controlling the temperature on the heater is working!
- Although not strictly classed as flammable, this wax will burn. Avoid contact with flammable fabrics, e.g. placing near the curtains.
- In the event of a small fire, foam, carbon dioxide, dry chemical powder, sand or earth may be used to extinguish it. For a large fire use foam or water spray.

What do I do in the event of an accident?

- In the event of a large spillage, any wax entering the drains will solidify and cause blockages. The local health authority will need to be notified if this happens.
- Allow spilt hot wax to cool and solidify, then scrape up for disposal.

How do I store it?

Hard depilatory waxes can be kept for up to six months in tightly closed jars in cool dry conditions, away from possible sources of contamination.

How do I handle it?

- Adequate protective clothing must be worn when handling wax in a molten state.
- It is recommended that advice be sought from the individual awarding body and professional organisation that is favoured by your training establishment.
- To ignore their recommended guidelines may invalidate any assessments taking place, but more importantly may remove insurance protection.
  (Refer to **Professional basics**, 'You, your client and the law'.)

Warm wax

What is it?

This is a soft, thick liquid. It may vary in colour from warm honey to amber or light brown.

Soft wax is supplied in a tin or plastic tub, which fits into a special heating unit.

There are many soft waxes on the market and it is recommended that the wax be heated only in the correct heater, following the manufacturer's instructions, as the temperatures for best performance may vary slightly.

What is it made of?

It is composed mainly of refined gum resin and hydrocarbon tackifiers. This gives the wax its sticking properties.

What are the hazards?

Warm wax is classed as non-hazardous if used in correct professional circumstances.

What are the first aid measures?

- If used at the correct temperature and with the correct procedure for hair removal, this wax poses no hazard.
- High temperatures should be avoided, as this will cause thermal burns.
- If an overheated wax has solidified on the skin, leave it in place and consult a doctor.
- If in contact with the eyes, irrigate immediately with copious quantities of cold water for at least five minutes. Obtain medical attention.
- If inhaled, move the person away from exposure to fumes from molten products. If irritation persists, obtain medical attention.
- If ingested, no special treatment is necessary.
- If accidental skin contact with the heated product occurs, cool the affected area by plunging it into cold running water for at least ten minutes. *Do not remove the adhering material.* Obtain medical attention. If a limb is completely surrounded by wax, the wax should be split to avoid a tourniquet effect.
- If skin contact with the cold product occurs, wash thoroughly with soap and water.

What are the fire-fighting measures?

- Although not strictly classed as flammable, soft wax will burn above 200° C. Avoid contact with flammable fabrics, e.g. placing near the curtains. Ensure that the thermostat on the heating unit is in working order by regularly maintaining the equipment.
- In the event of a small fire, use carbon dioxide, dry powders or foam.
- *Do not use water on soft wax.*

What do I do in the event of an accident?

- When soft wax is molten, care must be taken to prevent burns by ensuring that application temperatures are kept to the minimum necessary for adequate product performance.
- At no time is it necessary to heat the product above 60° C.
- Ensure good ventilation in the working environment.
- Where accidental overheating occurs the source of heat should be disconnected and the molten product left undisturbed until cool. Make sure that all persons are aware of the potential hazard.

Warm wax heater

How do I store it?

Soft wax may be maintained as a cool liquid within its own container, or heated within the unit on a daily basis. It may keep for up to six months in cool dry conditions.

How do I handle it?

- Handle in the same way as for hard wax.
- Adequate protective clothing must be worn when handling wax in a molten state.
- It is recommended that advice be sought from the individual awarding body and professional organisation that is favoured by your training establishment.
- To ignore their recommended guidelines may invalidate any assessments taking place, but more importantly may remove insurance protection.
  (Refer to **Professional basics**, 'You, your client and the law'.)
- Soft waxes are unlikely to cause any environmental hazards, but do remember that all waxes are generally non-biodegradable in the short term.

Cream waxes

Many manufacturers now produce a good quality cream wax. Cream wax contains ingredients such as moisturisers and azulene that help the skin condition. Azulene is anti-inflammatory and soothing, and is suitable for more sensitive skin types. (Azulene is the ingredient that will turn the cream a blue colour.)

Cream wax also works on slightly lower melting and working temperatures, thereby enhancing client comfort during waxing.

Cream wax has enhanced sticking properties, which means that it can be spread thinly and is thus very economical to use.

Refer to the soft waxing information in the COSHH details above.

Organic waxes

Organic waxes are very popular as they contain natural ingredients such as honey as well as the chemical ingredients they need to keep them stable. Organic waxes do not set when cold but become very liquid when heated.

Cold waxes

Some cold waxes, such as pre-coated wax strips, are available over-the-counter; others are supplied to salons by the manufacturer.

Retail strips

- These can be purchased from most large chemists and come in packs of 6–10 strips.
- They are usually made by the same companies that produce hair-removing creams.
- These pre-coated strips are double layered – one piece of wax paper is a non-stick backing strip from which the coated strip peels away, to be placed on the skin.
- They contain hydrocarbon resins so are sticky, but as they are cold, the adhering properties are not as effective as warm or hot wax.
- Most manufacturers recommend the strips be warmed between the hands before splitting and applying.
- The wax coating is quite fine and may not be sufficient to grip strong hair growth, so the strips are only suitable for light growth. They are not normally recommended for facial use, elderly people, diabetics and people with skin irritations.
- They can be used as a stopgap for quick removal of a light growth between waxing, and for special occasions should the client not be able to visit for warm waxing.
- Follow instructions on the individual packaging.

Reality Check!

Non-recoverable waste should be disposed of via a licensed waste contractor. A set fee is charged for a regular collection, e.g. a company called Rentokil will operate a weekly collection. Waxing waste should be put into a separate lined bin, ready for picking up by the disposal company.

Cream wax

Waxes with natural ingredients such as honey are popular

Roller waxing

Many manufacturers provide complete systems with disposable roll-on heads. These are proving very popular in salons and with therapists offering a mobile beauty therapy service.

The applicators look a little like a roll-on deodorant stick, and come in various roller head sizes for different parts of the body. They can be disposed of after use. Alternatively, refill cartridges can be used and the head attachments taken off for cleaning and sterilisation.

Some salons favour the client purchasing the whole roller applicator, which the salon then keeps for that client to avoid cross-contamination.

Other products used in waxing

Pre-waxing lotion

What is it?

This is a cleansing lotion applied to the area before treatment to cleanse and remove any grease or dirt on the skin that may prevent good hair removal.

What is it made of?

The product usually contains ethanol and camphor oil in a cosmetic lotion. The ethanol is an alcohol for cleansing, and the camphor has anti-bacterial and anti-inflammatory properties as well as being anti-viral. It is also a counter irritant.

What are the hazards?

If used properly, this product has no hazards.

What are the first aid measures?

- If ingested, drink milk or water.
- If it goes into the eyes, wash well with water. If irritation persists, seek medical advice.

What do I do in the event of an accident?

If spillage occurs, clean up with an absorbent material then wash with detergent and water to avoid a slippery floor.

How do I store and handle it?

No special precautions are considered necessary.

Purified talc

What is it?

It is a dry powder that is used as a light dusting over the area to be waxed. It ensures the hairs have a covering for the wax to adhere to and that the hairs stand away from the skin.

What are the hazards?

All dry powders can give respiratory problems if precautions are ignored and they are inhaled.

Avoid excessive use, especially near the nose and mouth.

This product is non-flammable.

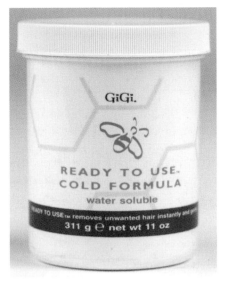

Cold wax

Pre-waxing lotion

What are the first aid measures?

- If ingested, drink milk or water.
- If inhaled, move the person to the fresh air and keep him or her warm.
- Avoid prolonged skin contact as this can lead to dry skin.
- If it goes into the eyes, wash well with water.

What do I do in the event of an accident?

Sweep or vacuum the powder up, avoiding dust.

How do I store and handle it?

Store in a cool, dry place, keeping containers tightly sealed.

After-wax lotion

What is it?

This is a soothing lotion used after treatment to help cool and calm the skin and prevent irritation.

What is it made of?

The product contains an emulsion of oils, waxes, water, water-soluble ingredients, emulsifiers, fragrance and preservatives.

What are the hazards?

If used properly, this product has no hazards.

What are the first aid measures?

- If ingested, drink milk or water.
- If it goes into the eyes, wash well with water. If irritation persists, seek medical advice

What do I do in the event of an accident?

If spillage occurs, clean up with an absorbent material then wash with detergent and water to avoid a slippery floor.

How do I store and handle it?

No special precautions are considered necessary.

Wax equipment cleaner

What is it?

This is a liquid with a very strong smell!

What is it made of?

It is a hydrocarbon solvent and a very powerful cleaner.

What are the hazards?

It is highly flammable and is hazardous. It should not be used in an enclosed space as the fumes are highly noxious.

What are the first aid measures?

- If it goes into the eyes, irrigate immediately with copious quantities of cold water for at least five minutes. Obtain medical attention.
- Do not inhale as this may cause dizziness. If it is inhaled, move to fresh air.
- If ingested, drink plenty of milk or water.
- Avoid prolonged contact with the skin. If irritation occurs, seek medical advice.

What are the fire fighting measures?

The cleaner is highly flammable. Evacuate the area and inform fire fighters of the hazards.

What do I do in the event of an accident?

- Clean the contaminated area with lots of detergent and water to avoid slippery floors.
- Do not absorb onto combustible material.

How do I store it?

Store in a cool place away from direct sunlight. Large quantities should be kept in a fire-resistant store.

Benefits and effects of waxing

Type of wax	Benefits	Effects
Hot wax	As hot wax needs to be heated to a high temperature it is extremely effective on strong hair growth.	The solid wax turns into a liquid when heated and when applied to the skin, it coats the hairs, gripping them firmly. The wax is applied with a disposable spatula unit in a thick layer. A lip of the wax is then lifted to allow a firm hold to take the whole patch off.

Possible drawbacks

Only really suitable on longer hair growth – results not good if the hair is shorter.

Hot wax may cause a slight skin reaction, so not suitable for sensitive skin, or sensitive areas.

Application is a skill that needs a lot of practice to master.

As the wax needs to be kept at a constant working temperature it can be time-consuming if the wax keeps over-heating and therefore needs time to cool again.

The wax needs to be applied quite thickly, so it can be quite costly in materials.

Wax should not be applied over the same area twice, as the skin may burn.

Can be messy to apply so it is hard to keep the equipment clean.

These considerations need to be thought about when choosing equipment.

Type of wax	Benefits	Effects
Warm wax	More comfortable on sensitive skins than hot wax, and can be reapplied over the same area. Even short hairs can be successfully removed with warm wax. The equipment is easy to maintain and keep clean. Very little preparation is needed and application is easy and quick.	Warm wax is applied with a disposable spatula, in a very thin coating and a fabric or paper strip is applied over the top of the wax for easy removal – rather like a plaster coming off. The wax and hairs adhere to the strip. A single strip can be used over again until it reaches saturation point.

Other methods of hair removal

Hair removing creams

These creams use chemicals to break down the hair structure. The chemical is calcium thioglycollate and it attacks the hair keratin layer. The hair dissolves and can be scraped or washed away. Most over-the-counter preparations have a full list of instructions for use, and timings may vary. This type of product is not always suitable for young or sensitive skins and a reaction can occur. The re-growth is soft and with a tapered end, so the hair does not feel spiky and sharp.

Cutting or clipping

Scissors will trim the hair. They can be used in between treatments, as this does not distort the follicle. Scissors can obviously shorten long 'whiskers' but are not ideal for achieving a smooth finish. This is not a long-term solution to superfluous hair.

Shaving

Shaving is the chosen option for many people. It is a quick-fix option and can produce clean results providing care is taken, a clean razor is used, and a suitable lubricant is applied to the skin. Many razor companies have recognised the large female market and have designed razors, creams, shaving foams and after-shaving preparations in feminine colours and with attractive smells.

However, shaving is a double-edged sword! The ends of the hair are chopped at skin level and are very blunt, so the re-growth is spiky and gives stubble.

Shaving is not for the face or arms, as once started it becomes quite a chore – if the hair growth is dark and thick, it could become a twice-weekly job.

Plucking

Plucking of the eyebrows has always been done, but as the hairs are taken out individually plucking is not suitable for removing hairs from large areas. The hair is pulled out of its follicle, and if the hair is taken out in the right stage of growth, re-growth can take some time. The hair grows back with its natural tapered end so does not feel spiky to the touch. Care must be taken to avoid infection. The tweezers should be clean and disinfected, and the skin cleaned and wiped with antiseptic. Avoid applying make-up straight away as the follicle is open and there is a risk of infection.

Threading

Threading is similar to plucking. It is practised mostly in Asian communities and is sometimes seen in the Mediterranean. A piece of cotton is entwined around the fingers and twisted over the hairs. The hair gets caught up in the thread and is plucked out of its follicle. This is quite a skill and requires practice.

Abrasives

An abrasive glove or pumice stone is rubbed over the skin and the hair is broken off at the skin's surface. There are many over-the-counter preparations that have this effect. They come in glove or mitt form and are sold as 'a sensible alternative to waxing and shaving'. They tend to resemble fine sandpaper in appearance.

For best results the skin must be dry, and the glove is rotated in a gentle circular fashion. **Do** rub gently. **Do** rub in circular motions. **Don't** rub up and down.

The fine powder that appears is an accumulation of skin **exfoliation**. This means skin cells are shed. This makes the product ideal on dry rough skin, provided that soothing body moisturising creams are applied after use.

Check it out

Prices vary from salon to salon. You can expect to pay higher prices in top salons in the West End of London.

In your local area get two or three price lists from salons offering waxing treatments. How much do they charge? What are the types of wax they use, and which treatments do they offer?

Remember

A good tip to pass onto the client who has booked for a waxing treatment is to take a couple of mild over-the-counter painkillers. This helps to block the pain-transmitting nerve endings in the skin so it is less painful. It must be a medicine that the client has used before, with no adverse reaction.

Remember

Not all methods of hair removal are suitable for all clients. A full consultation will be needed to establish which method is suitable and agreeable to you both.

Remember

A patch test would be advisable for people with a sensitive skin.

Consult with the client

BT6.1

Before you can effectively consult with the client and decide on her or his waxing or lightening needs and draw up your treatment plan, you need to have thorough background knowledge of all the products. So, look closely at 'Hair facts' (page 312) and 'Wax facts' (page 315) before deciding on your recommendations.

In this outcome you will learn about
<ul><li>consultation techniques</li><li>discussing and agreeing the service and outcomes</li><li>maintaining client modesty</li><li>contra-indications to waxing.</li></ul>

The first three of these topics have been discussed elsewhere. Refer to the following:

- Consultation techniques: pages 10–12, 19–21
- Discussing and agreeing the service and outcomes: pages 29–30
- Maintaining client modesty: page 28
- Contra-indications (general): pages 21–22.

Contra-indications to waxing

A contra-indication means that the treatment cannot be carried out, as the client is unsuitable for this particular treatment. Refer to **You and the skin**, pages 148–149, for photographs of types of infection.

It may be that an area has to be protected or avoided, e.g. where a mole or skin tag is present.

The areas to be treated should be examined in good lighting to judge if any of the following conditions are present:

- skin diseases or disorders
- open skin, infection, inflammation or healing skin (scabs present)
- bruising
- very thin or papery skin (diabetics have thin skin that does not heal very well because of poor circulation)
- sunburn – after a sun bed or natural tanning
- recent scar tissue
- moles, warts or any unidentified skin problems
- varicose veins or broken capillaries on the legs
- cold sores, eye infections, styes or colds when treating the face
- unidentified lumps, breast-feeding and mastitis when treating under the arm
- previous reactions to treatment
- excessive ingrown hairs from previous treatments.

The client would also not be suitable for treatment if he or she had just had heat treatment, for example infra-red treatment or a sauna or steam bath.

Prior to or during menstruation, clients may have a lower pain threshold and the skin may be more sensitive and may react unpredictably. You can suggest clients take an over-the-counter painkiller to help, but only if they have used them before with no adverse reactions.

Look out for moles or skin tags which may restrict the treatment in the area

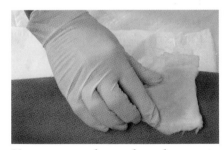

Use a pre-wax cleaner from the manufacturer to cleanse the area

Cover the mole with petroleum jelly to prevent the wax adhering to it – this will ensure you do not cause any damage to the mole

A contra-action is an unfavourable reaction of a client to a treatment.

Even when you have been faultless in hygiene, safety and product use, your client may react to the wax – even if she has had the same treatment for years. It could be a reaction caused by medication being taken, it could be under the influence of fluctuating hormones or it could be that an allergic reaction has developed.

Possible contra-actions to waxing may be immediately visible, either during or after the treatment. They may also appear when the client goes home or back to work. Either way you should act responsibly and make your client aware of what action to take.

Unfavourable skin reaction

Recognised as redness or soreness to the area, this could be caused by the wax being too hot on the skin, by an allergic reaction or from too vigorous scraping of the spatula on the skin during application. Stop the treatment, apply a cold compress to the area, and apply and give aftercare cooling lotion for the client to continue applying.

Burning or blistering

Recognised as a burning sensation, this is caused by the wax being too hot. Was it tested on the therapist, and a little applied to the area prior to treatment?

Refer back to the individual waxes for first aid recommendations (pages 318–319).

Swelling in the area

Recognised as the area being tender and the skin having a puffy appearance, swelling is caused by the wax having too high a temperature or by the strips being lifted off in an upward motion rather than back on themselves.

Refer back to the individual waxes for first aid recommendations.

It is also advisable to give your client an aftercare leaflet to take away and refer to, so that any potential contra-action can be avoided and maximum benefit is gained from the treatment.

> ### Remember
>
> The golden rule is: 'If in doubt – don't treat!'
>
> Always get a doctor's written approval where appropriate and keep it with the record card along with the client's signature agreeing that the treatment can go ahead.
>
> It is much better to be safe than sorry!

> ### Remember
>
> There is usually a slight reaction to hair removal and that is to be expected, but a strong reaction should not occur.

Prepare for the treatment 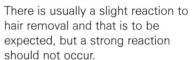 BT6.2

> ### In this outcome you will learn about
>
> - the working environment
> - personal appearance
> - sterilising tools
> - environmental conditions
> - the client's position and safety
> - hygiene
> - personal protective work wear
> - patch testing or sensitivity testing.

Most of these topics have been discussed elsewhere. Refer to the following.

- The working environment and legal, hygienic and treatment requirements: pages 23, 25–27
- Personal appearance: pages 8–10, 26, 67
- Sterilising tools: page 25–26
- Environmental conditions: pages 31–36
- The client's position and safety: page 42–46

- Hygiene: page 23–27
- Personal protective work wear: pages 32, 34, 67.

Learning about these topics will help you form a professional assessment and give the best treatment that is tailor-made to your client's requirements.

The working environment

Preparation for waxing is an essential part of the professional beauty therapist's role regardless of the treatment being carried out.

Good preparation sets the whole atmosphere of any treatment, creating a calm and efficient impression. If preparation is not in place, the client will pick up on the fact and that can detract from the benefits of the treatment.

In the case of waxing, preparation is vital. Most wax needs preheating so that the client is not kept waiting. All equipment and materials should be in place to avoid leaving the client alone.

Preparation of the working area

Many salons have designated rooms or areas that are permanently prepared for waxing with heaters and all necessary products never leaving the room.

The golden rule here is to leave everything fully prepared for the next therapist to use. This means replenishing anything that has run low, cleaning and being tidy during the treatment. It would be most off-putting for a new client to find the remains of the previous client's treatment.

The preparation of the working area should include the following.

Prepare your working area carefully

- Protective covering for the couch, so that any spillage or residue is easily removed and will not cause permanent damage.
- Where plastic sheeting is used, paper couch roll should be placed over the top. This prevents cross-infection, as the paper can be replaced easily; it also provides client comfort.
- Two waste bins, both with inner liners, should be placed behind or under the couch: one for general waste; one for wax waste – this is for contaminated materials, which will be put into a designated bin for collection by a licensed removal firm for incineration.
- The chosen heating unit for the wax type to suit the client's needs and enough wax product for the area to be treated. Obviously a lip wax requires a small amount of product, but a full leg wax will mean the heater needs to be quite full. Remember that it may take a full half-hour to heat the wax to a working temperature, so that needs to be the first job of the day. (Many salons keep a heater on all day, in anticipation of clients dropping in without appointments.)
- Antiseptic cleaner for the skin, or the manufacturer's recommended skin cleanser.
- Talcum powder.
- Fabric or paper strips which are compatible with the manufacturer's requirements for the wax chosen.
- Disposable gloves, usually vinyl with a talc-impregnated lining so they are easy to put on – refer to your individual professional body's guidelines for use.
- Disposable wooden spatulas or a suitable applicator – again refer to your professional body's guidelines (there are no spatula requirements for roller waxing, of course).
- Tissues, cotton wool and a jewellery bowl for the client.

- A pair of scissors and tweezers in a container soaking in suitable disinfectant to sterilise – the scissors may be required to trim the hair length prior to treatment, and the tweezers to remove the odd stray hair which has escaped the wax.
- After-wax lotion or oil.
- Aftercare leaflets for the client to take away.

Client positioning

- The couch should initially be placed in an upright position to allow the client to be comfortably seated, and then placed into the appropriate position for the area to be treated. A pillow covered with a towel and protected with couch roll should be used.
- Help the client into a comfortable and relaxed position. Offer a covered towel as a prop, should she or he require extra support under the knees or in the small of the back.
- Ask the client to place protective couch roll around the panty line if doing a bikini wax, or around the bra if doing an underarm wax, rather than just assuming the client would be comfortable for you to touch those areas.
- Remember, when the couch is in a semi-reclining position and the client is having the front of the legs waxed, it is very comfortable. However, you must lower the couch head so it is flat again before you ask her to turn over, otherwise she will be in a very awkward position.

> **Reality Check!**
>
> Accidents can and do happen. Advise the client not to wear her favourite expensive underwear when having a wax. Protect the client's clothes with towels and tissues. If the client is having a bikini wax prior to her holiday, she should wear her swimsuit or bikini bottom for waxing to ensure that the line is right. If not, an old pair of briefs with the same leg shape will give the correct line.

> **In the salon**
>
> Many salons have names for bikini styles of waxing. A 'Hollywood' is full and total hair removal – this is high maintenance and can be painful, with the client visiting the salon very regularly.
>
> A 'Brazilian' is not quite total removal, but a small line of pubic hair is left centrally in a vertical line. This allows for a narrow thong bikini to be worn. Some salons call this a 'Mohican', or a 'landing strip'.
>
> Remember to check which names your salon uses so you don't find you remove more hairs than your client wanted.

Patch testing or sensitivity testing

A patch test should be carried out on a clean, dry area of skin, usually on the forearm as this is hair free. Consult with your own awarding body and professional therapies federation, as they may insist you carry out a patch test on the area you are treating.

> **Remember**
>
> If a reaction is occurs, it will be noticeable as redness in the area of the patch test, which may also be itchy. This will indicate either that the wax type is not suitable for the client, or that waxing cannot take place at all.

Having heated the correct type of wax to be used for the client, test it on yourself for the correct temperature, then apply a small circle of wax to the client's forearm. Remove as for hair removal and note any immediate reaction on the skin.

Put the details onto the client's record card and ask her to monitor the result for the next 24 to 48 hours.

You must be tactful when informing the client that she is not suitable for treatment if there is an adverse reaction to the patch test. Be discreet, too, and tell her somewhere private, rather than in the middle of reception where everyone can hear.

Warm wax and roller wax operate at much lower temperatures than hot wax, so an alternative product might prevent a reaction from occurring. Another patch test will be required using the different product. If that proves satisfactory, and the client is happy, then the treatment can go ahead.

Plan the treatment

BT6.3

- aims of the treatment plan
- preparation of the client
- selecting equipment.

These topics have been discussed elsewhere. Refer to:

- Discussing and establishing treatment plans: pages 10–12, 19–21
- Preparation of the client: page 330
- Selecting equipment: 'Wax facts' page 315.

Aims of the treatment

During the consultation the therapist needs to discuss the realistic outcomes of a waxing treatment.

Unrealistic aims of waxing

It would be unrealistic to believe that:

- waxing is permanent hair removal
- waxing makes the hair growth weaken
- all the hairs grow back at the same time
- waxing lightens the hair colour
- the hairs grow back with a sharp, spiky feel to them
- waxing does not hurt.

Realistic aims of waxing

- Waxing lasts for 3-6 weeks depending on hair growth.
- As the blood supply to the hairs is increased with waxing, the hairs may grow back slightly more thick and coarse.
- The hairs grow back spasmodically as the hair growth cycle for each follicle is different.
- Waxing does not change the hair colour.
- Shaving and cutting blunts the ends of the hair, making them feel spiky; after waxing the hair grows back with its natural tapered end, feeling smooth to the touch.
- Waxing feels like a plaster being taken from the skin. Pain thresholds will vary and some clients will feel more than others.

Reality Check!

It is important to be honest with your clients, so they know what to expect. Honesty between therapist and client is part of the ethical conduct that maintains high professional standards for all beauty therapists.

Remove unwanted hair

BT6.4

In this outcome you will learn about

- application of wax
- checking hair-growth patterns
- health and safety
- applying the product
- sugaring.

Application of wax

Check this list before you apply the wax:

- Is the working area fully prepared and the wax pre-heated?
- Are you fully prepared with protective clothing and gloves?
- Have all safety and hygiene precautions been observed?
- Are manufacturers' instructions being adhered to?
- Has a full consultation been carried out?
- Can the treatment proceed with no contra-indications present?
- Has a patch test for sensitivity been carried out before the treatment?
- Has the client had a full explanation of the treatment so she or he knows what to expect?
- Has the client been fully informed with regard to aftercare and homecare?
- Has a record card been filled out for the client, or the existing one updated?
- Has the area for waxing been examined in a good light and the best method of waxing decided and agreed between the therapist and client?
- Has the area to be waxed been cleaned so it is grease-free, has it been talced, and has pre-wax lotion been applied?

Checking hair-growth patterns

The direction of your wax application will depend upon the way the hair is growing, which varies in different areas of the body.

Closely examine the direction of the hair, from the point where it comes out of the skin to its tip. Always work in the direction of the hair growth and you will get great results.

The legs

Most hair on the front of the leg along the shins grows downwards towards the foot. However, the hair along the calf muscle (gastrocnemius) often starts to grow across the leg, going sideways and downwards. This is often dictated by the pressure of clothing on the hairs.

Along the top of the thigh the hair starts to grow inwards towards the inner thigh, but the bikini line tends to grow down and inwards.

The abdomen

The hair around the navel grows upwards from the pubic hairline, and then forms a circle around the navel. You may need several small strips to completely remove the circular pattern. Be careful if the client is menstruating – she may wish to avoid the area because of pressure. Do not wax a client on the abdomen if there is a possibility she may be pregnant.

a) front of legs   b) back of legs

Direction of hair growth on legs

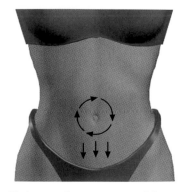

Hair growth pattern on abdomen

The arm

The hair on the forearm tends to grow sideways across the arms, rather than downwards towards the hand and wrist. It usually grows from the inner to the outer sides.

Underarm hair varies – some clients have perfect circles of hair around the pit of the arm, some have downward hair and some have hair growing sideways. Very often more than one strip is required to remove underarm hair.

The face

Hair on the upper lip tends to grow in the male pattern of a moustache, i.e. downwards from the nose towards the upper lip, with some longer hairs growing down on the side of the lip.

Chin hairs often grow straight outward or down, depending on the strength of the hair.

Health and safety

Health and safety information for the different types of waxes used in a salon is included on pages 318–323, along with potential hazards and first aid measures.

Refer to **Professional basics**, 'You, your client and the law', pages 31–47 for legislation affecting all beauty treatments.

Below are general precautions for safe practice when waxing.

- Do not have any naked flame near waxing preparations or equipment as the ingredients make them very inflammable.
- Do not have heating units near anything flammable, e.g. curtains, in case the thermostat breaks and the wax ignites.
- Do not have the heater on a glass-topped trolley, in case the glass breaks and molten wax spills.
- Do a thorough consultation, check for contra-indications and carry out a patch test prior to treating the client.
- Firmly stretch and support the skin in fleshy areas to avoid bruising, especially in the bikini and underarm areas.
- Be aware of your own professional guidelines regarding insurance cover and the use of gloves and protective clothing.
- Thorough moisturising after waxing can help to avoid the problems of ingrown hairs, which is when the hair grows back under the skin causing infection. This is always a problem with continual waxing.
- When hot waxing, never allow the wax to become too cool on the skin as it will be too brittle to remove effectively, and may cause the client a great deal of discomfort.
- With hot wax always test the temperature on yourself and carry out a small patch test on the client to avoid giving a burn.
- With organic wax do not allow too much of a build-up on the muslin strip as this can cause undue lifting of the skin during removal.
- With organic wax it is important to keep the angle of pull on the muslin strip horizontal to the skin's surface, as the hairs can break off at the skin's surface and bruising can occur in fleshy areas.

A thin layer of wax is more effective than a thick layer on a strip. Too much wax builds up on itself and does not coat the hairs. It is therefore less effective.

For maximum comfort and minimum embarrassment give the client lots of towels to protect her modesty, especially with a bikini wax. Plenty of protection will make the client feel more secure and means that the therapist can manoeuvre her into good

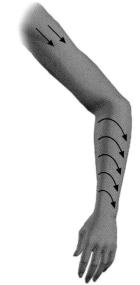

Direction of hair growth on the arm

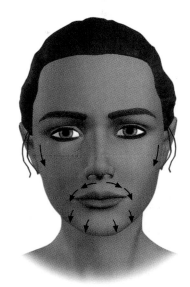

Direction of hair growth on the face

positions for easy and effective removal. Ensure that the waxing area has adequate ventilation, especially with hot wax, which can give off fumes when first heated.

Risk assessment for hot and warm wax equipment

Refer to **Professional basics** for a complete discussion of risk assessment.

Hazard: only look for hazards that you could reasonably expect to result in significant harm under the conditions in your workplace. Use the following examples as a guide:

- **Fire** (e.g. from electrical flex or lead)

- **Burning of equipment** (through low wax level in the tank)

- **Burns to skin** (not testing wax temperature first on self)

- **Ejection of materials** (spitting hot wax)

- **Electricity** (e.g. poor wiring)

- **Manual handling** (spillage possible if moving when in liquid form)

- **Falling machinery** (if not securely positioned on a trolley)

- **Contamination** (poor waste disposal of contaminated wax strips)

- **Cross-infection** (ignoring possible contra-indications)

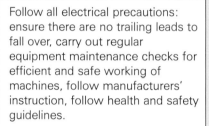

Remember

Follow all electrical precautions: ensure there are no trailing leads to fall over, carry out regular equipment maintenance checks for efficient and safe working of machines, follow manufacturers' instruction, follow health and safety guidelines.

Many of the topics in BT6 are covered in the **Professional basics** section, or in G1 'Ensure your own actions reduce risks to health and safety'.

Applying the product

Leg wax

The lower leg is a simple area to treat as the hair growth can be seen easily. The hairs usually grow towards the ankle on the front of the leg, but may go slightly sideways on the calf. Hair growth may be coarse if the client has shaved the area and results are usually good as the hair growth in the area is strong. Moving the leg around slightly will allow access to the ankle hair if the growth pattern is not straight down. The client may ask for the toes to be waxed too.

1 The client can be lying down, or sitting up for the front of the legs. Remember, though, to put the couch back into a flat position before the client is turned over for the backs of the legs.

2 It is important that the client's clothing is protected, so provide a towel for cover. Be aware of protecting the client's modesty if repositioning is required.

3 Cleanse the area and prepare for waxing following the usual sanitising procedure.

4 Start from the ankle and work up the leg systematically.

5 To keep the skin taut at the knee, ask the client to bend it.

6 Turn the client over (lowering the couch) and follow the same routine with the back of the leg. Pay special attention to the hair growth, which may be not straight down.

7   Do not apply wax to the back of the knee. There are usually no hairs present here, but if there are a few, then tweeze them.

8   If completing a full leg wax continue up the thigh at the front and then turn the client over, again paying attention to the direction of growth.

Step-by-step warm wax application for legs

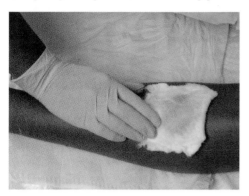

1 Clean the whole area to be waxed with a suitable antiseptic wipe or hibitane on damp cotton wool.

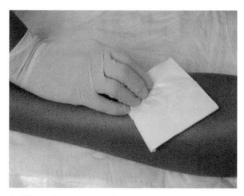

2 Blot the area with a tissue to ensure the skin is dry and grease free.

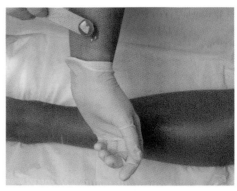

3 Test the wax on your inner arm to make certain you will not burn the client.

4 To avoid cross-infection drizzle the wax onto another spatula – it will also help you check that the consistency is workable.

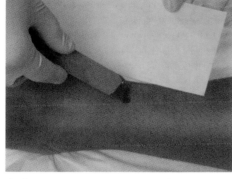

5 If temperature is acceptable to you, apply a small area onto the legs to check with the client that the temperature is tolerable for her.

6 Following the hair growth, i.e. downward, apply a thin even strip of wax to the leg, approximately the width of the paper strip.

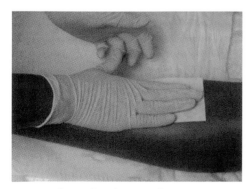

7 Press down firmly over the wax strip, to ensure all the hairs are fully attached to the strip.

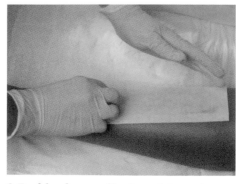

8 Peel back a small edge of the strip to hold onto.

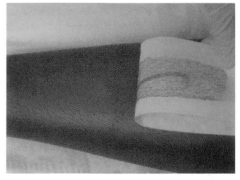

9 Holding the ankle, grip the wax strip edge and pull the strip off. It is almost a peeling back of the strip, but it must be quick, to minimise pain.

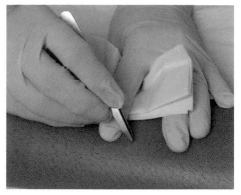

10 Any missed hairs, too short for the wax to pick, can be plucked out. Sterilise the tweezers first.

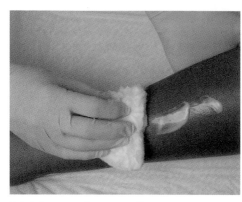

11 After-wax lotion will remove any wax residue.

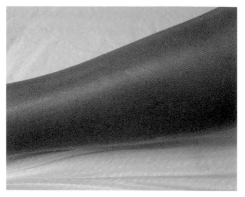

12 The finished result should be a moisturised, hair-free front of leg.

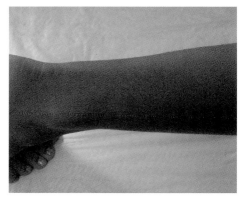

13 Ask the client to turn over – remember to ensure you put the back of the bed down first. Repeat the cleansing and blotting process.

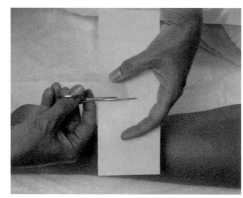

14 As the hairs grow in different directions, you will need to cut the wax strips into manageable sizes.

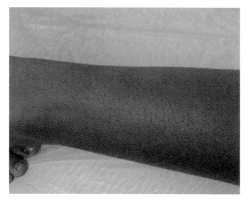

15 Check the direction of the hair growth, which may be diagonal as shown here. Remember to test the wax again – first on yourself and then on your client.

NB Some awarding bodies only expect gloves to be worn if there is a danger of drawing bodily fluids, for example, underarm or bikini line. Therefore, it may be permissible to wax legs without gloves.

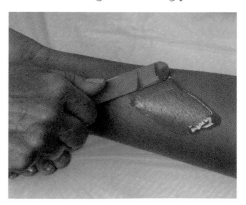

16 Apply a thin even strip of wax to the leg, following the hair growth, i.e. diagonally as shown here, and repeat the process as for front of leg.

Warm wax is applied in a thin film using a spatula in the direction of hair growth with a firm press, without hurting the client.

1   Test the wax prior to use on the inside of the wrist. If it is at a comfortable temperature for the therapist, it should be fine for the client, but also test a small patch on the wrist or ankle of the client depending upon the area to be waxed.

2   Take up a manageable amount of wax on the spatula and twist it so that it stays on the end. Remove any excess on the side of the pot. In the other hand have a folded tissue covering the palm to catch any drips from the spatula and any spillage during the transfer from pot to client.

3   Transfer the wax onto the skin following the hair growth, holding the spatula at a 90° angle, and spread a strip-sized width of wax onto the hairs. (As skill levels increase and practice is gained, you will be able to apply and quickly remove longer strips.) Support the skin with the free hand.

4   Firmly press the fabric or paper strip and rub down several times to bond the wax to the hairs in the direction of the hair growth. Leave a small flap free at the end of the strip with which to grip the strip for removal.

5   Using the flap, grip firmly, stretch the skin slightly with the free hand and pull the strip away from the skin, going back against the hair growth, with the strip almost going back on itself, in one swift movement. Try not to lift upward as that may cause skin damage. The swiftness of the hand really does make a difference to the pain the client will feel. Do not hesitate, or stop halfway through, as that is just prolonging the agony.

6   Apply a little pressure to the area with your hand to help reduce the tingling and pain, which occurs after strip removal.

7   Work in a logical sequence over the whole area to be treated taking care not to miss any hairs, but avoid overlapping the strips as that will mean the skin may be sore in that area.

8   The strip will last for several removals before it becomes too laden with wax to pick up any more hairs. When that stage is reached, fold the wax strip in on itself so that the clean side is on the outside and place it in the bin with a liner that is designated for contaminated waste. Use a fresh strip for the next removal and continue.

Remember

Check with your own professional body with regard to the use of spatulas. Most state that once the spatula has come into contact with the skin, it has become contaminated and should be thrown away and a new one used for the next application.

In the salon

Some manufacturers make strips for use with water-soluble wax. If the correct washing instructions are followed the fabric strips are boiled and re-used.

9   After the waxing is complete, if any stubborn, stray hairs remain, they should be tweezed out with a sterile pair of tweezers. With warm wax it may be possible to reapply a strip over an area with lots of hairs remaining, as there is little skin reaction at low temperatures. This is not advisable with the higher temperature of hot wax.

10 Apply afterwax lotion liberally and go over aftercare with the client.

11 Clearing up can now take place. This is as important as the rest of the treatment as cross-infection can occur through the contaminated waste. Dispose of used spatulas, wax strips, gloves and couch roll in the appropriate bags (unless the strips are to be used again).

12 Clean the equipment with the recommended manufacturer's cleaner and clean the plastic couch covering. Wash hands and begin with the next client.

Step-by-step warm wax application for eyebrows

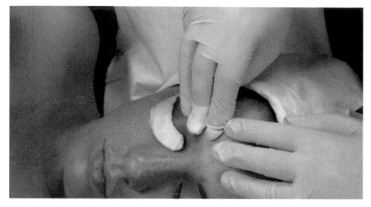

1 Cover the closed eye with a damp cotton wool round and cleanse the eyebrow area with suitable cleanser. Cut up some small pieces of paper or material strips.

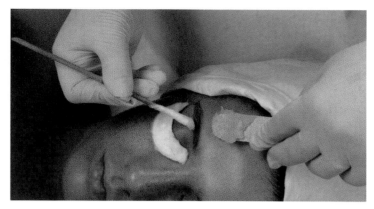

2 Decant petroleum jelly onto a spatula, using a covered orange stick; apply to hairs you do not want to remove. This barrier stops the wax sticking to the hairs.

3 Remember to test the wax on your forearm, before applying to the client. You do not want to burn the delicate eye area.

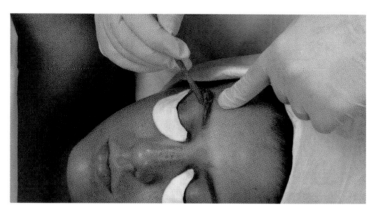

4 Apply a small amount of wax to the area under the eyebrow, working in the direction of the hair growth. Take care not to dribble wax onto the client's face.

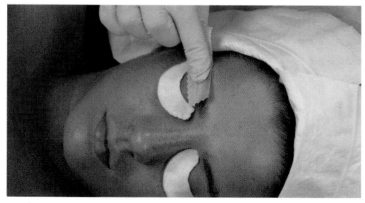

5 Using a small piece of wax strip, press onto the arch, under the eyebrow. Smooth over with your finger, to ensure all of the hairs are stuck to the strip.

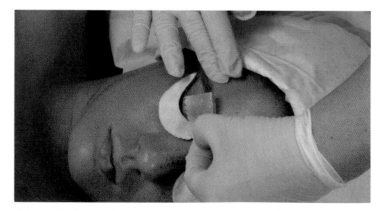

6 Stretch the eyebrow. Remove hairs against the hair growth i.e. working inwards towards nose. The movement needs to be quick to avoid pain, and it is like peeling back on the strip. Apply after-wax lotion.

1 Cleanse the eyebrow area, having removed make-up, and follow all the usual sanitising procedures.

2 Cut a large wax strip into smaller manageable strips.

3 Discuss the shape required with the client taking into account face shape and the direction of hair growth.

4 Apply a suitable barrier cream to the eyebrows not being removed - this will prevent the wax adhering to them and avoid accidental total eyebrow removal.

5 Apply a small amount of wax to the hairs being removed, following the direction of hair growth (an orange stick may be a more suitably sized applicator than a spatula).

6 Press the small strip firmly to the skin.

7 Remove the strip against the hair growth and continue to shape the eyebrow as required.

8 Use a hand mirror to consult the client at every stage, and be flexible to client suggestions.

9 Follow aftercare and home care routines.

Step-by-step warm wax application for the lip and chin

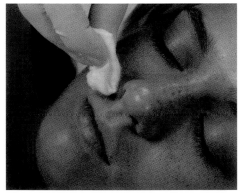

1 Cleanse the upper lip area. The skin should be clean and grease-free. Blot if necessary.

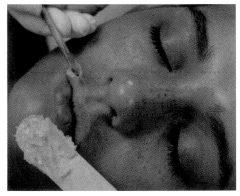

2 Decant petroleum jelly onto a spatula, using a covered orange stick, and cover the lip up to the lip line.

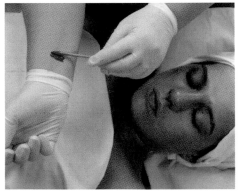

3 Remember to test the wax on your forearm, before applying to the client.

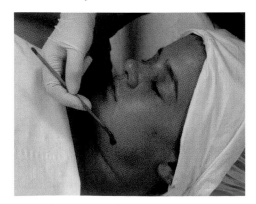

4 Patch test a small drop of wax near the area, to test the temperature is acceptable to the client.

5 Build up a good layer of wax on upper lip. Ask the client to smile slightly to help stretch the skin. Remove as for all hot wax application and apply after-wax lotion.

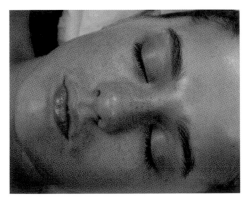

6 The finished result.

Step-by-step warm wax application for underarms

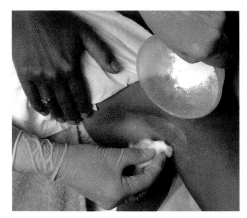

1 Protect the client's clothing with couch roll and cleanse the area. A light dusting of talcum powder will absorb any residue perspiration and make the hair stand out from the skin.

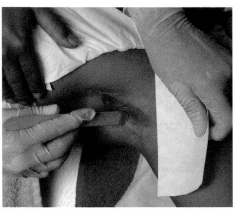

2 After testing on yourself, apply the wax, going with the hair growth. If hairs are diagonal then go in that direction.

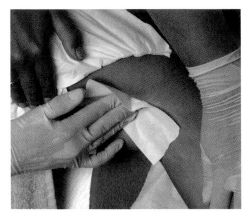

3 Firmly press the strip down to bond the hairs to it.

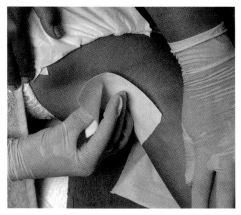

4 Stretch the armpit area and, if necessary, ask the client to help, with her free hand.

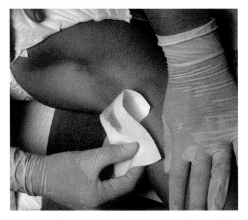

5 Grip the edge of the strip and quickly and firmly remove the strip against the direction of hair growth.

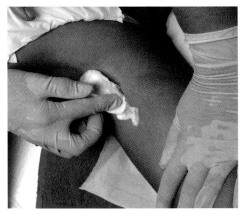

6 Should any blood spots appear, apply light pressure with a clean tissue and then wipe them away. Apply after-wax lotion.

1   The client's armpit should be stretched and extended as far as possible.

2   The client should be in a semi-reclining position or flat down on the bed, depending upon client preference.

3   Follow the standard procedures for cleansing and hygiene.

4   Study the hair growth carefully as underarm hair can be very diverse in its growth, and some underarm hair can grow in circles.

5   Small strips should be used, and the hair may need trimming before treatment.

6   Remember to protect the bra with couch roll or tissues.

7 The skin can be extremely delicate and there is a danger that infection may occur causing glands to swell.

8 Never treat the underarm if mastitis is suspected.

9 Aftercare and homecare are extremely important for underarm treatment.

Treatment time guide for warm wax

Area	Time
Eyebrows	10 minutes
Facial (lip and chin)	15 minutes
Full leg	45 minutes
Half leg (up to knee)	20–30 minutes
Underarm	15 minutes
Bikini line	5 minutes
Forearm (wrist to elbow)	20 minutes

The above is a guide only – the time it takes to complete a wax treatment will depend upon the amount of hair growth, how strong the growth is, and how experienced the therapist is. In time and with experience, timings can greatly improve as the confidence and judgement of the therapist improves.

However, it is important to remember to be cost effective when waxing with both time and use of materials.

Remember

The abdomen is also suitable for warm wax hair removal, although it is not a range in NVQ Level 2. The same application techniques would apply.

Step-by-step hot wax application for legs

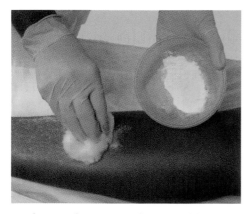

1 Cleanse the area with a suitable cleanser, to make sure that the skin is dry and grease free. Apply a light dusting of talcum powder – this will make the hairs stand up.

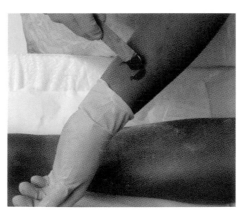

2 Test the hot wax on your forearm before applying any to the client.

3 Decant a good amount of hot wax from the pot onto another spatula, to avoid contamination. The consistency of wax should be like soft treacle.

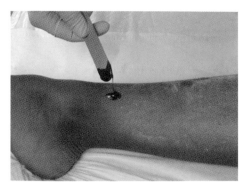

4 Test a small patch of wax on the client, to avoid burning the skin.

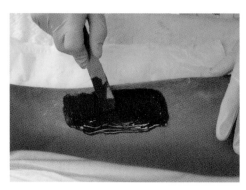

5 Working against the hair growth to begin with, apply the wax in a figure of eight shape. As you keep applying, you will build up a thick patch of wax.

6 When the wax layer looks set, pressure from the knuckles will help bond the hot wax to the hairs. The wax takes on a matt finish as it cools.

7 Using the same techniques as with a wax strip, flick a lip up, and gripping firmly, quickly remove the patch of wax – against the direction of hair growth.

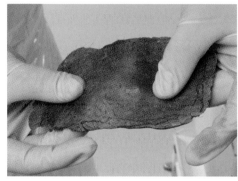

8 The hairs should be clearly visible, embedded in the wax strip you have removed.

Hot wax application is a skill that needs more practice than warm waxing, but many beauty therapists trained in hot wax prefer to use it. As the temperature is higher, the removal of strong coarse hairs is very effective and it gives a nice clean finish.

Unlike warm wax, hot wax is applied as a thicker layer, which is built up by firstly going with the hair growth and then against the hair growth, until sufficient thickness for removal has been achieved. The procedure is as follows.

1   Test the wax on yourself on the inner wrist. Then, if the temperature is comfortable, test a small patch on the client on the area to be worked upon. If the client confirms that she is happy with the feel of it, commence the treatment.

2   Look closely at the hair growth in the area, as this affects both application and removal.

3   Gather a manageable amount of wax onto the spatula, and keep the spatula twisting to avoid drips, wiping any excess onto the edge of the heater. A tissue in the free hand, held underneath the spatula, will catch any drips on the way from heater to couch.

4   The wax should be the consistency of icing ready to go on a cake: spreadable but not too thick. Apply the wax, and build up several layers, working firstly against and then with the hair growth. Ensure that the edges are quite thick too, as when the wax is removed, the edges may break off if too thinly applied.

5 Try not to make the strips too large as this makes them difficult to remove. Two or three applications should give a covering about 3 mm thick. Avoid the temptation to apply too many layers, as the wax will just build up on itself and not adhere to the hairs.

6 The trick is to be quick, and apply several patches in one go. As the first patch is setting slightly, the second and third can be applied. Do not let any of them dry out totally on the skin, as they will become brittle and break off, and will hurt the client when removed.

7 A thick lip on the edges of each patch will allow a firm grip when removing.

8 As each strip starts to set slightly, press with the fingers. It should feel dry but still supple to the touch, and the lip can be flipped up.

9 Grip the lip you have created and with the other hand pull the skin slightly away from the wax patch to minimise client discomfort. Be quick and firm, and swiftly remove the wax against the direction of hair growth.

10 Immediately soothe the area by applying pressure to it. Quickly move onto the next patch as that will be setting.

11 Fold each wax strip in on itself, with the hairs inside, and put them into the lined bin for disposal into the collectable waste bin.

12 Should there be any small remains of wax, press the larger patch over the area and the remains should be picked up easily.

13 Work methodically all over the area to be waxed in a pattern, so that all hairs are removed, but avoid overlapping and therefore over-waxing.

14 Any hairs that have escaped may be tweezed away, and the result should be clean and clear. The skin will be slightly pinker than with warm waxing because of the higher temperature.

15 Aftercare and homecare advice can be given. A soothing after-wax lotion can be applied, and a nice gesture is to provide the client with a small sample-size aftercare lotion to take away and apply at home.

16 Clearing up can now take place. This is as important as the rest of the treatment, as cross-infection can occur through the contaminated waste. Dispose of used spatulas, wax, gloves and couch roll in the appropriate bags.

17 Clean the equipment with the manufacturer's recommended cleaner and clean the plastic couch covering. Wash hands and begin with the next client.

Treatment time guide for hot wax

Area	Time	Area	Time
Eyebrows	10–15 minutes	Underarm	15 minutes
Facial	10–15 minutes	Bikini line	15–20 minutes
Full leg	45–60 minutes	Forearm	20 minutes
Half leg	20–30 minutes		

Remember

Some of the older wax heaters have a second tub. This was because the used wax was reheated and passed through a small filter, a bit like a sieve, and then reused. This is no longer acceptable practice and is not hygienic. Ignore the second tub on the machine.

Remember

This treatment guide is very dependent upon the skill of the therapist. Hot wax needs to be nurtured up to the correct working temperature and consistency, and then used quickly.

It may cool down and start to solidify, in which case the heater needs turning up, which sometimes causes the wax to get too hot. Time is then spent waiting for it to cool down to a good consistency, and the client is kept waiting. Then the whole cycle starts again.

This has a great effect on treatment times, which is why hot wax is considered to need more training and a higher skill level.

Sugaring

What is it?

Sugaring is the removal of hairs using a paste. This is has been used for hair removal for centuries in Eastern tradition and has become very popular in salons in the West.

Many people prefer this method of hair removal, as they find it less painful than waxing.

What is it made of?

Sugar paste is made up of sugar, water, citric acid (lemon juice) and oil with other natural ingredients. Most manufacturers of sugar paste will not reveal the proportions of their recipe, so it does have to be purchased from a sugaring wholesaler. It can be used in either a paste or as strip sugar.

What are the hazards?

Sugar paste ingredients are completely natural and form no threat to health in their natural form. However, as the product needs to be heated for use, great care should be taken as burns could occur.

What do I do in the event of an accident?

- In the case of burns flood the area immediately with cold water for a minimum of ten minutes (twenty minutes for burns to the eyes). Cover with a sterile, non-fluffy dressing and seek medical aid.
- If ingested, seek medical advice.
- To avoid accidents only a person who has been fully trained in the art of sugaring should use sugar paste.

How do I handle and store it?

Most suppliers send out their products in firm plastic tubs. Like warm wax, the product can be heated in the tub.

Store sugar paste in a cool, dry place, and keep containers airtight to avoid the product degenerating. The normal shelf life is about 12 months, but if looked after, it may last up to two years.

The main reason for product deterioration is continual over-heating.

Types of treatment paste

Soft paste

Soft paste often needs no adjusting, especially if the weather or the practitioner's hands are warm. If the paste becomes wet and sticky, a little hard paste can be added to absorb the moisture. If the paste becomes hard, add steam or water to adjust. Soft paste is ideal to be used with strips.

Super-soft paste

Super-soft paste needs less time to heat and is ideal for use by practitioners with cool hands. It often needs no adjusting, especially if the weather or the practitioners' hands are warm. If the paste becomes wet and sticky, a little hard paste can be added to absorb the moisture. If the paste becomes hard, add steam or boiled water to adjust. Super-soft paste is also ideal to be used with strips.

Waxing

Preparation – you, your working area and the client.

⬇

Two waste bins with liners.

⬇

Choose wax most suitable for client and area. Heat it up half an hour before appointment.

⬇

On the trolley:

- antiseptic cleaner
- talc
- fabric or paper strips
- disposable gloves
- wooden spatulas
- tissues and cotton wool
- jewellery bowl
- scissors and tweezers
- after-wax lotion
- record card

⬇

Consultation, with record card. Fully explain treatment.

⬇

Wash hands.

⬇

Test on self and patch test on client.

⬇

Area to be clean and grease free. Commence treatment.

⬇

Afterwax – wash hands.

⬇

Aftercare and homecare.

⬇

Dispose of used spatulas, etc. Clean working area.

⬇

Wash hands.

⬇

Start again with next client.

Firm Paste

Firm paste is darker in colour and takes longer to heat. It is ideal for use by practitioners with hot hands and in very hot weather. It often needs adjusting, especially if the weather or the practitioner's hands are cool. If the paste becomes hard, adjust with steam or boiled water. Firm paste is not recommended for use with strips.

Hard Paste

Hard paste is darker in colour and takes longer to heat. It needs adjusting within a few minutes of use and is not recommended for use with strips, as it has to be at a higher temperature.

Extra Hard Paste

Extra hard paste is the darkest in colour and takes the longest to heat. It needs adjusting within a few minutes of use and so is not recommended for use with strips. This paste is mainly used abroad in hot humid climates.

Benefits and effects of sugaring

- As the product is made up of natural ingredients and the working temperature of the paste is low, it is very effective on a more sensitive skin as well as some skins that would react to waxing and would therefore be contra-indicated. Clients do say that it feels less painful than warm waxing.
- Sugar paste is water-soluble so less inclined to stick to everything. It is very easy to wipe down both the skin and other surfaces.
- Very short hairs can be removed as the paste grips the hairs and not the skin, so there is not the wait for re-growth as there is with waxing.
- Sugaring is very successful on facial hair as the hairs are pulled cleanly out. The soft vellus hair is left intact whilst the coarser hairs are removed – this leaves the face with a natural look.

Strip sugaring

Strip sugaring is applied in the same way as warm waxing. It has all the benefits and effects of sugaring, as well as the advantage that you can heat it in a microwave. Those in mobile businesses favour its use.

Care must be taken when heating strip sugaring in a microwave as the centre of the tub is much hotter than the outside and there is a risk of burning.

Pre-care for sugaring

Sugaring sticks best to the hairs when there is no grease on the skin, and when the hairs are of a good length to grip.

If a regular client is booking for a sugaring treatment, she can be gently reminded of the following; if the client is new, these considerations need to be discussed for maximum results.

24–48 hours before treatment:

- **No** body lotion applied to area
- **No** bubble baths
- **No** body or baby oil

A least three days before treatment:

- **No** shaving of the hairs

> ### Remember
>
> Most sugaring wholesalers will supply the complete kit for strip sugaring. There are lots of complementary accessories available, should the therapist wish to purchase them.
>
> It is advisable to carry out a little research and shop around for the best purchases, for both value for money and reliability of aftercare service. Comparing prices and wholesalers will give good indications as to which manufacturer to choose.

It will be too late to explain these considerations to the client, once she is in the salon expecting to be treated.

The receptionist should also be aware of the expected pre-care for sugaring, so that if a new client makes enquiries about sugaring, she can be primed before the salon visit. The last thing a salon needs is an angry or disappointed customer.

Step-by-step sugar depilation

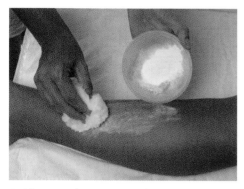

1 Cleanse the area, so that it is clean, dry and grease free. A light dusting of talcum powder can be applied to the area.

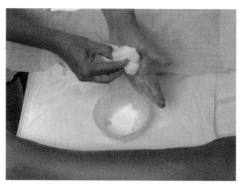

2 Apply talcum powder to your palms to ensure they remain free from grease and perspiration.

3 Test sugar paste temperature on yourself, on the inner wrist, to avoid burning the client.

4 Decant a small amount of sugar paste from the pot onto another spatula, to avoid contamination. The consistency of the paste should be like soft treacle.

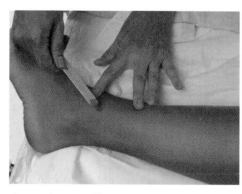

5 Test this small patch of paste on the client, to avoid burning the skin.

6 Draw off some of the paste onto your fingertips. (Cool hands are best for this.)

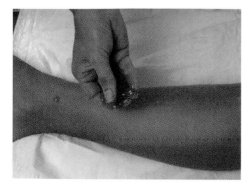

7 Using a circular wrist and hand motion, begin to work the paste between the fingers.

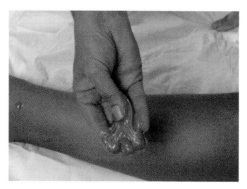

8 The paste begins to cool and become more treacle-like in consistency. It is now ready to use.

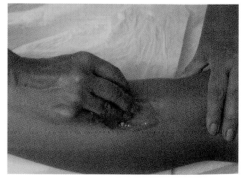

9 Firmly spread the paste onto the hairs, keeping the skin taut in the area.

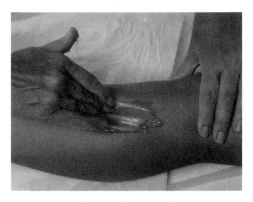

10 Drag and spread outwards, pressing as you go.

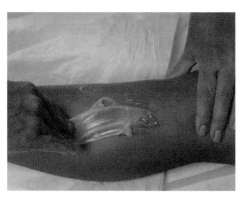

11 Spread the paste in the direction of hair growth.

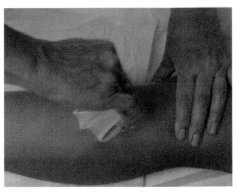

12 Begin flicking the edge of the paste inwards towards the centre of your patch, just as in waxing, but without leaving the skin.

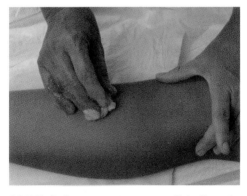

13 Work the paste into a small ball and remove.

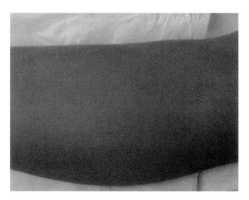

14 The successful result should be a hair-free, clean area, with no remaining paste on the leg.

Items required

- Sufficient sugar and a heating unit to pre-heat the sugar to the required temperature.
- Paper and plastic sheeting to protect the couch and surrounding area.
- Paper to protect the client's clothing.
- Antiseptic lotion to cleanse and degrease the skin.
- Talcum powder to dry the skin and lift the hair.
- Cotton wool for the application of products.
- Spatulas.
- Tissues.
- Scissors to cut long hairs or strips (in autoclave).
- Tweezers for the removal of stubborn hairs (in autoclave).
- Soothing lotion.
- Barrier cream.
- Orange stick.
- Two bins with bin liners.
- Disposable gloves and a protective apron.
- Pillow.
- After-sugaring lotion.
- Cleanser.

- Towels.
- Strips of muslin, or, fibre.
- Jewellery bowl.

Preparation of the couch

- Cover the base of the couch with plastic sheeting, and dispose of this after use.
- Place paper tissue over the top of the sheeting where the client will lie.
- Put the couch in an upright position with a pillow, towel and tissue for hygiene.

Preparation of trolley

- Wipe over the whole area with antiseptic lotion.
- Place the wax heater on the top of the trolley and position it away from the client. Ensure there are no trailing wires.
- Make sure all products required are on the trolley and to hand. This promotes a professional image and saves time.

Preparation of client

- Check for contra-indications to prevent any harm to the client and operator.
- Examine the area and note which way the hairs are growing.
- Explain the treatment to relax the client and prepare her for the feeling.
- For leg sugaring, remove the lower garments (skirt, trousers, etc.). Place a modesty towel over the lap with protective paper tissue.
- For underarm sugaring remove the client's upper garments. Place a modesty towel around the upper chest with protective tissue.
- For bikini sugaring remove the lower garment and ask the client to place a folded tissue each side of her briefs.
- For facial sugaring cover the client's upper half with a towel and paper tissues.
- Wipe the area to be treated with antiseptic or cleanser, and toner if working on the face, to remove dirt and grease enabling the wax to adhere to the skin and hair.
- Ensure the client is in a comfortable position for the area to be treated.
- Make sure all the surrounding area is protected with paper towels.
- Apply a fine dusting of talc to the area. This dries and lifts the hairs away from the skin so that the sugar can get a firm hold on the hairs and remove them successfully.

Areas to sugar

There are many areas which can be treated:

- eyebrows
- upper lip
- abdomen
- chin
- toes
- bikini line
- face
- underarm
- legs.

Discretion must be used when discussing areas to treat. Allow your client to tell you the areas she requires to be treated; you may have different opinions.

Consultation

Before starting treatment it is necessary to discuss certain contra-indications with your client. These points should be noted on the record card and kept in a safe place for future reference (refer to the **Professional basics** section, pages 17–18).

Contra-indications

- **varicose veins/ulcers** – sugaring would aggravate the condition
- **defective circulation** from **diabetes** – the skin is easily bruised and damaged
- **skin diseases** – cross-infection could occur
- **cuts, abrasions, recent scar tissue** – sugaring might worsen the problem and cause cross-infection
- **stings or sepsis** – sugaring might cross-infect or cause client discomfort
- **warts or hairy moles** – protect with barrier cream
- **hyper sensitive skin** (due to wind or sunburn) – the client might experience discomfort
- **high blood pressure** – circulation problems might occur
- **areas of discomfort to client**, e.g. bruises
- **recent hemorrhage or operation**.

> **Remember**
>
> The golden rule is: if you are unsure about whether there is a problem, request a physician's approval.

Hygiene and sterilisation

Two important points to follow during treatment are:

- Disposable gloves must be worn.
- Sugar paste must be disposed of after use and not reused.

This is to avoid the spread of infections.

Other health and safety precautions are as follows.

- Serum may be excreted from the skin along with small amounts of blood. Students are strongly advised not to touch such areas and to ask the client to treat the affected area.
- Cotton wool, tissues, spatulas and wax should be disposed of in a sealed dustbin liner in the main bin.
- Tweezers and scissors should be sterilised in an autoclave.
- Antiseptic lotion should be used to sanitise the area to be treated, the treatment area, trolley and equipment.
- During hot wax treatment, scrape residue wax onto a large spatula, not onto the sides of the machine.
- Refer to Professional basics, 'You, your client and the law'.

Safety precautions

Certain rules must be followed to ensure client and operator safety.

- During sugaring, have folded tissues in one hand to catch drips to prevent them dropping onto the client.
- Check the machine, wires, plugs, etc.
- Do not rest the machine on a glass-topped trolley.
- Do not heat the paste near inflammable materials.
- Do not over-heat the paste.
- Always test the temperature in relation to the client's tolerance.
- Protect the client's clothing.
- Do not re-apply immediately after removing a strip.
- Explain the procedure thoroughly and warn the client of a possible skin reaction.
- Explain the aftercare procedure.

- Ensure all equipment is clean and sterile.
- Do not leave heating paste unattended.
- Do not heat paste too near the client.
- Check contra-indications.
- The therapist should be familiar with the machine, e.g. what temperature is required for the treatment.
- Apply barrier cream to moles and birthmarks.
- Make sure you avoid the area behind the knee.
- All heaters must comply with British Safety Standards.

Testing paste temperature

Once the therapist has tested the paste, test a small amount on the client to check tolerance and also to prepare her for the feeling. This is usually done on the inner ankle.

Contra-actions

You must stop sugaring if a treatment is applied and the area reacts by:
- swelling
- blisters
- becoming sore.

A normal reaction to sugaring is:

- slight heat builds up in the area
- blotchy red patches appear
- the area is a little itchy.

These reactions must only be mild. Any other reaction would prevent treatment from either being carried out or being continued.

Application of sugaring

1   Take up a manageable amount of paste, and if it needs it, adjust the consistency with a few drops of water. Mould it to make it elastic enough to use.

2   With the spreading technique, massage the paste onto the area with fingers and thumb. The skin will need to be stretched and supported, as in a wax application.

3   Make sure the edges are thickly enough applied to make a lip for easy removal.

4   Remove the paste with a firm flicking motion without hurting the client.

5   Work methodically over the whole area to be treated, so that all hairs are removed.

6   Using the antiseptic wipes and soothing lotion that is compatible with the product used, wipe over the area.

7   Provide aftercare and homecare advice.

Top and bottom lip area

1   Work from the corner of the mouth, towards the centre of the lip in small strips.

2   Ask the client to open her mouth or twist to the opposite side before applying paste against the hair growth.

3   Place a hand on top of the area to soothe it.

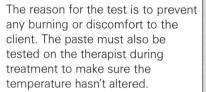

Remember

The reason for the test is to prevent any burning or discomfort to the client. The paste must also be tested on the therapist during treatment to make sure the temperature hasn't altered.

4   Move to the other side of the couch and repeat on the opposite side.

5   A second application may be necessary.

6   Some manufacturers recommend diluted witch hazel be applied after treatment on this area to soothe it.

Step-by-step sugaring for lip and chin

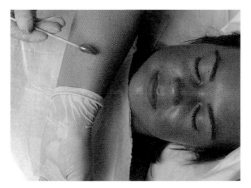

1 Prepare the client by covering the clothes, and clean the area to be sugared. Patch test the paste on yourself for correct temperature.

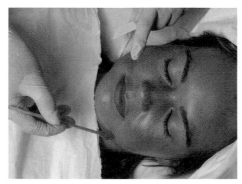

2 Test the paste on the client prior to application – remember her temperature tolerance may be different from yours.

3 Work from the outer edge of the upper lips inwards.

4 Use a small length of paper or fabric wax strip to help grip the hairs. Press down to bond the hairs to the strip.

5 Using the same removal technique as for waxing the upper lip, quickly remove the strip – avoiding contact with the nose.

6 Carry out the same procedure on the other side of the upper lip, and apply after-sugar lotion.

Chin and jaw line

1   Use strips if the hair is long; if too long, trim with scissors.

2   Treat as for the top lip, using wider strips working first against and then with the hair growth.

3   If the hair is strong, apply worked paste and remove it strip by strip.

4   Ask the client to lift her neck and use her thumb and index finger to pull the skin taut. (Cover a maximum of three times.)

Neck

1   Work by hand, unless the hair is particularly strong.

2   Work first against the growth and then with the growth.

3   Witch hazel may be applied after sugaring to prevent the skin from drying.

Underarms

Step-by-step sugaring for the underarms

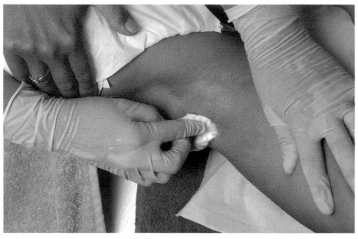

1 As with the procedure for warm wax application on the underarm, protect the clothing, cleanse the area and make sure the skin is dry and grease free.

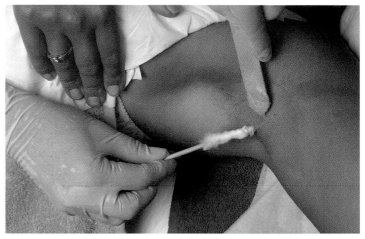

2 Look for skin tags or moles in the armpit and, should you find one, cover with petroleum jelly to avoid causing any damage.

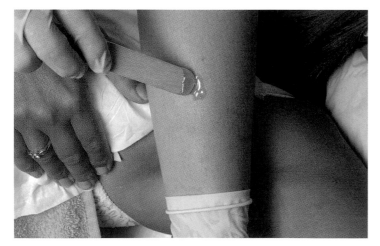

3 Test the paste on yourself.

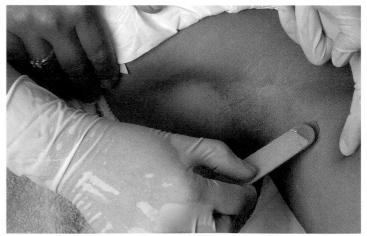

4 Apply a test patch on the client and remove in the same way as for warm wax, following the direction of hair growth. Pluck any stray hairs out and apply after-sugar lotion.

1   Look at the direction of hair growth and check how to support the area for maximum effect, asking the client to help keep the underarm skin taut.

2   Work from the elbow to the breast; apply the paste against hair growth with the inside of the index finger, which could be in a different direction if stripping. Avoid dipping and bumps in the skin.

3   Gloves should be worn.

4   Take a strip and press firmly leaving room at the ends to flick.

5   Hold away from this point with your fingernails and flick forwards.

6   Always flick long and low, not forgetting to place a hand on the skin after treatment.

7   Then work from the breast to the elbow if necessary, still with the client's support.

8   Treat the other side in the same way.

9   Dry the area and remove any remaining hairs with tweezers and a pad.

10 Apply after-sugaring lotion using gentle massage techniques.

11 Give aftercare advice.

Eyebrows

Treat as for warm waxing.

Lower legs

1   Prepare as for other sugaring areas. The client may wish to have the feet and toes included.

2   Treat the ankles in small flicks in both directions.

3   Treat the knees first against, then with the hair line, then from the side of the knee, and then from the opposite side of the couch.

4   Ask the client to place her leg flat and treat the side of the knee asking for the client's assistance, treating first against then towards hair growth.

5   Treat in rows from the ankle to the knee, first against and then with hair growth

6   Always start with the backs of the legs, with the ankle flexed and with short flicks.

7   Give aftercare and homecare advice as usual.

Aftercare and homecare

Once you have finished an area you must soothe it with a lotion before commencing another area. This can be done with after-sugar lotion or cream spread over the area with cotton wool.

The client should also follow the guidelines below for 24 hours after she has left the salon:

- Do not take a hot bath or shower.
- Do not sunbathe or use a sun bed.
- Do not use perfumed products on the area (body lotion, deodorant, make-up, perfume).

> **Remember**
>
> Sugaring, like hot waxing, is a skill that develops over many hours of practice. All skills that include a certain amount of dexterity take time. Practice makes perfect and treatment times will improve with experience.

The bleaching agent then mixes with the hydrogen peroxide and oxygen is released. The oxygen that enters the cortex oxidises the melanin to oxymelanin, which bleaches out the colour.

Contra-indications to bleaching

In a good light, cleanse the area to be bleached and look for:

- open or broken skin
- the presence of infection or disease
- moles or warts
- recent sunburn
- recent scar tissue
- healing skin, i.e. scabs
- swelling or unrecognised inflammation
- recent heat treatment or sun bed treatment
- eye infections, such as sties, etc.
- loss of pigment present already in the skin
- over-pigmentation of the skin colour of the area
- failure of the patch test.

The patch test is carried out in a similar way to an eyelash tint patch test.

Cleanse an area in the elbow and apply a small amount of the mixed bleach product. Leave for five minutes, or for as long as the manufacturer's instructions state, and remove the bleach with damp cotton wool. Over the next 24 hours the client must check for any adverse reaction to the bleach and report back before the treatment can be carried out.

It is likely that a reaction will occur almost immediately if there is to be one. A burning or stinging sensation with redness and itchiness are common. Remove the bleach immediately and place a cool compress to the area.

Safety precautions for bleaching

Please refer to the COSHH regulations for first aid and safety on pages 35 and 75. Also refer to the **Professional basics** section, 'You, your client and the law' for employee's responsibilities under the Health and Safety at Work Act (page 31).

Step-by-step bleaching for the forearms

> **Remember**
>
> Because of the strong nature of the ingredients in bleach, always do a patch test prior to the treatment for the client's well-being and the therapist's protection.

> **Remember**
>
> - Always follow the manufacturer's instructions for mixing and application.
> - Never apply bleach after a hot bath or shower as the pores are open and bleach will enter the skin and cause irritation.
> - Ensure the client's clothing is protected as bleach will also make fabrics lose their colour.
> - When bleaching the eyebrows, do not allow any mixture to fall into the eye.
> - Always wear protective gloves.
> - Never leave the client as the bleaching process is taking place.
> - Never mix products from different manufacturers as the stability may not be compatible.
> - Never exceed the processing time and do not guess – use a clock.

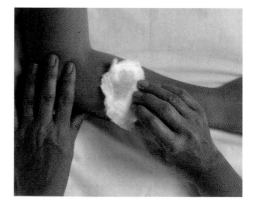

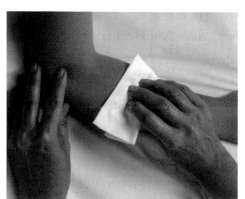

1 Cleanse the area well, checking for contra-indications, broken skin or signs of infection. Never treat unless a patch test has been completed 24 hours before.

2 Provided no contra-indications are present, blot the skin with a tissue to keep the skin clean, dry and grease free.

3 Follow manufacturer's instructions for mixing the bleach and apply all over the forearm in light strokes. Leave for recommended time and wipe off with damp cotton wool.

Step-by-step bleaching for the upper lip

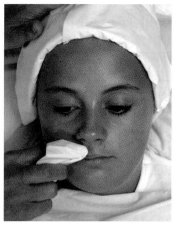

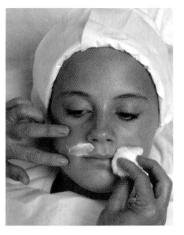

1 Cleanse the upper lip.

2 Blot with a tissue to dry the skin.

3 Apply a small amount of paste all over, avoiding going too far into the nostrils – it may make the client inhale.

4 Wait for manufacturer's development time, and remove with damp cotton wool. Give aftercare and homecare advice to the client.

1   Ensure that the area is free from all traces of grease and make-up products as these would cause the bleach not to be effective.

2   Wash the area with lukewarm water and dry.

3   Mix the bleach according to the manufacturer's instructions.

4   Cover the surrounding area with a suitable barrier cream to prevent the bleach spreading to other areas.

5   Apply the mixture to the area with a spatula or fine brush. Try to ensure that the bleach goes mainly on the hairs and not on the skin.

6   Leave the bleach on the hairs in accordance with the manufacturer's instructions. The colour and the coarseness of the hair will also determine processing times – the finer the hair the quicker the results.

7   Check the process every 3-5 minutes by removing a small section of bleach with damp cotton wool. If the hair is not sufficiently lightened, re-apply the mixture and allow more time, making sure its development is carefully monitored.

8   When the hair has reached the required lightness remove the paste with cool water.

9   Should the client complain of stinging or irritation, remove the bleach immediately with damp cotton wool and rinse the area thoroughly. White spots may appear if the bleach is left on too long.

10 Apply a soothing lotion and give aftercare advice.

- You were too slow when ripping off the strip. Be bold and confident, and it will be less painful and give a better result. Try not to lift upwards when removing the strip; always try to bring the strip back on itself.
- The hairs were too long and got into a tangle in the wax. Hair can be trimmed back with scissors prior to treatment.
- If the skin is very red after the first strip, it means the wax is too hot or too much pressure is being applied with the spatula. Try not to scrape it hard across the skin's surface as it will hurt.

Test your knowledge

Choose the correct answer to each of the questions below.

1   Waxing is a:
   a   permanent method of hair removal
   b   temporary method of hair removal
   c   long-lasting method of hair removal
   d   short-term method of hair removal.

2   Hot wax is most suitable for use on:
   a   strong hair growth
   b   weak hair growth
   c   bent follicles.

3   Hair removal creams are:
   a   suitable for all skin types
   b   not suitable for all skin types
   c   a painless method of hair removal
   d   a permanent method of removal.

4   Warm wax is:
   a   most suitable for all areas
   b   easy to apply
   c   not easy to apply
   d   a temporary method of removal.

5   Hot wax works best at a temperature of:
   a   48–68 ºC
   b   20–30 ºC
   c   60–80 ºC
   d   15–20 ºC.

6   Warm wax works best at a temperature of:
   a   48–68 ºC
   b   40–43 ºC
   c   60–80 ºC
   d   15–20 ºC.

7   The main ingredients used in hair removal wax are:
   a   resins and beeswax
   b   starch and flour
   c   sugar and water
   d   crystals and polish.

8   Pre-wax lotion must be used to:
    a   dry up the skin
    b   cleanse the area
    c   make the area smell nice
    d   make the hairs stand on end.

9   Talc is used to:
    a   make the skin smell nice
    b   provide a coating for the wax to stick to
    c   make the hairs stand away from the skin
    d   make the skin white.

10 After-wax lotion helps:
    a   soothe the skin
    b   stop the area going pink
    c   makes the skin smell nice
    d   helps calm the client down.

11 A patch test must always be carried out, to:
    a   try out the heat of the wax on the client
    b   see if the client is suitable for treatment (i.e. no reaction occurs)
    c   let the client know it hurts
    d   give the client a bald patch on her arm.

12 After-care is important, because:
    a   it prevents the client from irritating the area after the treatment
    b   it stops you from being sued for poor treatment
    c   it's just part of the job
    d   it stops the client from picking at the area.

Remove hair using waxing techniques
What your assessor is looking for   Unit BT6

Once you have practised and feel fairly confident about all the skills in this unit, you can then think about how you can develop your techniques to meet employer expectations of a good therapist who can wax well. An employer or assessor would be looking for the following, especially if you were asked to perform a trade test for a job application.

*   Minimise any wastage of product, strips or consumables you use during the treatment, including couch roll, tissues and cotton wool. Imagine *you* were paying for all of the items you used – you will soon realise that money is wasted if you throw away half-used products. When waxing, try not to end up with little bits of fabric or paper strips, or if you do, save them for small areas, such as when you do a lip wax or eyebrow wax. Split couch roll and tissues where possible and be economical with the amount of wax used.
*   Minimise discomfort to the client by developing good techniques for the removal of wax – be firm, confident and quick. Remember to smooth the area afterwards – a soothing touch really does calm the nerve endings.

- Keep checking your client's well-being and be sympathetic. Even though some seasoned clients go to sleep when being waxed, it can be quite painful – it depends upon the pain threshold of the individual. Now is a good time to introduce other treatments, discuss possible enhancing treatments, and take the client's mind off the waxing process.
- Keep an eye out for any contra-actions which may arise, and follow the appropriate procedure. Give good immediate aftercare, and then homecare advice. It may be that the treatment has to stop, and you invite the client to come in at a later date when the area has calmed down – or you might offer an alternative treatment if one is available.
- Work methodically in a logical sequence, so you do not miss any chunks of hair growth. In time, your own technique will develop and you will find yourself automatically working in a patchwork pattern, which works well for you. An employer does not often dictate how you achieve the end result, nor do many awarding bodies, but a good clean result is essential.

As this is a full practical unit, simulation is not allowed for any performance evidence within this unit.

The areas to be treated include the eyebrows, face, legs, underarm, bikini line and forearm.

As well as performing the treatment and leaving a good clean result, the assessor will be checking that you have:

- checked for contra-indications
- given the correct treatment advice
- told the client what to avoid
- recommended home care products
- carried out the treatment in a safe manner.

Remember that waxing is a skill that requires a lot of practice to improve both your technique and cleanliness. Before attempting an assessment, make sure you have had sufficient practice to feel confident and self-assured in your knowledge of what to tell the client.

Although the areas of the body are specified, you may be able to cluster your assessments. One client may have several areas waxed in one treatment, and they all count.

Be careful that the length of hair is right. If the hairs are too short the wax does not have enough of the hair shaft to adhere to, so the results will be patchy. If the hairs are too long, it will be advantageous to trim them down with scissors before starting. Otherwise the hair will become tangled and again the results will not be clean.

Be very careful to check the direction of hair growth, as that will dictate the direction for your wax strips. Show that you understand the relevance of hair growth even if it means using smaller strips, say for a circular direction of underarm hair growth.

Be clean and hygienic, and check with your professional body about when to use gloves. The best clean results on the skin will be spoilt by an unhygienic treatment approach and a messy workstation with wax on the floor.

Do not forget to test the wax on yourself and to carry out a small patch test on the client before you begin – burning the client's skin will not gain a competent assessment.

The assessor is looking at the whole approach, including client care, hygiene and a good result.

Provide manicure and pedicure treatment

Units BT7 and 8

This unit focuses on the treatment of natural nails and cuticles on hands and feet. These two units have been combined in the book as many techniques are common to both skill areas.

In this unit you will cover the following outcomes:

7.1/2/3 ⎫ Consult with clients, prepare and plan for manicure and pedicure treatments
8.1/2/3 ⎭
7.4/5/6 ⎫ Improve the appearance of the natural nail and cuticle
8.4/5/6 ⎭ with massage and polish application
7.7/8.7 Complete the treatment

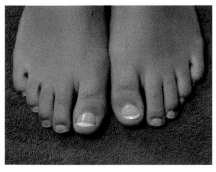

A pedicure is the professional threatment of feet, toes and nails

The practices of improving the appearance of the natural nail and cuticle is known as manicure and pedicure. A **manicure** is the care of hands and fingernails. This is a popular treatment in salons as smooth skin, well shaped and varnished nails are vital to promote a well-groomed appearance. Regular professional attention will help prevent minor nail damage, e.g. hangnails, spilt and brittle nails. This treatment is becoming increasingly popular with men who have regular treatments as part of their professional lives.

A **pedicure** is the professional treatment of feet, toes and nails. This treatment greatly enhances the appearance of feet and toenails which are often a neglected part of the body. Professional attention to the nails and surrounding skin encourages nail growth, keeps cuticles pushed back and can prevent minor skin conditions, e.g. corns and ingrowing toenails.

Consult with clients, prepare and plan for manicure and pedicure treatments

BT7.1/2/3 and 8.1/2/3

In this outcome you will learn about

- preparation of the working area
- consultation
- nail shapes
- contra-indications to manicure and pedicure

- equipment
- products required.

Preparation is the key to being a professional beauty therapist regardless of the treatment being carried out.

Preparation of the working area

Many salons have a designated working area for manicure and pedicure treatments. Sometimes this in in the reception area. But wherever you carry out your treatment you should ensure all materials equipment and products are within easy reach. The area required for manicure and pedicure varies greatly, with more versatility in manicure than pedicure.

Manicure	Pedicure
Client across a couch	Sitting only – can be combined with a manicure
Sitting across a table	
At a manicure station	
In a hair salon while having hair done	
Client lying on a beauty couch while having a facial	

Working areas for manicures and pedicures

Consultation

Whichever method you use to carry out your treatment, you need to be prepared. Have all the equipment, materials and products you will need to hand and also keep with you a client record card to ensure a professional treatment. The consultation should cover the following points:

- contra-indications
- skin and nail conditions (treatable)
- occasion (e.g. wedding)
- products used
- contra-actions

- varnish used
- homecare advice
- sales
- next appointment / recommendations
- therapist's name.

Nail shapes

At the consultation stage it is also important to consider the shape that would most suit your client: discuss this with the client. You will need to consider his/her working environment. Nail shapes should usually conform to the shape of the fingers for a more realistic and natural appearance. The following are shapes to be considered.

Square

This shape is usually most suitable for manual workers or clients who do a lot of work with fingertips, e.g. typists, pianists.

Round

This is a good shape for clients who require a short neat style. It decreases the likelihood of breakage or injury. It is suitable for clients with large square hands.

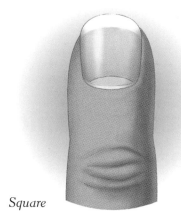

Square

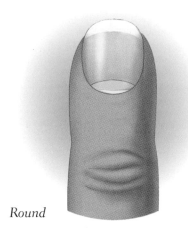

Round

Oval

This shape can appear to lengthen the fingers for a more elegant appearance. It is usually suitable for small hands.

Pointed

This shape is liable to breakage due to the exaggeration of the shape. It is therefore most suitable for special occasions.

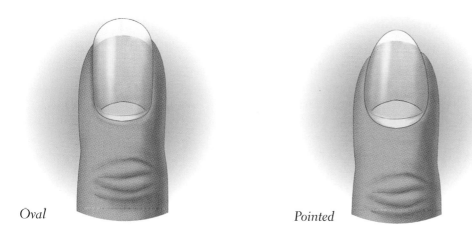

Oval   *Pointed*

In the salon

Helen comes into the salon for a manicure and polish. She has badly bitten nails, but she insists that her nails should look look good enough for a special evening out.

What approach would you take?

What would you do?

Contra-indications to manicure and pedicure

It is important to establish at the consultation stage if contra-indications are present. A contra-indication means that the treatment cannot be carried out, as the client is unsuitable for this particular treatment, or that the treatment needs to be adapted. If an area with a contra-indication is treated, there is a risk of contamination and cross-infection occurring.

The area to be treated should be examined in good light to judge if any of the following conditions are present. Details should be recorded on the client record card. Here are the most common contra-indications that are found and associated with manicure and pedicure treatments. The term **onychosis** is used to describe any nail disease.

Fungal infections

Fungal infections spread very rapidly and often thrive in damp areas, and can appear soft and spongy. Fungal infections should not be treated.

Check it out

When you watch the television, look at the hands of the celebrities and people in the news. Look at the shape of their nails. Do they follow the guidelines for nail shapes listed above? Could you make any adjustments or other recommendations?

Onychomycosis (pronounced on-i-ko-my-ko-sis) or ringworm

This is a fungal infection caused by the tinea unguim fungus, otherwise known as ringworm. The infection invades beneath the free edge, spreading into the nail bed and then attacking the nail plate. The nail plate becomes brittle, rough and opaque, and separation starts to occur due to the build-up of scales between the nail bed and nail plate. This can also make the nail plate appear very thick. Yellow discoloration may also be present.

Ringworm of the hands is a highly contagious disease caused by a fungus (tinea unguim). The symptoms are papular, red lesions, which occur in patches or rings over the hands. Itching may be slight to severe.

Athlete's foot (ringworm of the foot) – in acute conditions deep, itchy, colourless blisters can appear. These can appear singly, in groups, and sometimes on only one foot. They spread over the sole and between the toes, perhaps involving the nail fold and infecting the nail. When the blisters rupture they become red and ooze. The lesions dry as they heal. Fungus infection of the feet is likely to become chronic. Both the prevention of infection and beneficial treatment are accomplished by keeping the skin cool, dry and clean.

Bacterial infections

This type of infection is usually characterised by swelling, tenderness and redness in the area. Bacterial infection is a contra-indication to treatment.

Paronychia (pronounced par-on-ik-ee-ah)

This is a bacterial infection of the nail fold, the two types of bacteria generally responsible being staphylococci and streptococci. In paronychia, the nail fold is damaged either from a bad manicure, or by the hands being constantly immersed in water and harsh detergents. The symptoms are erythema, swelling and tenderness around the nail fold. There may be signs of slight shrinkage of the nail plate, which is separated from the nail bed. If the condition is not treated then the symptoms are accompanied by pus formation under the nail fold. After this, other types of bacteria set in, turning the nail plate a dark brown or black colour. Eventually, if the condition is not treated, a fungal infection known as candida takes over. Candida is the worst form of paronychia and is hard to destroy. The more common form of paronychia is very often found amongst dental and nursing staff. **Paronychia should not be manicured.**

Whitlows

These are small abscesses at the side or base of nail. The skin around the nail becomes soft and open to infection by herpes simplex virus or by bacteria, usually through a prick with a dirty pin or other sharp object. **Nails with this condition cannot be manicured.**

Onychia (pronounced on-ik-ee-ah)

This is the inflammation of the nail matrix, accompanied by pus formation. Improper sanitisation of nail implements and bacterial infections may cause this disease. **Nails with this condition cannot be manicured.**

> **Remember**
>
> Ringworm is a highly contagious disease and must not be manicured. If in doubt refer client to a G.P.

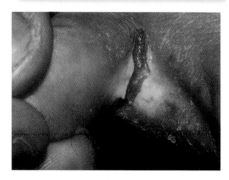

Athlete's foot (ringworm of the foot)

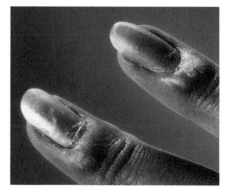

Paronychia

Viral infections

These infections are very common and treatment can be adapted by using a waterproof dressing and avoiding the area. However, viral infections are highly contagious if touched.

Verruca vulgaris (common warts)

These are small and highly contagious. They are caused by a viral infection. They are rough and hard and can be darkish in colour or natural skin tone. They are found either singly or in groups and appear around the nail fold area. They create pressure above the matrix, which can lead to deformities appearing in the growing nail plate (dystrophy). Warts should be left alone or untouched since they tend to disappear of their own accord, as suddenly as they appear. **Cannot be manicured unless covered**.

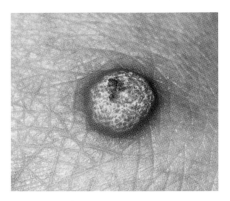

Verruca vulgaris (warts)

Verruca plantaris (verruca of the foot)

This condition belongs to the same family as the common wart, but instead of being raised on the surface of the skin, verrucas tend to grow inwards, so until they get fairly large the client can be unaware of having a verruca. They are often caught in swimming pool areas and are highly contagious. The skin's surface can be smooth and the appearance can be like a circular piece of hard skin with a black dot or dots in the centre.

Now you know what to look for, refer to your GP for advice on treating these conditions.

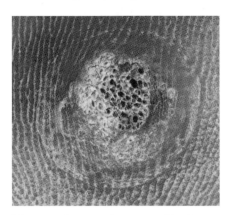

Verruca plantaris (verruca of foot)

Other contra-indications to manicure and pedicure

Onycholysis (pronounced on-ik-oh-lie-sis) or nail separation

This is a disorder where the nail separates from the nail bed (usually only part of and not the whole nail). It results from a build-up of debris found in the moist warm space between the digits, which attracts bacteria and fungal organisms, and in severe cases turns the nail plate a dark green or black colour. The infected nail plate grows faster than those that are uninfected. In feet, onycholysis occurs through wearing a tight-pinching shoe, poor general circulation and lack of attention to foot care. Non-infectious nails can be manicured or pedicured as long there is no fungal or bacterial infection. **Severe separation should not be treated.**

Onychocryptosis (or ingrowing nails)

This may affect either the fingers or toes. In this condition, the nail grows into the sides of the flesh and may cause infection. Filing the nails too much in the corners or over vigorous cutting is often responsible for ingrowing nails.

Other nail conditions

There are also other conditions that may require an amendment in treatment but are not necessarily a reason for stopping treatment.

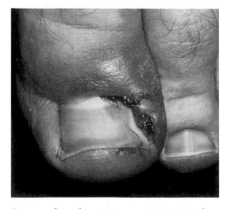

Paronychia due to ingrowing toenails

Split nails, brittle nails

Normally the result of abuse with drying agents, like those found in harsh detergents, cleaners, paint-strippers and film-developing fluids. Cotton-lined rubber gloves are good protection. Since the nail begins forming at almost the last finger joint, sometimes injury to the finger or diseases like arthritis can result in split nails. If accompanied by an overall dryness of skin and hair, split nails could indicate poor circulation.

Treatment will increase the circulation, bringing more nutrients and oxygen to help with cell regeneration. Hydrate the nail plate and surrounding skin with hot oil or paraffin wax. The use of a cuticle cream or oil for home use will be effective between treatments. **Manicure should be given.**

Blue nails

Usually a sign of bad circulation of blood or a heart condition. Manicures and pedicures may be given and massage usually helps circulation.

Beau's line

This is a disorder caused by an acute illness. As a result, the matrix temporarily stops producing new cells for the duration of the illness and, when it once again begins to reproduce, the period of the illness is clearly marked by a definite furrow or series of furrows. This grows forward and eventually disappears as it is cut away as part of the free edge.

This disorder is non-infectious and can therefore be manicured.

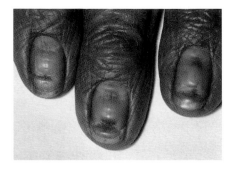

Beau's line

Nail / finger biting

This is a nervous habit where the individual bites and chews the free edge of the nail plate right down to expose the bulging nail bed below. The individual may also chew at the hardened cuticle and nail wall, causing a multitude of hangnails.

Should be regularly manicured. Massage and buffing will help to increase circulation and therefore stimulate growth. The use of special preparations to discourage nail biting may be recommended.

Hangnail

This is a condition whereby the cuticle around the nail plate splits leaving loose, flaky pieces of dry skin. It is caused by extreme dryness of the cuticle and from not keeping the cuticle free from the nail plate, so that it is stretched forward as the nail plate grows and eventually snaps leaving hangnails.

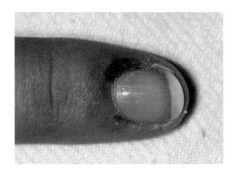

Finger biting

Splinter haemorrhages.

These appear as tiny streaks of blood under the nail plate, usually near the tip. Like nail separation, splinter haemorrhages can result from a traumatic blow to the nail. Sometimes, however, these red streaks can indicate a liver disease or possibly trichinosis (from improperly cooked pork).

Overgrown cuticles

This is caused by excessive cuticle growth that adheres to the base of the nail plate. Suggest that your client has a manicure or that she gently pushes the cuticle back with a soft towel after bathing and apply cuticle cream as often as possible. If the cuticles are very dry, a hot oil or paraffin wax manicure will help hydrate the area.

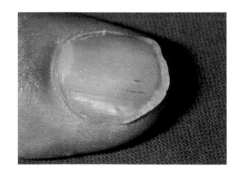

Splinter haemorrhages

Pits and grooves

Linked to both dermatological disease and systematic irregularities. However, many people who complain about pits and grooves in their nails have no apparent systematic diseases. It is very common and sometimes an unexplainable phenomenon, which can be dismissed with gentle buffing.

Flaking and breaking nails

This is a very common complaint, and can be due to lack of vitamin A and B2, general ill-health, incorrect filing, excessive use of enamel remover, or excessive use of solvents and harsh detergents. Use of a nail strengthener may help this condition if applied regularly. It is also advisable to keep the nails fairly short to prevent the nails breaking.

Bruised nails

This occurs when the nail receives a heavy blow. This shows as a dark purple patch on the nail and will grow out with the nail. In severe cases the nail may detach itself from the nail base. Unless there is damage to the matrix, a new nail will grow normally to replace it.

Severely bruised nails should not be treated.

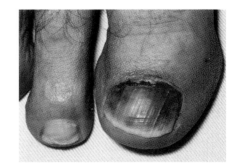

Bruised nails

Eggshell nails

These are recognised by the nail plate being noticeably thin, white and much more flexible than in normal nails. The nail plate separates from the nail bed and curves at the free edge. This disorder may be caused by chronic illness or may be of systemic or nervous origin.

Corrugations (or wavy ridges)

These are caused by uneven growth of nails, usually the result of illness or injury. When giving a manicure to a client with corrugations, buff to minimise ridges and use a ridge filler when painting for a smoother finish.

Furrows (depressions)

In the nails these may either run lengthwise or across the nail. These are usually the result of an illness or an injury to the nail cells, in or near the matrix. The nails are fragile, so care must be taken.

Leuconychia (pronounced loo-ko-nick-ee-aah) or white spots

These appear frequently in the nails but do not indicate disease. They may be caused by injury to the base of the nail or they might be air bubbles. As the nail continues to grow, these white spots eventually disappear. This is a very common disorder.

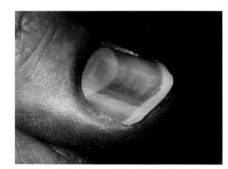

Koilonychia (spoon nails)

Koilonychia (spoon nails)

The nail plate is flat or concave giving a spoon-shaped appearance. This can be a hereditary condition, can be due to anaemia, or can be caused by the clients' contact with oils, soaps or detergents. The nails of newborn babies are often spoon shaped but this usually changes during their first year.

Onychogryphosis (claw nails)

The nail plate of this condition is usually grainy and fibrous which gives it a thick curved appearance. It is more common with toenails and is often caused by ill-fitting shoes. On the hands it is usually caused by trauma, although in some cases it can be caused by psoriasis of the nail. The nails should be kept short to prevent the nail looking too claw like. However, care should be taken when cutting as this can cause bleeding.

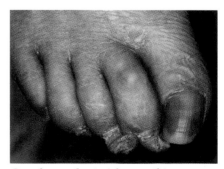

Onychogryphosis (claw nails)

Check it out

Have a really good look at your own fingernails and toenails. Can you identify any of the conditions mentioned?

Equipment

To ensure that no cross-infection or contamination occurs, the manicurist must make sure everything is clean. Some pieces of equipment are only designed for single use. Therefore, the cost of these items should be reflected when setting prices for manicure and pedicure treatments.

Emery board

This has two sides, a coarse side for shortening nails and a fine side, which is used for shaping and bevelling. These cannot be cleaned, and should be used once only and disposed of, or given to the client.

Orange stick

The two ends of the orange stick each have different purposes. The pointed side is used to apply cuticle cream and buffing cream. The other side, when tipped with cotton wool, can be used to clean under the free edge, remove excess enamel and ease back cuticle. When tipped with cotton wool this should be disposed of after each use. If not tipped they are for single use only.

Cuticle knife

This is used to mould back the cuticle and remove any excess attached to the nail plate.

Cuticle nipper

Used to remove hangnails and dead skin around the cuticle.

Nail scissors

Used to cut nails.

Toenail clippers

Used to cut and shorten nails prior to filing.

> **Remember**
>
> To sterilise all metal equipment, it should be placed in a chemical steriliser or autoclave. While performing the treatment, cleanse with a suitable sanitising solution.

Nail buffer

A pad covered with chamois leather and with a handle. Used in conjunction with buffing paste. Buffing adds sheen, stimulates circulation and growth at the matrix. Useful in pedicure, male manicure or when nail varnish is not going to be applied. To clean wipe with a suitable cleansing solution.

3-way buffer

This is used to smooth the nail and to remove any longitudinal and horizontal lines. Wipe between use with a suitable cleansing solution.

Nail brush

To brush the nails and clean them effectively. Also used to clean the therapist's nails. Wash in hot soapy water or sterilise in a chemical solution.

Hoof stick

Usually plastic, may be wooden, with a rubber end to ease back the cuticle. Pointed, and may be tipped with cotton wool to clean under free edge. When using from nail to nail, clean with a steriliser. On completion of treatment, sterilise in a cold sterilising solution.

Hard skin rasp/file/grater

To be used after the feet have been soaked and can be used in conjunction with hard skin remover. Use on areas of hard skin in a rubbing action with light pressure. Wash after use in hot soapy water and remove debris, sterilise in chemical solution.

Pumice stone

As with hard skin rasp.

Manicure bowl

This contains warm soapy water and sometimes a few drops of oil or a soaking solution. This softens the cuticle ready for pushing back. To clean, wash in hot soapy water and dry thoroughly.

 Some chemical solutions may dissolve the glue that attaches the rasp element or bristles in this equipment.

Towels

A clean towel for each client. It is useful to protect it with couch roll. Remember to have a separate towel for your personal use.

Couch roll

Dispose of all pieces after use.

 Remember

All metal equipment should be regularly checked, e.g. hinges and springs on scissors and clippers. Also check that cutting surfaces are smooth and sharp. Once sterilised all equipment should be stored hygienically, to prevent contamination occurring.

Tissues / cotton wool

Use a different tissue or piece of cotton wool for each hand / foot.

Spatulas

Break wooden spatulas after use. Wipe clean plastic or metal spatulas with a suitable cleansing solution when using between different products. Sterilise in chemical solution after use.

Products required

The following products are required for manicure and pedicure treatments:

- cuticle cream
- buffing paste
- hard skin remover
- massage medium
- talcum powder

- nail varnish / enamel
- base and top coats
- nail hardeners
- nail strengtheners.

For all these products use the cut-out system, or use pump action dispensers. When using pump dispensers, do not allow the spout to come into contact with the client's hands or feet. Chemicals contained within varnishes will prevent infection spreading, but to avoid any infection use the client's own product or sell the product to the client.

Improve the appearance of the natural nail and cuticle with massage and polish application BT7.4/5/6 and 8.4/5/6

In this outcome you will learn about

- products used in manicure and pedicure treatments
- suggested manicure procedure
- suggested pedicure routine
- nail painting
- massage
- specialist treatments.

Products used in manicure and pedicure treatments

Nail enamel/varnish remover

A solvent used to dissolve nail enamel. It is usually a mixture of acetone, glycerol and perfume. Acetone can have a drying effect on nails and surrounding skin. Some products also contain ethyl acetate.

Nail enamel/varnish thinners

A solvent used to thin down thick nail varnish/enamel, usually ethyl acetate. Nail enamel/varnish remover should not be used for this purpose due to the oil content contained in the remover. This may cause the varnish to discolour or separate.

Cuticle cream/oil

An emollient (softening, soothing) agent applied to cuticle to make it pliable. Creams contain soft white paraffin, mineral oils and some also contain lanolin. Oils are a mixture of almond and jojoba and mineral oils.

Cuticle remover

A liquid or cream designed to dissolve and break down the cuticle to make removal easier. This contains potassium hydroxide (which is caustic), water and glycerol. As it is caustic, cuticle remover should be rinsed off the nails and skin directly after use. This product can be used as a nail bleach.

Nail hardeners

Used to strengthen fragile nails. It is a liquid which is painted on and allowed to soak into the nail plate. It acts as a binder to harden the nail.

Nail strengtheners

A mixture of powder acrylic and liquid plastic is painted on. Once set will reinforce the nail but still be flexible. This product is often combined in a base coat.

Rough skin remover

A cream or lotion containing abrasive particles, oils, emollients, perfume and water. Used to soften skin and aid removal of hard skin.

Buffing paste

An abrasive paste used in conjunction with a chamois buffer to smooth out ridges on the nail plate. The abrasive elements in the paste may be a mixture of kaolin, chalk, silica or talc.

Hand cream/massage cream

A cream that provides lubrication for massage and softens skin. It contains emollient, glycerol, lanolin, water, emulsifiers, colour and perfume.

Hand lotion

Contains the same elements as hand cream but has a higher water content. It is therefore less sticky than cream.

Nail enamels and varnishes, base coat and topcoat

These products all have the same basic contents:

- a film firming plastic e.g. nitrocelluose
- a plastic resin e.g. aryl sufonamicide
- a gloss e.g. formaldehyde
- a plasticiser e.g. castor oil for flexibility
- solvents to dissolve other substances causing the nail enamel to dry e.g. ethyl acetate.

Coloured enamel/varnish

Colour is given by the addition of pigments, and a pearlised effect is made by adding, for example, bismuth oxychloride (for a metallic shine).

Base coat

Applied before colour, to prevent staining of the nail plate and to give a smooth surface for the coloured varnish to stick to.

Topcoat

Applied after colour, to give extra durability against knocks and wear for cream colours. Pearlised varnishes/enamels already have these additives to give this durability.

Nail bleach

Cuticle remover may act as a mild bleach, but 20% hydrogen peroxide will be most effective on stains, e.g. dyes and nicotine.

Nail white pencils

Used on the underside of the free edge when coloured varnish is not used. Use moistened.

Nail repair kit

Used for splits or tears in nails – comprised of fibrous tissue and liquid adhesive.

Quick dry spray

Contains solvents that evaporate and speed up the drying process.

Suggested manicure procedure

Step-by-step manicure

If you do specialised manicures and pedicures at your salon using a particular brand of products, you will probably go on a course which shows you how to use their products and gives an order for the procedure that should be followed. You therefore need to adapt your treatments at all times according to the manufacturer's instructions. However, whichever products you use, the basic principles for manicure and pedicure are the same.

Before starting the treatment, always carry out the following steps.

- Ensure equipment is sterile and all materials and products are easily accessible.
- Complete your consultation form, check for contra-indications on client and discuss the needs of the client.
- Remove all the client's jewellery, including watches, so that a thorough treatment can be carried out. Keep in a safe place.

> **Remember**
>
> Many of the products used in manicure and pedicure treatments are covered by COSHH regulations. Always refer to manufacturer's instructions prior to use.

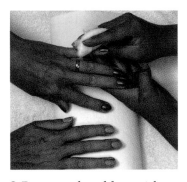

1 During the consultation discuss your client's needs, preferred shape of nails, and type of polish required. Providing there are no contra-indications present you are ready to begin.

2 As your nail bar has all equipment and stock ready to begin treatment, ask the client to pick her choice of varnish – dark, plain, frosted or French manicure.

3 Remove the old varnish and check the nails for ridges and possible problems as you go.

4 Cut the nails into shape if required, using sterilised scissors. Nail clippings need to be caught in a tissue and disposed of.

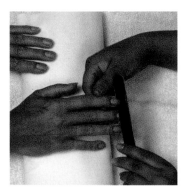

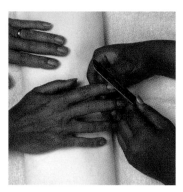

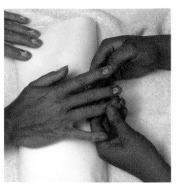

5 File the nails using an emery board working outside in, one way, one side then the other – avoid using a 'sawing' action. (There are different thicknesses of emery board.)

6 Bevelling seals the free edge layers to prevent water loss and mechanical damage.

7 Using an orange stick, decant and apply cuticle cream around the cuticles.

8 Gently massage the cream into the cuticles. This softens skin, making removal easier.

45° degree angle

Direction of filing stroke

Bevelling seals the free edge layers to prevent water loss and damage

Remember

Do not use a sawing action as this can cause the layers of the nail plate to split and separate.

Remember

The nail is made of three separate layers. 'Bevelling' holds the layers together and prevents splitting if the edge is traumatised.

Remember

There are some commercially prepared soaking preparations on the market, along with manicure bowls, to prevent spillage.

9 Soak the hands in warm water (tested by you first) to absorb the cuticle cream and to soften them.

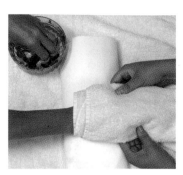

10 Remove one hand at a time and dry the hands thoroughly.

11 Apply cuticle remover with a cotton wool bud. It is caustic, so take care to apply sparingly and not onto the surrounding skin. Refer to COSHH regulations and manufacturers' instructions.

12 Using a hoof stick, flat to the nail plate, gently push the cuticle back, using circular motions.

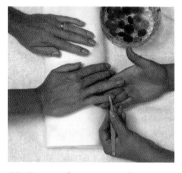

13 Depending upon the amount of work to be done on the cuticle, you may need to use the cuticle knife to ease the excess away from the nail plate.

14 Cuticle nippers may be used to trim off the excess cuticle; use a tissue to dispose of the waste.

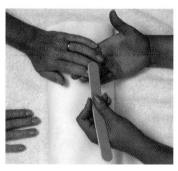

15 Bevel again, to give a smooth finish to the free edge.

16 Using a suitable medium, begin your hand massage with light effleurage movements. Support the hand and effleurage right up to the elbow.

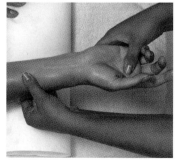

17 Circular thumb frictions get rid of tension in the flexors and extensors of the forearm.

18 Do circular frictions over the back of the hand.

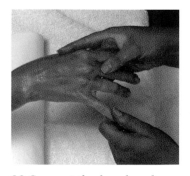

19 Support the hand and give gentle circular manipulations to each finger – this will free tension in the knuckles. Do not pull on the finger or make the circles too big.

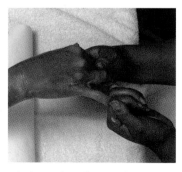

20 Grip the client's finger between your bent first and middle fingers and pull and twist gently down the length of the finger.

21 Interlock the clients' fingers with your own, and supporting the forearm, gently manipulate the wrist. First backwards . . .

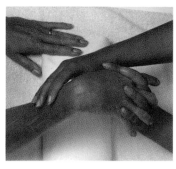

22 . . . and then forwards, to loosen the wrist and get rid of tension.

23 Apply circular thumb frictions to the palm. Stretch the palm out slightly.

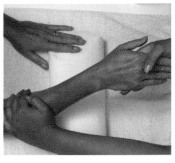

24 Finish your massage with effleurage up to the elbow.

25 With warm soapy water, gently wash the nails with a soft brush to remove any grease from the massage medium.

26 Apply a suitable base coat. Some nail systems have joint strengtheners or corrective properties within the base coat.

27 Apply the varnish of the client's choice, with clean strokes, without flooding the cuticle area.

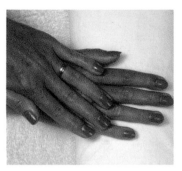

28 Topcoat will give a professional finish and the results should look good for some time.

Suggested pedicure routine

Before starting the treatment, carry out the following steps.

- Check for contra-indications, specifically: athlete's foot, bunions, corns, verrucas, ingrowing toenails and nail disease.
- Client should be seated comfortably with modesty towel over lap, and legs to knee exposed, to allow full pedicure with massage treatment.
- Therapist should have all materials to hand, be in a comfortable position with towel and single paper tissue roll on lap. Paper tissue to be replaced constantly through treatment to prevent cross-infection.

NB The client's feet may be pre-washed prior to commencement of treatment.

> ⚠ **Remember**
>
> Diabetes may not be considered a contra-indication to manicure and pedicure but in some cases diabetes can cause limited sensation in the feet due to poor circulation. If this is the case GP approval is required. In the case of varicose veins: avoid massage – a doctor's approval may be necessary.

Step-by-step pedicure

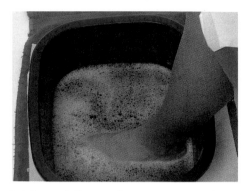

1 After a full consultation, remove the nail enamel and soak the feet to soften and refresh them.

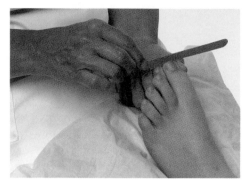

2 Using an emery board, file the toenails straight across – avoid any shaping, as it could cause ingrowing nails.

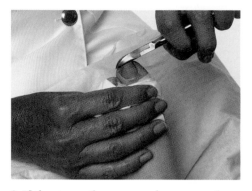

3 If the toenails are very long, use the clippers to get rid of the free edge, before filing.

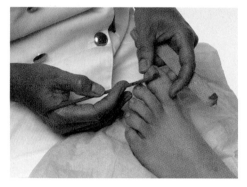

4 Apply cuticle cream and massage into the cuticle.

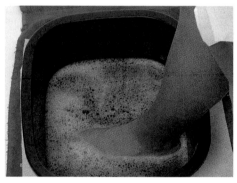

5 Soak the first foot in clean warm water, and repeat with second foot.

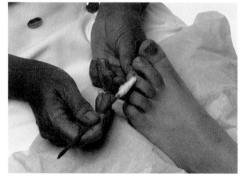

6 Apply cuticle remover with a cotton wool bud. It is caustic, so be careful only to apply sparingly and not onto the surrounding skin.

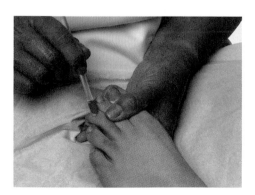

7 Using a hoof stick, flat to the nail plate, gently push the cuticle back, using circular motions.

8 Depending upon the amount of work to be done on the cuticle, you may need to use the cuticle knife to ease the excess away from the nail plate.

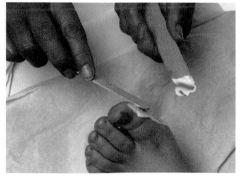

9 Rough skin remover may be applied to the areas that need attention, most commonly the ball of the foot, the heel and the side of the big toe.

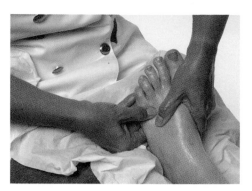

10 Apply massage medium and begin with effleurage to the whole foot, and follow with thumb frictions to the upper foot.

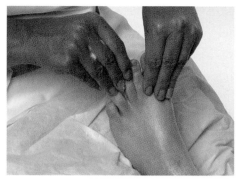

11 Follow the massage routine, as for manicure (see pages 382–383) – toe manipulations are really relaxing.

(see pages 382–383)

12 Finish with effleurage over the whole foot and lower leg.

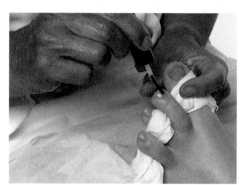

13 Paint toenails with client's choice of colour, using a base coat and top coat for extra durability. Remember to give the varnish plenty of time to dry, before the client puts her shoes back on.

Remember

Do not file nails to shape into the nail groove – keep free edge straight (square) or slightly rounded, to avoid problems with ingrowing nails.

Check it out

Do a small survey by asking how your friends and members of your family file their nails.

Are they filing correctly?

Nail painting

When painting nails, it is important to remember the following points.

- Try not to use more than four strokes per nail.
- Hold nail enamel in non-working palm of hand and use finger to support nail being painted.
- Always allow coats to dry before re-applying. This prevents smudging and streaking.
- When painting large wide nails, leave a thin unvarnished line at each side of the nail to produce a slimming effect.
- Avoid flooding the cuticles with nail varnish, as this has a drying effect on the skin.
- Tidy up any flaws with a cotton wool bud soaked in varnish remover.

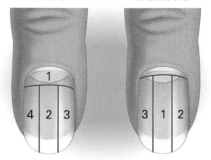

Method 1   Method 2

This is the better method for wide nails

In the salon

Jane has ridges on the nail plate and feels they are more noticeable when painted.

What recommendations could you make?

What colour varnish would you advise the client to wear?

Can you give any homecare advice?

Selection of colour

When selecting a coloured enamel it may help your client if you remember these few rules.

- Very bright colours draw attention to hands or feet.
- Dark colours make nails look smaller.
- Small hands or feet usually suit a light colour.
- Oval-shaped nails suit most colours.
- Orange, peach or beige tones emphasise the bluish tinges to the skin often seen in clients with poor circulation.
- Pearlised nails reflect the light and will emphasise any flaws in the nails.
- Coloured enamel is not suitable for very short / bitten nails, or hands and nails that are in poor condition.

Drying nail enamel

Nail enamel will dry quite well on its own, but on occasions it may be necessary to speed the process up. The application of either a topcoat dryer or quick dry spray can be used. Nail drying preparations do not completely dry the varnish but form a barrier over the surface to prevent smudging. Always refer to manufacturers' instructions and be aware of COSHH regulations when using these products.

French manicure

This is a popular way of varnishing fingernails that gives a natural look. Kits that are sold usually contain white and flesh coloured enamels. Always refer to manufacturers' instructions for application. A suggested method of application follows.

1 Apply base coat.
2 Apply white enamel to free edge only. Allow to dry.
3 Apply flesh-coloured varnish to entire nail.
4 Apply a topcoat.

Helping your client select a nail polish colour

Check it out

Investigate a range of salon products that you can buy for manicure and pedicures and a range of products that you can purchase in a local store.

French manicures are very popular and are often chosen by brides

The finished results give a healthy, natural look

Risk assessment for manicure and pedicure treatments

Refer to **Professional basics** for a complete discussion of risk assessment.

Hazard: only look for hazards that you could reasonably expect to result in significant harm under the conditions in your workplace. Use the following examples as a guide:

- **Allergies** (allergic reaction to chemicals used, nail enamel remover, nail polish, cotton wool)

- **Cross-infections** (infections spread from contaminated tools, or lack of sterilisation)

- **Skin breakage/bleeding** (caused by misuse of cuticle knife, or cutting the skin with cuticle nippers, or cutting the skin when using nail clippers/scissors)

- **Irritation** (caused by scratchy tools, lack of lubricant when using knife on the nail plate)

- **Contamination** (caused by ignoring contra-indications to treatment)

Massage

Hand/foot and arm/leg massage (to elbow or knee) is included in manicure and pedicure treatments. See the **Related anatomy and physiology** section for information on the relevant bones, muscles and blood circulation. The effects of massage on blood circulation are described on page 194.

Massage helps to:

- moisturise skin
- aid desquamation (shedding of skin cells)
- improve poor nail conditions
- stimulate blood supply, aiding cell regeneration
- relax tired muscles
- aid with the removal of waste products from the tissues
- aid client relaxation.

Types of massage movements

Effleurage

Effleurage movements are used for:

- introducing medium to area
- introducing hands to area
- helping relaxation with long flowing moves
- soothing nerve endings.

Petrissage

Petrissage movements are used for:

- increasing the blood flow feeding the muscular tissue and feeding cells
- desquamating cells from the surface of the skin
- increased removal of waste
- stimulating tissues, using deeper, more localised kneading or friction movements.

Tapotement

Tapotement movements, such as hacking and cupping where hands work briskly to stimulate the area, are used for:

- breaking down areas of tension and nodules and adipose tissue.

This type of movement needs adaptation depending on the area being treated and tissue density, e.g. not over a bony area.

Step-by-step arm massage

1 With effleurage movement, apply oil or cream.

2 With your left hand, effleurage one side of arm 3 times from out to in.

3 With your right hand, effleurage the other side of arm 3 times in to out.

4 Carry out thumb rotaries up the arm in 4 lines (2 at front and 2 at back).

5 Petrissage side of arm with your left hand out and in, and repeat on the other side from in to out 3 times.

6 Thumb-flicks in between the metacarpals 2 times between digits.

Manicure/pedicure

Ensure all equipment is to hand and sterilised

⬇

Consult to establish client requirements (discuss occupation to help with suitable nail shape)

⬇

Select nail colour

⬇

File/cut if required

⬇

Cuticle work

⬇

Apply specialist product according to manufacturers' instructions if required

⬇

Massage

⬇

Buff

⬇

Paint

⬇

Homecare/aftercare advice

⬇

Record details on record card to include shape and varnish colour.

7   Rotaries in between metacarpals 2 times between every digit.

8   Thumb-flicks again, in between the metacarpals 2 times between digit.

9   Rotaries to phalange joints, traction 2 times, full mobilisation – 3 in one direction (in towards your client), then repeat in the opposite direction away from your client.

10   Effleurage whole hand once.

11   Rotaries on carpals, traction of hand 2 times.

12   Full mobilisation of carpals, 3 times in one direction (in towards client).

13   Knead the palm with your thumbs.

14   Effleurage arms alternately 6 times and finish with pressure on the fingers.

Specialist treatments

In some cases, the condition of a client's hands or feet might mean that a standard manicure or pedicure is not enough, and so a specialist treatment would be recommended. These treatments include abrasive products for hard skin and electrically heated mittens for intensive moisturising. It is vital when using these products that you follow manufacturers' instructions. You may need to attend specialist training courses to use some of the products.

Product	What it does	Benefits
Abrasives and exfoliants	These products contain abrasive particles, which help remove (desquamate) excess skin. This type of product is especially useful for pedicure treatments	Softens and removes hard skin while conditioning. For best results, feet should be soaked prior to application. A massage product should be applied to the area after use, to help replace lost moisture, making the skin feel soft and smooth.
Thermal masks	These products are usually wax- or oil-based, and they are applied to a well-moisturised area in a heated liquid form. The treated area is usually wrapped in either foil or cling film to maintain heat. The mask is usually left on for 15 minutes, but you should always check the manufacturer's instructions. An example of a thermal mask is paraffin wax.	Intensive re-hydration and softening of skin and nail plate. Ideal for dry skin conditions. Increases circulation, promoting healthier growth. Decreases joint stiffness. Relaxes aching muscles. Increases absorption of moisturising products.

Specialist treatment products

Step-by-step paraffin wax treatment

This can be used for both manicure and pedicure treatments. It is applied after the cuticle work and before the massage.

1 Prepare your working area and decant the melted paraffin wax into a bowl lined with tin foil.

2 Test on self, prior to application on the client, over a sheet of tin foil, with a towel underneath it.

3 If the temperature is suitable, paint on a good even coating of the wax, working quickly before the wax sets, turning the hand to paint both sides.

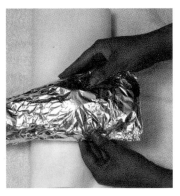

4 Wrap the hand in the tin foil, to retain the heat.

5 Wrap both hands in the towels and allow the heat to soothe and soften.

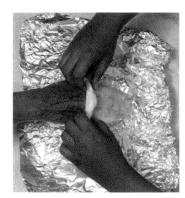

6 The wax cools and hardens, which makes removal easy – just peel it off. Any paraffin wax left in the bowl can be given to the client to use as a home treatment.

Contra-indications

- Skin infections
- Varicose veins
- Nail diseases
- Hypersensitivity.

Risk assessment for paraffin wax equipment

Refer to **Professional basics** for a complete discussion of risk assessment.

Hazard: only look for only hazards that you could reasonably expect to result in significant harm under the conditions in your workplace. Use the following examples as a guide:

- **Fire** (e.g. from electrical flex or lead)

- **Burning of equipment** (through low wax level in the tank)

- **Burns to skin** (not testing wax temperature. first on self)

- **Ejection of materials** (spitting hot wax)

- **Electricity** (e.g. poor wiring)

- **Manual handling** (spillage possible if moving when in liquid form)

- **Falling machinery** (if not securely positioned on a trolley)

Warm oil treatment

This treatment can also be offered in a salon. It is useful when treating dry hands / feet, cuticles and flaky nails.

The oil used should always be vegetable-based, for example:

- sweet almond oil
- olive oil
- cocoa oil.

Step-by-step warm oil treatment

1   Warm oil, either by immersing a suitable container in hot water or by using an infra-red lamp.

2   Proceed with treatment – do not apply cuticle massage oil at this stage. Soak fingers or toes in warmed oil for 5 minutes.

3   Massage in oil and wipe off any excess with a tissue.

4   Continue with routine.

NB It is not necessary to carry out a massage with this treatment.

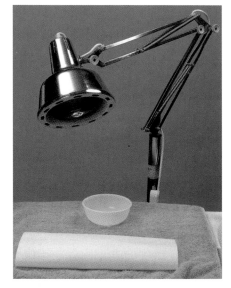

Preheat the oil in a plastic bowl

Soak the cuticles to help soften, and massage

Risk assessment for warm oil equipment

Refer to **Professional basics** for a complete discussion of risk assessment.

Hazard: only look for hazards that you could reasonably expect to result in significant harm under the conditions in your workplace. Use the following examples as a guide:

- **Fire** (e.g. from electrical flex or lead)

- **Burning of equipment** (through light bulb burning out)

- **Burns to skin** (lamp too close to skin, left on too long, treatment not timed)

- **Ejection of bulb** (hot bulb falling onto skin, not screwed in properly, lamp should not be directly over the skin)

- **Electricity** (e.g. poor wiring, trailing leads)

- **Manual handling** (outer casing is hot and will burn, if towel is not used for protection)

- **Falling machinery** (if supporting arm is not screwed in properly)

- **Contamination** (from brushes and equipment not sufficiently sterilised)

- **Cross-infections** (ignoring possible contra-indications)

Thermal mittens and booties

These are electrically heated items of equipment that are used on the same principle as thermal masks, with the added advantage of:

- maintaining heat more effectively
- being easy and less messy to use
- being more cost-effective over a period of time, as no special product is required.

Step-by-step thermal treatments

1 Apply a moisturising product to the area.

2 Apply cling film to improve the re-hydration process.

3 Place hands/feet in mittens/booties for 10–15 minutes.

4 After that time continue with cuticle work and the rest of the treatment.

Removal of nail extensions

A client may come into the salon with nail extensions in place. If the client wishes to have these extensions removed rather than have maintenance performed on them, you need to know how to remove the extensions without damaging the natural nail plate. You need to use products recommended for the removal of nail extensions. The time it takes to remove them will need to be taken into consideration when booking the appointment for the client. With some types of extension this procedure can add 30 minutes to the treatment time.

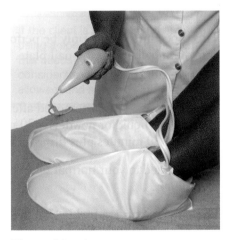

Thermal booties

Cuticle massage cream

Description

- An emulsion of oils, waxes, water and water-soluble ingredients, emulsifiers, fragrance and preservatives.

Ingredients

- All ingredients are commonly used in cosmetic preparations and meet acceptable standards of purity.

Hazards

- Considered to be non-hazardous under normal conditions of use.

Flammability

- Non-inflammable.

First aid procedures

- Ingestion: drink milk or water.
- Eye contact: wash well. If irritation persists, seek medical advice.

Spillage

- Clean using absorbent material, wash with detergent and water.

Handling and storage

- No special precautions are necessary.

Non-acetone nail polish remover

Description

- A mixture of organic solvents.

Ingredients

- All ingredients are commonly used in cosmetic products and meet accepted standards of purity.

Hazards

- The product is considered hazardous if precautions are ignored.

Flammability

- Inflammable.

First aid procedures

- Ingestion: drink milk or water and seek medical advice.
- Inhalation: avoid inhalation. If affected, remove to fresh air and keep warm.
- Skin contact: avoid. If prolonged contact occurs, wash well with water. If irritation persists, seek medical advice.
- Eye contact: wash well with water for a minimum of 15 minutes. If irritation persists seek medical advice.

Spillage

- Clean using liberal quantities of water.

Handling and storage

- Avoid contact with skin and eyes.
- Store in a cool place away from direct sunlight. Keep tightly sealed and store in a fire-resistant cupboard.
- Fire: advise fire service of storage quantities.

Acetone

Description

- Dimethyl ketone or 2-propanone.

Ingredients

- This product is commonly used in cosmetic products and meets accepted standards of purity.

Hazards

- Considered to be hazardous unless normal safety procedures are followed.

Flammability

- Flammable.
- Flash point 17.2 = Highly flammable.

First aid procedures

- Ingestion: drink plenty of milk or water.
- Inhalation: may cause dizziness, remove to fresh air.
- Skin contact: avoid prolonged contact with the skin. If irritation persists seek medical advice.
- Eye contact: rinse, seek medical advice.

Spillage

- Clean contaminated area with lots of water, wash with detergent and water to avoid slippery floors. Do not absorb with combustible material.

Handling and storage

- Cool place away from direct sunlight, in a fire-resistant store.
- Fire: contents are flammable. In case of fire evacuate areas known to contain products and inform fire fighters of their presence.

Your questions answered

What will happen if I don't check for contra-indications?
Infections of the hands and feet can be spread very easily – especially warts and verrucas.

Can I use a dark-coloured varnish on short or bitten nails?
Lighter colours will make the nails appear longer; a dark colour will draw attention to bitten and badly kept nails.

What happens if I don't keep the cuticle knife flat and wet?
Keeping the knife flat helps prevent cutting the skin, and wetting the knife prevents scratching the nail plate.

Why can't I use foam toe separators between the toes when painting the toenails?

Tissues are used because they are disposable. Foam separators may harbour germs and cause infections to be passed from client to client.

Test your knowledge

1   *How would you recognise a verucca?*

2   *Is athlete's foot a virus, fungus, or bacteria?*

3   *How should you cut toe nails?*

4   *What is the purpose of a hoof stick?*

5   *Why should a base coat be used before applying varnish?*

6   *What salon treatment could you recommend for a client with very dry skin or cuticles?*

7   *What is leuconychia?*

8   *Why do you bevel the nail when filing?*

9   *What are finger and toenails made from?*

10   *What nail shape suits most colours of varnish?*

11   *List five things that you should include in a consultation.*

12   *How should you store acetone?*

13   *If the nails have corrugations, what treatments could you offer to minimise this?*

14   *Why is it important to heat up the remover when removing nail extensions?*

Provide manicure and pedicure treatment
What your assessor is looking for   Unit BT7 and BT8

You cannot do any simulation within this unit, but the evidence can be gained quite easily. Remember to keep all paper evidence of any actions, feedback or witness statements that you have been given to support this work.

Your assessor will observe your performance on at least **three** occasions for both manicure and pedicure treatments (a minimum of six treatments for both the units).

- Treat both male and female clients for manicure (BT7).
- Use all consultation techniques.
- Use all the equipment and materials listed in the range.
- Apply all types of hand and foot treatments listed in the range.
- Apply all massage mediums.
- Apply all types of nail finish listed in the range.
- Maintain suitable environmental conditions (ventilation, heat, etc.).
- Prepare the client to suit the treatment.
- Deal with contra-indications that may prevent or restrict the treatment.
- Deal with contra-actions.
- Provide treatment advice.

Evidence of these can be provided by the observation of your assessor, but also by written work, projects, witness statements, photographic and video evidence and APL statements.

You must prove to your assessor that you have the necessary knowledge, understanding and skills to perform competently on all ranges within the criteria for this unit.

Plan and promote make-up activities   **BT10**

Introduction

Make-up is fun! Most of us love make-up and, given the chance, will play with the products, will try colours out on the hand, or watch as someone else has a 'make over'– even if we don't usually wear much make-up ourselves. With careful planning and preparation, giving a make-up demonstration or advice is easy and can be very enjoyable for both the therapist and the clients.

This unit is about providing make-up and product advice to a variety of clients through various activities, such as one-to-one sessions or group demonstrations.

This unit is complemented by the information on health and safety in *Professional basics* (pages 31–37), risk assessment in *Unit G1: Ensure your own actions reduce risks to health and safety* (pages 50–77), the skin in *You and your skin* (pages 133–163) and make-up in *Unit B9: Provide make-up treatment* (pages 281–310). As you work through this unit, refer closely to all the information you have learnt so far.

In this unit you will cover the following outcomes:

BT10.1 Prepare and plan for the make-up activity

BT10.2 Carry out the make-up activity

BT10.3 Complete the make-up activity

Prepare and plan for the make-up activity   **BT10.1**

The best way to make sure that your make-up promotional activity is a success is through careful planning. Planning a make-up promotional activity is dependent on many factors, so it is important to ask lots of questions when first setting up and planning your demonstration.

The types of questions to ask will depend upon whether the session is going to be:

- a one-to-one session to enhance a client's image
- a group demonstration to promote a business, salon or mobile client base.

One-to-one make-up

A one-to-one make-up activity usually takes place in a salon, in a well-lit cubicle or working area, and takes little organisation, except for clean tools, a good selection of make-up products and the necessary accessories of tissues, cotton wool and cotton buds, as well as a large mirror.

When the client books in for a make-up lesson, it is a good idea to suggest she brings her existing make-up – it might simply be that the client has excellent products and colours, but she just does not know how or where to use them, or she might be concerned about overusing them.

When you give a make-up lesson, not only are you guiding the client through the product type and colour, you are teaching her the correct application to assist her to create the same effect when you are not there. The best way to do this is to ask the client to follow your lead. You do one side of the face, and she matches the technique on the other.

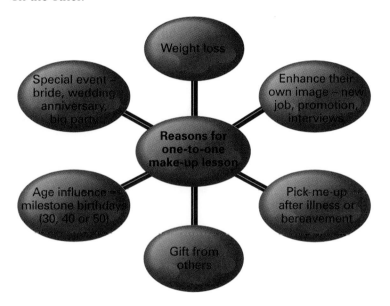

Reasons clients book a one-to-one make-up lesson

Group demonstrations

Local clubs and societies are often looking for opportunities to engage interesting speakers. You could offer to give a talk to the local Women's Institute (WI), mother and toddler group, slimming group, or women's group, or your salon might be approached by one of these groups asking for a make-up demonstration. This is your opportunity to talk about the various treatments your salon offers.

All of these groups are potential customers, so a professional, yet friendly approach is essential, and your aim is to encourage them to come into your salon for treatments!

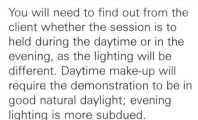

Remember

You will need to find out from the client whether the session is to held during the daytime or in the evening, as the lighting will be different. Daytime make-up will require the demonstration to be in good natural daylight; evening lighting is more subdued.

A 'make-over' is a great present for a milestone birthday

Remember

Always refer to the client's skin type for the products most suitable for her skin – the wrong type of product will produce a poor finish, as will the wrong colour.

Questions to ask when organising a demonstration of make-up

- How many people will be there?
- Where is the event to be held?
- What facilities are there – lighting, tables, mirrors, chairs?
- Date and time of the event?
- Duration of the demonstration?
- Type of event, e.g. bridal fair, WI meeting, slimming club?
- Outcomes expected?

Meeting individual needs and interest

When organising a demonstration, you will need to consider:

* the age group of the audience – this will impact on the type of make-up and how much
* the size of the group
* the type of demonstration – face painting would interest a mother and toddler group but may not interest the WI, for example
* the time of day when the event is to be held – day make-up or evening make-up
* different product types which might include:
  – emphasis on products with sunscreens and protection from the environment
  – products designed for sensitive skins/hypo-allergenic products
  – suitable cosmetic make-up for treating skin disorders, port wine stains, etc.

Venue and format

Some points to bear in mind:

* Where the event is to be held is very important. The venue can be anywhere from the local village hall, to a hotel (most commonly used for bridal fairs), to someone's home. Find out where and when, and then consider both the risk assessment aspect and health and safety implications.
* You will need to check whether your insurance will cover you to do the demonstration. You should not assume that your public liability and indemnity insurances are valid when you are working away from your own premises (see *Professional Basics*, pages 40–41).
* Accidents happen, and it is your responsibility to ensure that both you and your audience are adequately protected; both externally, for problems with the building, fire regulations, etc.; and for internal areas, such as safe seating, and non-slip flooring.
* Ask the group's organiser if the premises have an up-to-date fire certificate, if there has been a recent risk assessment of the building, and what access and exit facilities are available. Are there fire exits?
* Will a first aider be present at the demonstration? What happens if a member of the group has an accident or is taken ill? This needs to be considered before the event so that contingency plans can be put in place – after the event is too late and may leave you and the organiser with serious issues of compensation or neglect charges.
* If the demonstration is for people who have disabilities, then responsibility should be taken by the organisers to ensure that sufficient carers are present to support the audience. It should not be your responsibility to take disabled guests to the toilet, or deal with a medical emergency – you are not trained to do so. Find out if there are facilities for disabled people such as ramps and toilets.
* For your own safety, ask the organiser about parking and how to get into the building. A dark parking area may leave you vulnerable, and carrying your demonstration materials, make-up and stand up several flights of stairs because the lift is not working may not be very practical. Ideally, easy access on the ground floor is preferred, with well-lit parking available. You may need to enlist some help in setting up.

Does the client want bridal make-up or make-up for a special evening event?

Budget and cost

The other important aspect of the group demonstration is who pays and for what. The issues of budget and cost should be sorted out at the planning stage. If your salon is approached by an organisation, the organiser will usually ask how much you charge for a make-up demonstration. Some salons would consider this an ideal opportunity to enhance their client base and a means of advertising, and would therefore agree to the demonstration for free. Other salons would look at the time involved, the wages of the member of staff to be covered and the cost of materials, and then calculate a set fee to cover their overheads. This is down to the individual salon – there is no right answer.

The timing of the demonstration may affect the issue of cost. If the therapist goes in her own time after work to an evening event, then she may expect to be paid for it. Often, bridal fairs are held over a weekend to allow people who work during the week to attend. This may mean the therapist is working on her only day off, Sunday, and she may wish to be paid. If she attends on Saturday, who will cover her clients in the salon? This could become expensive if a relief therapist has to be brought in or clients cancelled to allow the therapist time to attend a demonstration she is giving, with no charge.

However, often it is worth the investment for the publicity generated, and the profile of the salon can be raised enormously. Lots of business comes out of demonstrations, and further treatments can be linked into the make-up demonstration – facials, top-to-toe bridal treatments, skin improvement, and so on.

All of this needs discussing with the organisers and your line manager within the salon before you agree to the demonstration.

Products

The number of people attending the demonstration will affect how many products, testers and display materials you will need. This will also depend upon the type of demonstration you do. If it is a complete make-over, using one model whom you have brought along, to display your skills and entice people into the salon for treatments, then you will only need products for one. If you will be selecting a model from the audience, you will need one set of everything for each skin type.

If you are doing a demonstration en masse, where the audience actively participates, following your lead, applying their make-up as you go along, then many more products are required, unless everyone brings their own. As you are applying make-up to a clean skin, which has a make-up base or moisturiser on it, skin care products are essential, as well as a selection of make-up.

Active participation is a good idea, and encourages the audience to have the confidence to apply their own make-up. Make sure that everyone has a clear view of you and the step-by-step application.

It is essential to have a selection of make-up at a group demonstration

Timing

It is important that you know how long you are expected to speak for and how long your full demonstration will take. If you are expected to take the whole meeting time, which may be several hours, you should have some activities which the audience can participate in, like a draw for a free treatment, to keep the interest high.

Have a dress rehearsal with a model before the day of the demonstration, so that you know how long the actual make-up application takes, and then add time for an introduction, and a question and answer session afterwards. This will allow you at the planning stage to tell the organiser that you will need a minimum of, say, an hour and a half, in which to work.

Setting up the room

The key to a successful demonstration is visibility. The audience needs to be able to see what you are doing, or they will lose interest and potential clients will have been lost. For good communication to take place, you also need to be heard, and a microphone may be needed for larger venues. A raised platform or stage is good for larger audiences, but it does not create an intimate friendly feel, so it will depend upon the number of people and the facilities the venue has.

The best room set-up is a horse-shoe shape, with you and your model at the open end, with an eye-catching display behind you and all materials close at hand. This ensures everyone has a good view, you have command of the room, and are able to make lots of eye contact to check that the audience understands your techniques and remains interested.

Try to be organised, so once you start and get into the swing of things, you do not have to return to your car for tissues, or stop the demonstration for any reason. This will break the attention span of your audience, and you will not appear to be professional.

Think through what you will need beforehand, and work logically so that nothing is missed.

To prepare your model	To carry out the make-up	To support the demonstration
A turban	Clean make-up brushes	Treatment leaflets
Eye make-up remover	and clean sponges	Price lists for
Cleansers	Concealers	the salon
Toner		Product information
Moisturisers	Foundations	Gift vouchers
Tissues	Powders	Display materials
Cotton wool rounds	Blushers	Testers
and buds	Eye make-up	A draw prize
A waste bin	Liners	(optional)
A cape to cover clothing	Mascara	
	Lip liners	
	Lipsticks/lip gloss	
	A mirror	
	A brush or comb	

What you will need

You should allow:

- 15 minutes to set up
- a 10-minute introduction
- 10 minutes to choose a model and hold a mini-consultation
- 30–45 minutes for the cleanse, tone and moisturiser, then actual make-up application
- 15 minutes for questions and answers
- 10 minutes to pack up.

Check it out

Try various room layouts and conduct a mock demonstration. Take it in turns to be the speaker and place rows of chairs in a circle or other formation – you may need to draw the seating plan to scale on paper. Observe health and safety rules, to ensure everyone has an easy exit route.

Displaying product information or pamphlets is a great way to promote products

Remember

A promotional activity:

- lets potential customers try treatments or products they have not experienced before
- retains existing customer loyalty
- conveys an impression of activity and change within the salon
- attracts new clients
- improves customer satisfaction
- improves your public relations standing within the community.

Carry out the make-up activity

BT10.2

Introducing the demonstration

Once you have fully prepared your working area and the room is set up in a user-friendly manner so that everyone can see and hear you, you may begin.

It is important to consult with your model prior to starting – have a quiet word with her to ensure that your objectives marry up with her needs, and that she has no contra-indications present.

An introduction is always a good ice breaker, rather than just starting and hoping everyone will pay attention. It is a good idea to begin with something along the lines of 'Good afternoon, everyone – my name is Janine from Tranquillity salon, and I'd like to welcome you to Fern Hall for this demonstration'. Then tell the audience exactly what is going to happen and at what point they can ask questions. For example, 'I am going to give a make-up demonstration for about half an hour, talking you through the various stages, with some professional tips, and then there will be a question and answer session. After the tea break, we can talk about products and treatments.'

Remember

In your introduction, make sure you:

- smile at everyone
- talk to the whole room
- make lots of eye contact
- confirm that everyone can see and hear you
- introduce your model
- talk about your salon and the treatments it offers
- discuss the outcomes of the make-up demonstration.

Communication skills

For tips on general communication skills, refer to *Professional Basics*, pages 10–11. Below are some specific tools for a short presentation:

- Pace your speech pattern – try to speak slowly and clearly, rather than very quickly, which is what often happens when you are nervous. Pace is literally the speed of the words. A calm, slow, measured speech reflects reassurance and confidence – the speaker is concentrating on getting across the message. Although interest and enthusiasm are important, these can sometimes lead to a more rapid delivery. Panic, anxiety and lack of confidence can produce fast, muddled speech.
- Do not be afraid of short pauses or silence while you are either allowing the information to sink in, or you are concentrating on applying the make-up. Break up the silence if you think it has gone on too long by commentary such as 'Always apply foundation after the skin has been moisturised. Allow the moisturiser to be absorbed for a few seconds before continuing with the foundation …'.
- Pauses can be either a comfortable silence, allowing reflection upon what has been said, or can be very awkward, even menacing. Judging a pause and knowing when to break it, takes a little patience and skill. Hesitation in speech patterns may indicate uncertainty or stress, or just tiredness, where the brain function is slowing down.
- Varying the tone of your voice enlivens speech and helps retain the listeners' attention. Flat, boring tones will not engage the audience and will not help them understand what is being said to them.
- Pitch is most noticeable when it is either high or low, and often reflects the emotional state of the person. Someone who is depressed often talks in a low, failing pitch, quite slowly, whereas a raised pitch conveys excitement, enthusiasm or anxiety. Voice coaches recommend to people in the public eye, who have to make a lot of speeches, to lower the pitch slightly and slow down their normal rate and rhythm of speech.
- The use of graphics, a PowerPoint display (if you have the technology and the facilities are available), or pictures of make-up and 'before and after' shots all add interest.

Check it out

On television, watch a politician being interviewed, a celebrity picking up an award, or a newsreader. How does the tone vary? What is the person's body language saying? Compare three different styles and discuss in class – which do you think is the best?

- Make plenty of eye contact and try not to focus on one person as this may make them uncomfortable. Include everyone in your field of vision.
- Respond kindly to those who ask questions, really listen to their query, rather than interrupting them, and nod to show you have understood. If you answer one person well, it encourages others to ask questions, too.

As well as talking through your demonstration, remember not to stand in front of the model as you are working – the audience will not be able to see. You need to perfect the art of working at the side so that your actions are plain to see, and you can stop at each stage to show the audience the type of effect. For example, 'After foundation and powder application, the skin colour is even and blemishes are well covered, but the colour comes with the application of blusher, lipstick and eye products, so don't expect too much colour in the face at this time.' Then show the audience your 'blank canvas', with just foundation and powder on.

> **Remember**
>
> Check your working area is tidy and clean throughout the demonstration – an untidy work station does not look professional.

> **Check it out**
>
> If you have the facilities to do so, video your presentation to the class (this will also be good key skill evidence) and time how long it takes. How was your speech pattern? What was your body language like? What could you improve?

Complete the make-up activity   BT10.3

After the make-over has been completed, hold a question and answer session. Have you:

- met the objectives
- checked the finished result with the client
- been cost-effective, both with time and product use
- carried out the treatment in a commercially acceptable time
- filled in a client record card
- obtained the audience's details for a promotional mailing
- tidied away and left the area immaculate
- enough products for other demonstrations, or will more need to be ordered?

Potential client information

Whenever you give a group demonstration, it is a good idea to ask the potential clients if they would be happy to give you their personal details to be included in a mailing list for special offers and promotions. (Refer to *Professional Basics*, page 39, for the correct storage of data under the Data Protection Act.)

Selling skills

Unit G6 Promote additional products or services to clients covers selling skills, including using open questions to aid the sale, and how to close when interest is shown.

Features and benefits

A **feature** is an aspect of the product which is useful, but not necessarily part of the action of the product, such as a plastic, unbreakable bottle for travelling, or a pump action for easy dispensing.

A feature of a one-to-one make-up demonstration may be that it can be performed privately in the salon, and the client may not have to travel too far.

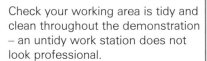

Displaying products and gift packs helps 'advertise' a product's key selling points

A feature of a group session is that it can be fun having company, and for the client who is shy, there is safety in numbers!

A **benefit** is the key selling point for the products to the client's advantage, for example a cream moisturising cleanser helps keep the moisture in the skin, or a cream foundation has a high moisture content to help a dry skin.

A benefit of a one-to-one make-up demonstration may be that it can be tailor made to suit the client's needs, and that a greater amount of understanding may take place because of the intimacy of just client and therapist.

A benefit of a group session is that the therapist reaches a wider audience and the client may interact with friend within the audience and it provides a good opportunity for discussion with others.

Self evaluation

After the event, it is important to look at your performance and judge if you were happy with all aspects of it. Ask yourself:

- How do I think it went?
- What would I change if I could?
- Was I fully prepared?
- What would I do differently next time?
- What sort of feedback did I get from the audience? Were they interested and attentive? If not, why not?
- Did the client(s) show full understanding of my instructions, and did she (they) show interest in purchasing a product, or booking a treatment?

Test your knowledge

1   List five questions to ask the organiser when planning a make-up demonstration.

2   Name two benefits of a one-to-one make-up lesson.

3   Name two benefits of a group make-up lesson.

4   What insurance details should you check when going to an event outside the salon?

5   Why is it important to consider budget and costing of a demonstration?

6   List five things which will support your demonstration.

7   List three benefits of a promotional activity such as a make-up demonstration to the salon.

8   When introducing yourself to an audience, list three things you should do.

9   Why is it important to vary your speech patterns when giving a talk?

10   How could you add interest to your presentation?

What your assessor is looking for

Unit BT10

- A one-to-one make-up lesson and a group demonstration (three or more people)
- How you would plan a demonstration, with an action plan, timings and products, and materials required
- High standards of health and hygiene
- A risk assessment has been discussed and all legal requirements fulfilled
- Up-to-date client record cards
- Good, clear communication skills suitable for the situation and the size of the audience
- An immaculately kept working area throughout the demonstration
- The opportunity to promote and sell additional treatments or products incorporated within the demonstration
- A full evaluation of the activity has taken place

Provide nail art service

BT13

Nail art complements your manicure and pedicure skills, is great fun, and makes a popular service to offer your clients.

It requires the same professional skills as your manicure and pedicure units – including practice and confidence. Once you start to feel confident with your manicure techniques and the application of polish, nail art is a natural progression. It looks lovely on both the natural nail and artificial nails.

Most of the outcomes of this unit are the same as the manicure and pedicure units:

BT13.1 Consult with the client

BT13.2 Prepare for the service

BT13.3 Plan the service

BT13.4 Provide nail art service to clients

BT13.5 Complete the service.

The consultation is similar to that for a manicure: look for contra-indications which would prevent the treatment taking place, talk to the client and discuss her treatment needs. Hygiene requirements and your personal presentation are exactly the same as for any other treatment.

Setting up your working area is the same as for manicure: you need a good, steady surface so that your hands, and the client's hands, have something to rest on, and you will usually need to be opposite her, as in the manicure position.

All tools and equipment should be sterilised and set out, ready to go. When putting out your nail art kit, it is a good idea to have it all on a tray or box with a small lip around the edge. That way, if you do knock over your rhinestones and flat stones, they are contained on the tray and easily retrievable, instead of being all over the floor! (If they get dirty, they have to be thrown away.)

Generally, clients wanting nail art tend to have nails in good condition, and plenty of free edge to work with – people with bitten nails and small nail plates tend not to want to draw attention to them with jewels and coloured polishes. Little preparation should therefore be needed to the nail before commencing.

Remove any old polish, and check again for any contra-indications which may have been concealed by nail enamel. File the nail correctly and ensure the nail is left clean and free from debris. The cuticle should be neat and undamaged.

At this stage, some salons offer a brief hand massage to soften and nourish the nails – it is a pleasant extra for the client, but do remember to ensure the nail plate is left grease-free afterwards, so that the base coat can dry. A quick wipe over with nail polish remover, or a gentle scrub with a nailbrush and warm soapy water, will be sufficient. Dry the hands and nail plate thoroughly.

Then you are ready to begin. Remember where possible to follow manufacturers' instructions and use the accompanying base coat and topcoat for products.

Also, do remember your posture. You will want to get as close as possible to the nail you are working on, which means you will be tempted to bend over. In concentrating hard, and aiming for symmetry and artistic flair, you may not realise how hunched over your position has become. By the end of your ten applications, your back and neck muscles will let you know they have been over-stretched. Also, if you have three or four clients for nail art in the day, you could really suffer with backache.

Try to remain in an upright position, with the hand raised towards your eyes if possible, resting on a manicure pad, or even a towel-covered box, so that you are not continually bent over. Keeping upright also means you will not inhale glue fumes, which can cause headaches and nausea.

The following pages show examples of nail art. The ranges you will be asked to cover are:

- coloured polishes
- rhinestones
- flatstones
- polish secures
- painting techniques
- base coats
- glitters
- blending
- topcoats
- transfers
- foiling.

You will need to be assessed on at least three occasions, but remember that some of these techniques can be covered on the same client: for example, you would apply base coat, a coloured polish, some rhinestones and a topcoat together in one treatment.

During treatment it is important to talk through maintenance and aftercare, so that your client can look after your creation. This is much the same as manicure aftercare:

- use rubber gloves for household chores
- keep nails as jewels, not tools
- do not pick or peel off the products
- allow no solvents or chemicals near the hands which will dissolve the glue or topcoat (surgical spirit, for example)
- have regular manicure treatments to keep the nails in top condition.

Give your client the manicure aftercare leaflet or card to take away and refer to, and introduce her to the other treatments the salon has to offer, with a price list.

Finally, remember to tidy up after the treatment and fill out the record card, in full.

Remember

Always wash your hands before and after treatment.

French manicure with rhinestones

1 The white of the French manicure is applied over the free edge after the base coat has dried.

2 The rhinestone is inserted into the wet top coat and positioned using an orange stick. Press firmly.

3 The final result. Less is more! Nail art doesn't have to be on every nail to be effective.

Coloured polishes and brushwork

1 Coloured polish application.

2 Using a fine brush, sweep laterally across the nail.

3 Finished tiger stripes. The top coat seals the black acrylic paint.

Glitter and flick

1 While one hand is drying, proceed with the other hand.

2 Apply glitter in the direction of the acrylic paint, as a highlighter. The glitter can contrast with jewellery.

3 The finished result with glitter application.

Transfers

Damp the transfer and apply to the nail. Seal with a top coat.

Step-by-step nail art

1 Apply a base coat to provide a smooth surface and prevent staining of the nail plate.

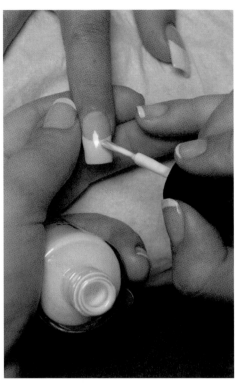

2 Apply the white tip to the free edge.

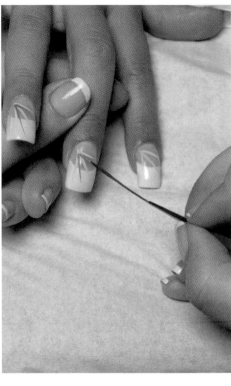

3 Using a thin brush, apply directional strokes in contrasting colours.

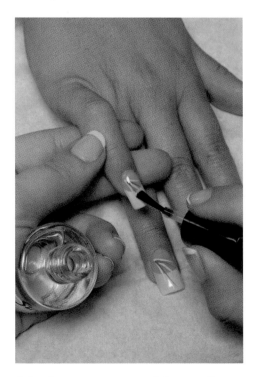

4 Apply a top coat to seal the acrylic design.

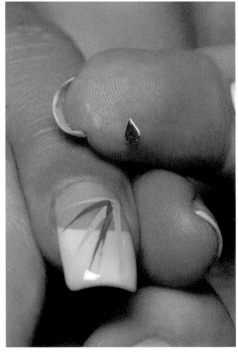

5 Apply the gem using a dampened finger and push into place with an orange stick.

6 Finished fan effect with rhinestones.

Paint effects

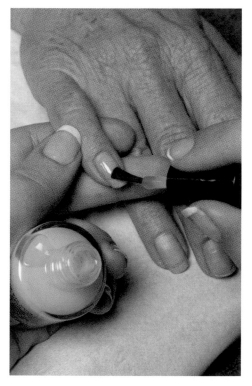

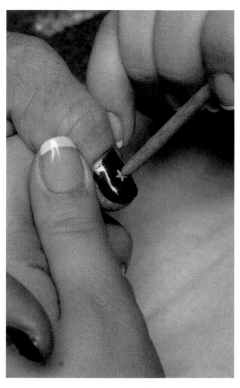

1 Apply the base coat to the clean nail plate.

2 Apply a dark base colour.

3 Apply gems to each nail using a blob of clear varnish. An orange stick will help with placement.

4 Apply strokes in a suitable colour of the client's choice with a thin brush.

5 Apply top coat to seal the varnish and secure the gems.

6 The finished effect.

Nail art products

Key skills Level 1 and NVQ Level 2 Customer Service

When completing tasks for your NVQ Level 2 Beauty therapy portfolio you will also be creating evidence that is suitable for your Key Skills portfolio and, if you take it, your NVQ Level 2 Customer Service.

The following is a guide to which evidence is most suitable for each and what is expected of that evidence for Key Skills Level 1. The Key Skills evidence is listed first, and the related Customer Service evidence follows.

Key Skills Level 1 Communication

C1.1 One-to-one discussion

This needs to be about different, straightforward subjects. Any of the following can be used as evidence.

- Practical units BT4–BT11: a treatment consultation with the client

- Unit G6: a discussion with a client on products or services

- Unit G8: one-to-one discussion for any tutorial interview with a subject or personal tutor

- Units G4 and G8: one-to-one discussion within your role as a receptionist or salon manager

If a discussion arises regarding the treatment page / treatments to do or jobs to be allocated, the discussion should be logged in your duty report form and signed by both parties.

- Units G4 and G8: discussion between two colleagues

Use a salon situation to discuss any practical issues that arise, and log it on the salon report sheet, or present the solution to a problem to your salon manager / assessor, e.g. 'Joanna and I are going to cover the clients for Suzette, who is off sick – I will do XYZ and Joanna will do ABC'.

C1.1 Group discussion

- Units G4 and G8: class discussion between all class members

Class discussion on a straightforward subject linked to Beauty therapy, e.g. cosmetic surgery or the use of Botox injections, permanent make-up or similar. Suggestions on how to improve the salon / client set up – salon organisation, client rota or similar topic.

Do an evaluation sheet on the results of your discussion and remember to get signatures.

Customer Service NVQ Level 2

If you complete the evidence for Key Skills Communication C1.1, you have also achieved the following elements for NVQ Level 2 Customer Service.

Element 1.1 Questioning and listening techniques for services and products

Element 5.3 Work with others to improve reliability of service

C1.2 Read 2 documents including an image
- Units G1, G4, G8, BT4–BT11

Dealing with any health and safety instructions or manufacturer's instructions relating to practical units BT4–BT11.

- How to use the autoclave. (See Professional basics, page 25.)
- Fire evacuation procedures. (See Unit G1, page 71.)
- Client booking-in sheet – allocation of jobs. (See Professional basics, page 12.)
- Salon rules and regulations for professional attire and safe footwear. (See Professional basics, pages 8–9.)
- Also use information from Unit G1 for safe practices within the salon and spillage procedures. (See page 61.)

Customer Service NVQ Level 2

If you complete the evidence for Key Skills Communication C1.2, you have also achieved the following elements in NVQ Level 2 Customer Service.

Element 1.1 Using products and services; Following manufacturer's instructions; Awareness of legal rights of customers.

C1.3 Write 2 documents including an image
- Units G4, BT4–BT11

Design a safety poster, which could be presented to the group, and a memo inviting students to attend the briefing. Also, a memo inviting students to attend a salon meeting could be sent.

Design an aftercare leaflet for any practical unit BT4–BT11, e.g. manicure, pedicure, waxing, facials. (See Unit BT6, pages 360 and 363.)

Customer Service NVQ Level 2

If you complete the evidence for Key Skills Communication C1.3 you have also achieved the following elements in NVQ Level 2 Customer Service.

Element 2.1 Design a client record card, bearing security of information in mind.

Element 5.3 Work with others to improve reliability of service.

Design a short questionnaire on the back of the record of evidence sheet, for customer evaluation of service or treatment.

Key Skills Level 1 Application of Number

N1.1 Interpret information from 2 sources

- Unit BT6

Refer to the waxing section to work out how many minutes it would take to conduct a waxing treatment, which type of wax would be most successful, and how long setting up and finishing the treatment would take. (See Unit BT6, pages 323–325.)

N1.2 Carry out calculations to do with amounts and sizes, scales and proportions, handling statistics

- Unit BT6

  - Work out how many treatments you would realistically get from one wax pot, using the volume and the amount of wax used each time.
  - Calculate the cost of the wax, and the cost per treatment, remembering overheads. You should now be able to calculate the profit margin per pot.

N1.3 Interpret results of calculations and present findings – must include 1 chart and 1 diagram

A bar chart, pie chart and / or line graph to show profit margins and overhead costs. This can be relevant to Key Skills Level 1 IT, too.

Customer Service NVQ Level 2

If you complete the evidence for Key Skills Application of Number N1.1, you have also achieved the following elements for NVQ Level 2 Customer Service.

Element 5.2 Using client feedback to improve service reliability

Design and conduct a short questionnaire on client preferences for type of wax used on different areas of the body. Give feedback to colleagues, based on the results, on the most popular choices and why.

Key Skills Level 1 Information and Communication Technology

You may need the help of your IT co-ordinator, because this Key Skill requires you to use ICT resources.

IT1.1 Find & explore and develop information – 2 different purposes; IT1.2 Present 2 pieces of information for different purposes – including: 1 with text, 1 with images, 1 with numbers

- Units BT4 and BT6

If you are creating client information sheets on, for example, waxing or facial treatments, you need to remember the following.

  - Check the spelling, punctuation and grammar.
  - Keep a log detailing: how you found the information you required; the file names you used to save your work; your reasons for choosing or rejecting information.
  - Keep **draft copies** of your work, and note on them why you decided to make changes.

Customer Service NVQ Level 2

Unit 4 Solve problems for customers

Using a computer, design a short questionnaire to gather information on customer problems.

Or you could relate your questionnaire to: availability of stock, quality of products or services, use of products or services, organisation of systems, booking, etc.

Element 4.2

Analyse the results and discuss in a staff meeting with colleagues the best way to solve the problem.

Design a poster explaining the new method of meeting the clients' problems. Include text, images and numbers. It could be a timed booking-in system, with a fixed penalty for late clients or non-arrivals.

Index